THE
INTERNATIONAL SERIES
OF
MONOGRAPHS ON PHYSICS

GENERAL EDITORS
W. MARSHALL   D. H. WILKINSON

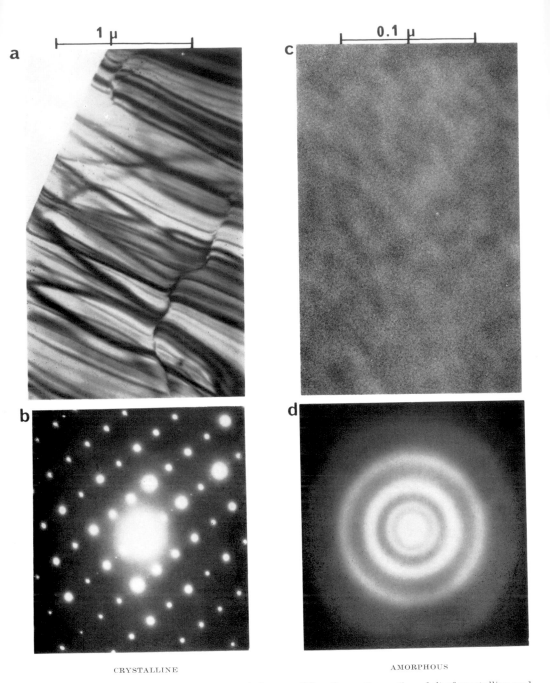

a   1 μ

c   0.1 μ

b

d

CRYSTALLINE   AMORPHOUS

Scanning electron micrographs (a and c) and electron diffraction patterns (b and d) of crystalline and amorphous arsenic triselenide (courtesy of L. Freeman, Cavendish Laboratory, Cambridge)

ELECTRONIC PROCESSES IN NON-CRYSTALLINE MATERIALS

BY

N. F. MOTT

Cavendish Professor of Physics in the University of Cambridge

AND

E. A. DAVIS

Royal Society Mr. and Mrs. John Jaffé Donation Research Fellow
Cavendish Laboratory, University of Cambridge

CLARENDON PRESS · OXFORD

1971

Oxford University Press, Ely House, London W.1

GLASGOW   NEW YORK   TORONTO   MELBOURNE   WELLINGTON
CAPE TOWN   IBADAN   NAIROBI   DAR ES SALAAM   LUSAKA   ADDIS ABABA
DELHI   BOMBAY   CALCUTTA   MADRAS   KARACHI   LAHORE   DACCA
KUALA LUMPUR   SINGAPORE   HONG KONG   TOKYO

PRINTED IN NORTHERN IRELAND BY THE UNIVERSITIES PRESS, BELFAST

PREFACE

TEN YEARS ago our theoretical understanding of electrons in non-crystalline materials was rudimentary. The classification of materials into metals, semiconductors, and insulators was based on band theory, and band theory starts from the assumption that the material is crystalline. According to band theory, an insulator is a material with an energy gap between the conduction and valence bands, and a transparent insulator is one in which the gap is greater than the quantum energy of visible light. Ordinary soda glass is an insulator and transparent; a gap seemed to exist but we did not know how to describe the gap. Even now we do not know how to calculate it, but the concepts that we have to use are fairly clear.

A milestone in the development of the subject was Ziman's quantitative explanation of the electrical properties of liquid metals, put forward in 1960. This was a weak-interaction theory, the effect of each atom being treated as small. The success of this theory prompted investigations of what happens when the interaction is large, as it must be when an energy gap exists. The keys to our present understanding have been the principle of Ioffe and Regel (1960) that the mean free path cannot be less than the distance between atoms, and the concept of localization introduced by Anderson in his paper 'Absence of diffusion in certain random lattices', published in 1958. In a sense, our book is written around these two themes. We have built a theoretical edifice on them, and since mathematical rigour is anything but easy in this subject we have not hesitated to guess at the approximate solutions of problems that at present are unsolved. Our aim is to suggest models that can be compared with experiment. We have chosen the experimental material, too, with a view to comparing it with our theory and our conjectures. Thus we have given a rather full account of what is known in October 1970 about the electrical and optical properties of certain amorphous semiconductors, in particular silicon, germanium, chalcogenide glasses, and selenium, which we think relevant. We have said much less about conduction in glasses containing transition-metal ions as they would in our view fit better into a book about polarons. Our chapter on impurity-conduction is not meant to be exhaustive; we include it because impurity-conduction is the most fully understood process of conduction in a random field. We have said rather little about the phenomenon of switching, fearing that anything we could write would be out of date too quickly.

Finally it is a pleasure to thank our many colleagues who are interested in non-crystalline materials and who have helped us to write this book. We are particularly indebted to Dr. T. E. Faber for making available to us some tables from his forthcoming book, to Dr. R. S. Allgaier for the table in the Appendix, to Dr. L. Friedman, Mr. C. H. Hurst, and Dr. F. Stern for help in correcting the proofs, and to Miss Shirley Fieldhouse for her help in preparing the bibliography.

N. F. M.
E. A. D.

Cambridge
October 1970

ACKNOWLEDGEMENTS

We wish to acknowledge the permission of the publishers of the following journals and the authors to reproduce the figures specified: *Physical review* (Figs. 2.5, 3.9, 5.8, 5.14, 6.1, 6.6, 6.9, 6.11, 6.12, 6.13, 6.15, 6.16, 6.18, 6.20, 6.26, 6.27, 7.27, 7.30, 8.6(a), 8.10, 8.13, 8.14(a) and (b), 8.19(a) and (b), 8.27, 8.28(a) and (b), 8.29, 9.27(a) and (b), 10.8, 10.12, 10.14, 10.22, 10.23); *Journal of non-crystalline solids* (Figs. 2.15, 3.18, 3.19, 3.28, 7.1, 7.23, 7.24, 7.25, 7.34, 8.2, 8.7, 8.8, 8.15, 8.20, 8.21, 8.32, 8.34, 8.35, 8.36, 8.37, 8.39, 8.40, 8.41, 9.8(a) and (b), 9.9, 9.10, 9.15(a) and (b), 9.20, 9.21, 9.24, 9.25(a) and (b), 9.28, 9.29, 9.35, 10.3, 10.4, 10.5(a) and (b), 10.7, 10.9, 10.13, 10.15, 10.17); (Fig. 3.2); *Philosophical magazine* (Figs. 3.3, 3.4, 3.7, 3.11, 3.13, 3.14, 3.15, 3.16, 3.26, 7.8, 7.17, 7.40); *Journal of vacuum science technology* (Fig. 3.8); *Review of modern physics* (Figs. 3.12, 6.8, 6.10); *Physics of condensed matter* (Fig. 3.20); *Physics letters* (Fig. 3.22(b)); *Compte rendu hebdomadaire des séances de l'Académie des sciences* (Fig. 3.23); *Advances in physics* (Figs. 3.24, 3.25, 5.17, 6.5, 6.7); *Journal of applied physics* (Figs. 3.29, 6.19, 9.33, 9.34); *Physical review letters* (Figs 5.13, 6.21, 7.36, 7.42, 8.16(a) and (b), 8.22, 8.23, 8.24, 9.7); *Advances in chemistry series* (Fig. 5.16); *Solid state communications* (Fig. 6.14); *Handbuch der Physik* (Fig. 6.22); *Helvetica physica acta* (Fig. 6.24); *IBM journal of research and development* (Fig. 6.23); *Journal of the physical society of Japan* (Fig. 6.25); *Zeitschrift für Naturforschung* (Fig. 7.3); *Progress in semiconductors* (Fig. 7.10); *Electronics letters* (Fig. 7.11); *British journal of applied physics* (Figs. 7.20(a) and (b), 7.22, 7.38, 9.19); *Thin solid films* (Figs. 8.1, 8.2, 8.12); *Applied physics letters* (Fig. 8.11); *Physica status solidi* (Figs. 8.17(a) and (b), 10.16, 10.18(a) and (b), 10.20); *Discussions of the Faraday society* (Figs. 8.38(a) and (b), 10.2); *Czechoslovak journal of physics* (Figs. 9.5, 9.6(a) and (b), 9.17); *Materials research bulletin* (Figs. 9.16, 9.26, 10.1); *Journal of the electrochemical society* (Fig. 9.31); *Contemporary physics* (Fig. 10.6).

Acknowledgements are also due to the following publishers and the authors for permission to reproduce figures: Nauka, Leningrad, from *Proceedings of the Ninth International Conference on the Physics of Semiconductors, Moscow* (Fig. 5.9(a) and (b)); The United States

Atomic Energy Commission, from *Proceedings of the Tenth International Conference on the Physics of Semiconductors, Cambridge, Mass.* (Figs. 7.21(a) and (b), 7.26(a) and (b), 7.37, 8.3, 8.25, 8.30, 8.31(a) and (b)); Benjamin, New York, from II–VI *semiconducting compounds* (Fig. 7.35(a) and (b)); Academic Press, from *Quantum theory of atoms, molecules, and the solid state* (Fig. 8.26).

We wish to thank also the following individuals for permission to use their unpublished material: P. D. Adams and S. Kravitz (Fig. 3.5(a) and (b)); and E. W. Collings (Fig. 3.6).

CONTENTS

1. INTRODUCTION 1

2. THEORY OF ELECTRONS IN A
NON-CRYSTALLINE MEDIUM
 2.1. Introduction 6
 2.2. Localized states 9
 2.3. The Kubo–Greenwood formula 10
 2.4. Vanishing of the conductivity when states are localized;
   the ω^2 law 14
 2.5. Situations in which states are localized in one range of
   energies and not localized in another 22
 2.6. Many-body effects and magnetic susceptibility 28
 2.7. The density of states 29
   2.7.1. Random distribution of centres in space 29
   2.7.2. Liquids, glasses, and amorphous solids 31
 2.8. Conductors and insulators 34
 2.9. Temperature-dependent conductivity 39
   2.9.1. Conduction due to electrons with energies near the
    Fermi energy 39
   2.9.2. Amorphous semiconductors; the mobility shoulder 43
   2.9.3. Thermoelectric power 47
 2.10. Hopping conduction for alternating currents 49
   2.10.1. Debye-type energy loss for hopping conduction 50
 2.11. Optical interband transitions in semiconductors 52
 2.12. The Hall effect 53
 2.13. One-dimensional problems 55

3. LIQUID METALS, SEMI-METALS, AND
SEMICONDUCTORS
 3.1. Introduction 59
 3.2. Scattering of electrons by a random distribution of centres:
   degenerate semiconductors 61
 3.3. Resistivity of liquid metals; Ziman's theory 63
 3.4. The absolute magnitude of the resistivity 66
 3.5. Resistivity of liquid alloys 68
 3.6. Thermoelectric power 70
 3.7. Hall effect 71
 3.8. Density of states 72

3.9.   Knight shift   74
3.10. Change in the magnetic susceptibility on melting   74
3.11. X-ray emission spectra   75
3.12. Amorphous metallic films; grain boundaries   76
3.13. Injected electrons in liquid rare gases   77
3.14. Effect of the density of states on the conductivity   79
3.15. Optical properties   81
3.16. Liquid and amorphous semi-metals   82
       3.16.1. Mercury at low densities   82
       3.16.2. Amorphous Mg–Bi alloys   84
3.17. Liquid semiconductors and semi-metals   86
       3.17.1. Semiconductors in class (d); selenium   89
       3.17.2. Tellurium   91
       3.17.3. Tellurium–selenium liquid alloys   94
       3.17.4. Liquid alloys of tellurium with metallic elements   97

4. PHONONS AND POLARONS
   4.1.   Introduction   102
   4.2.   Scattering of electrons by phonons   102
   4.3.   Thermally activated hopping   104
   4.4.   The distortion of the lattice round a trapped electron   107
   4.5.   Transitions from one localized state to another in a
          polar lattice   109
   4.6.   Hopping at low temperatures   112
   4.7.   Polarons in crystalline materials   113
   4.8.   Motion of a polaron in a crystalline lattice   115
   4.9.   Energy required to release a charge carrier from a
          donor centre   116
   4.10. Examples of hopping polarons   117
   4.11. Thermopower due to polarons   118
   4.12. Anderson localization of polarons   119
   4.13. Degenerate gas of polarons   120
   4.14. Polarons in liquids   120

5. THE METAL–NON-METAL TRANSITION
   5.1.   Introduction   121
   5.2.   Mott–Hubbard insulators   123
   5.3.   Band-theory description of Mott–Hubbard insulators   127
   5.4.   Behaviour near the transition point   128
   5.5.   The Hubbard Hamiltonian   131
   5.6.   Effect of long-range forces   132
   5.7.   Wigner crystallization   135
   5.8.   The excitonic insulator   137

5.9. Kohn's model for the Mott transition   140
5.10. Transition-metal oxides   142
5.11. The metal–non-metal transition in disordered systems   146
5.12. Conductivity near the transition point in a disordered system 148
5.13. Materials of high dielectric constant; the transition in
        doped titanates   148
5.14. Metal–ammonia solutions   150

6. IMPURITY BANDS AND IMPURITY-CONDUCTION
6.1. Introduction   152
6.2. Models of Twose and of Miller and Abrahams   157
6.3. Impurity-conduction in silicon and germanium   159
6.4. Thermopower   164
6.5. Anderson localization on the metallic side of the MNM
        transition   166
6.6. Anderson localization in cerium sulphide and vanadium
        monoxide   167
6.7. Impurity-conduction in ionic materials   170
6.8. Conduction in glasses containing transition-metal ions   172
6.9. Magnetic susceptibility   174
6.10. Hall effect   175
6.11. Magnetic polarons   175
6.12. Magnetic semiconductors   177
6.13. Magnetoresistance   181
6.14. Optical absorption and a.c. conduction   184

7. NON-CRYSTALLINE SEMICONDUCTORS
7.1. Introduction   188
7.2. Preparation and classification of materials   189
7.3. Studies of the structures of amorphous materials   194
7.4. Electrical properties of non-crystalline semiconductors   197
      7.4.1. Summary of theoretical concepts   197
      7.4.2. Temperature variation of d.c. conductivity   200
      7.4.3. Drift mobilities   207
      7.4.4. a.c. conductivity   211
      7.4.5. Thermoelectric power   219
      7.4.6. Hall effect   225
      7.4.7. Magnetoresistance   227
      7.4.8. Thermally stimulated conductivity   228
7.5. Photoconductivity and quantum efficiency   229
7.6. Optical absorption   237
      7.6.1. Absorption edges and Urbach's rule   238
      7.6.2. Interband absorption   248

7.6.3. Absorption at high energies   253
7.6.4. Modulation experiments   257
7.6.5. Intraband absorption   258
7.6.6. Absorption by phonons   261
7.7.   Other measurements   262
7.7.1. Photo-emission from non-crystalline semiconductors   262
7.7.2. Electron spin resonance   264
7.7.3. Magnetic susceptibility   265
7.8.   Non-ohmic conduction in strong fields   266
7.9   Switching in non-crystalline semiconductors   269

8. PROPERTIES OF AMORPHOUS GERMANIUM,
   SILICON, AND OTHER SEMICONDUCTORS
   WITH TETRAHEDRAL COORDINATION
8.1.   Amorphous germanium and silicon   272
8.1.1. Methods of preparation   272
8.1.2. Structure of amorphous germanium and silicon   274
8.1.3. Electrical properties of amorphous germanium   279
8.1.4. Electrical properties of amorphous silicon   291
8.1.5. Optical properties of amorphous germanium   298
8.1.6. Optical properties of amorphous silicon   307
8.2.   InSb and other III–V compounds   312
8.3. $CdGeAs_2$ and similar ternaries   315
8.3.1. Electrical properties of glasses of the type $CdGeAs_2$ 316
8.3.2. Optical properties of glasses of the type $CdGeAs_2$ 320

9. THE CHALCOGENIDE GLASSES
9.1.   Introduction   324
9.2.   Summary of electrical and optical properties of chalcogenide
       glasses   327
9.3.   Arsenic trisulphide As_2S_3 and the As–S system   331
9.4.   Arsenic triselenide As_2Se_3 and the As–Se system   347
9.5.   Arsenic tritelluride As_2Te_3 358
9.6.   Mixed binary systems   361
9.6.1. As_2Se_3–As_2Te_3 361
9.6.2. As_2Se_3–As_2S_3 363
9.6.3. As_2S_3–As_2Te_3 363
9.6.4. As_2Se_3–Sb_2Se_3 364
9.7.   Germanium telluride GeTe   365
9.8.   Multicomponent glasses   368

10. SELENIUM, TELLURIUM, AND THEIR ALLOYS
10.1. Structure of amorphous selenium and alloys of selenium   371

10.1.1. Isoelectronic additives Te and S 374
10.1.2. Univalent additives Cl, Br, I, Tl, Na, and K 375
10.1.3. Branching additives As, Bi, and Ge 376
10.2. Electrical properties of amorphous selenium and alloys of selenium 380
10.2.1. Electrical conductivity 380
10.2.2. Drift mobilities 382
10.2.3. Carrier lifetimes and ranges 387
10.2.4. Space-charge-limited current measurements 389
10.3. Optical properties of amorphous selenium and tellurium 391
10.4. Photogeneration in amorphous selenium xerography 398

APPENDIX 401

REFERENCES 410

AUTHOR INDEX 427

SUBJECT INDEX 434

1

INTRODUCTION

THE subject-matter of this book is those properties of non-crystalline materials that are due to the movement of electrons, particularly electrical conduction and optical absorption. Among non-crystalline materials are liquid metals and semiconductors, glasses, and amorphous evaporated films. A closely related subject also described in this book is the phenomenon of impurity-conduction in semiconductors, in which an electron moves directly (by tunnelling) from one impurity atom or point defect to another. Whether the material surrounding the impurities is crystalline or not, the impurity atoms are distributed at random, so that impurity-conduction provides a particularly simple example of the movement of an electron in a non-periodic field of force.

The book starts with a description of the theoretical concepts necessary to describe these phenomena. Chapter 2 sets out a theory of non-interacting electrons in a rigid non-crystalline array of atoms. By a rigid array, we mean a model that neglects the effect of phonons and of distortions of the lattice, such as polarons, produced by an electron. For many of the phenomena described in this book, this is legitimate; for instance, the resistivity of a liquid metal is determined mainly by the scattering of electrons that results from the disordered arrangement of the atoms, and the resistance of a disordered alloy is normally calculated without considering the energy that may be transferred to an atom when an electron is scattered.†

Confining ourselves then to a rigid array of atoms, we have to ask first which of the concepts appropriate to crystalline solids can be used in non-crystalline materials. The first concept, equally valid for crystalline and for non-crystalline materials, is the density of states, which we denote by $N(E)$. The quantity $N(E)\,dE$ denotes the number of states in unit volume available for an electron with given spin direction with energies between E and $E+dE$. As in crystalline solids, the states can be occupied or empty, and $N(E)f(E)\,dE$ is the number of occupied states per unit volume, where f is the Fermi distribution

† See § 3.1.

function. The density of states can in principle be determined experimentally, for instance by photo-emission (§ 7.7.1). In general, the available evidence suggests that the form of the density of states in a liquid or non-crystalline material does not differ greatly from the corresponding form in the crystal, except that the finer features may be smeared out, and some localized states may appear in the forbidden energy range in semiconductors. Figure 2.1 shows some of the forms that the density of states may take.

On the other hand, the description of individual electron states used for electrons in crystalline materials is not always appropriate for the non-crystalline case. In crystalline materials, assuming a perfect crystal and neglecting the effect of phonons, we describe each electron by a Bloch wave function

$$\psi = u(\mathbf{r})e^{i\mathbf{k}\cdot\mathbf{r}}, \tag{1.1}$$

where $u(\mathbf{r})$ has the periodicity of the lattice. The wave vector $\mathbf{k}$ is a quantum number for the electron. Because of phonons or impurities, scattering takes place, and a mean free path L is introduced; for instance, if there are N impurities per unit volume each with a differential scattering cross-section $I(\theta)$, the mean free path is given by

$$1/L = N\int_0^\pi I(\theta)(1 - \cos\theta)2\pi\sin\theta\,d\theta. \tag{1.2}$$

This formula assumes that the Fermi surface is spherical, so that $I(\theta)$ is independent of the initial direction of motion of the electrons. But it is, of course, characteristic of the conduction and valence bands of many crystalline solids that the energy $E(\mathbf{k})$ corresponding to the wave function (1.1) does depend on the direction of $\mathbf{k}$.

In non-crystalline materials there are two possibilities. One is that the mean free path is large, so that $kL \gg 1$. This is the case in most liquid metals, and in the conduction band of liquid rare gases. The wave vector $\mathbf{k}$ is then still a good quantum number, and a Fermi surface can still be defined; but, since the liquid or amorphous solid has no axis of symmetry, the Fermi surface must be spherical. In fact, since the mean free path is large, the deviation of the density of states from the free-electron form must be small. This will be shown in Chapter 3, which deals with liquid metals and other related problems. But if in a liquid or amorphous material the atomic potential (or pseudopotential) is strong enough to produce a band gap, or any large deviation from the free-electron form, then it must give strong scattering and a short mean free path ($kL \sim 1$). This in our view is the most important difference between the theories of crystalline and non-crystalline materials. In the latter case, phenomena frequently occur in which electrons have energies for which $kL \sim 1$. This is so, as we shall see in subsequent chapters, for the carriers in most amorphous and liquid semiconductors. Under such conditions the k-selection rule† breaks down in optical transitions (§§ 2.11, 7.6.2). For conduction processes when this is the case, there is much evidence that the Hall coefficient R_H is less than that predicted by the usual formula ($R_H = 1/nec$), and may even have the wrong sign (§ 2.12).

It was first emphasized by Ioffe and Regel (1960) that values of L such that $kL < 1$ are impossible; this leads us to expect that, when the interaction of the carrier with atoms is sufficiently strong, something new ought to happen. It was first conjectured by Gubanov (1963) and by Banyai (1964) that near the edges of conduction or valence bands in most non-crystalline materials the states are *localized*, and the concept of localization will play a large part in this book. There is nothing unfamiliar about the concept of localized states; they are simply 'traps', and the most direct evidence for their existence in amorphous materials is provided by measurements of the transit time for injected carriers (§ 7.4.3); if this shows an activation energy, a trap-limited mobility can be inferred. The new concept for amorphous materials is that a continuous density of states, $N(E)$, can exist in which for a range of energies the states are all traps, or in other words localized, and for which the mobility at the zero of temperature vanishes, *even though the wave functions of neighbouring states overlap.*

The first phenomenon for which this was generally recognized was impurity-conduction in doped and compensated semiconductors, which was first fully understood in the early 1960s. The centres in these materials are located at random positions, and in addition there is a random potential at each centre. This is discussed in Chapter 6. Our understanding of localization in this case derives from Anderson's paper (1958) on the absence of diffusion in certain random lattices which is central to our theme and is discussed in Chapter 2. In impurity-conduction, each time an electron moves from one centre to another, it emits or absorbs a phonon; processes in which it absorbs a

† This says that $\mathbf{k} - \mathbf{k'} \pm \mathbf{q} = 0$ when $\mathbf{k}$, $\mathbf{k'}$ are the wave numbers before and after the transition and $\mathbf{q}$ is the wave vector of the light.

phonon are rate determining, and in consequence the conductivity
contains an activation energy, so that it takes the form (Chapter 6)

$$\sigma = \sigma_3 \exp(-\varepsilon_3/kT),$$

and tends to zero at low temperatures.† We call this form of charge
transport *thermally activated hopping*, or just hopping. Hopping is
also responsible for an a.c. conductivity $\sigma(\omega)$ at frequency ω proportional to $\omega^{0.8}$. In this process, an electron hops between pairs of
localized states, absorbing or emitting a phonon each time.

The extension of the idea of localized states to non-crystalline
semiconductors is more speculative, but it seems highly probable that
such states do indeed exist near the extremities of a conduction or
valence band in most cases. If so, an energy E_C can be defined that
separates a range of energies in which states are localized from a
range in which they are not. This quantity E_C was first introduced by
Mott (1967), and the concept is developed in Chapter 2. For energies on
one side of E_C, charge transport is only possible by thermally activated
hopping, involving interaction with phonons, so that the mobility
tends to zero with temperature. For energies on the other side of E_C,
diffusion can take place even at the absolute zero of temperature,
and the diffusion coefficient contains no activation energy; since the
mobility μ is related to the diffusion coefficient D by the equation
$\mu = eD/kT$, the product μT is finite when $T \to 0$. We believe that,
when $T = 0$, the product μT shows a discontinuity at E_C; the reasons
are set out in Chapter 2. This leads us to the concept of a *mobility
shoulder* (see Fig. 2.17). Except at low temperatures, the charge
carriers in many non-crystalline semiconductors are in non-localized
states within a range of energy of order kT just above E_C; whether
or not this is so at a given temperature depends on the range in energy
of localized states at the band edge.

In Chapter 2, also, we develop formulae for the thermoelectric
power. Since the Hall effect appears anomalous, a measurement of the
thermopower is the most reliable method of determining whether the
carriers are electrons or holes.

Chapter 4 describes the effect of phonons. These are of three kinds:

(a) Phonons can scatter an electron with a non-localized wave
function, making a contribution to the resistance just as in a crystalline
metal or semiconductor.

---

† A variation at very low temperatures as $\exp(-\text{const}/T^{\frac{1}{4}})$ is predicted and found
in certain cases (Chapters 2, 6, 8).

(b) As we have seen, they can, by exchanging energy with an electron, enable it to hop from one localized state to an other, as, for instance, in impurity-conduction.

(c) They can be trapped by the electrons to form a *small polaron*. Effects such as polaron formation in which several phonons are trapped, so that the interaction between electron and phonon is not to be treated as a small perturbation, play a part in impurity-conduction in all polar semiconductors, and in other phenomena. In Chapter 4, therefore, a description is given of polaron behaviour in crystalline narrow-band semiconductors as an introduction to the related problems in non-crystalline materials.

Chapter 5 describes the metal–insulator transition, in crystalline materials as well as non-crystalline materials. There are two reasons for including this:

(a) In narrow-band semiconductors and impurity-conduction the correlation effects due to the repulsion between a pair of electrons often play an essential role, the predictions of the one-electron theory being qualitatively wrong.

(b) Much work on the metal–insulator transition is done by observing impurity-conduction and therefore can be understood only in terms of a theory that treats electrons moving in a non-periodic field.

The metal–insulator transition is essentially a many-body effect, and many-body theory, or at any rate a consideration of the interaction between the electrons, is important in several other problems. In particular, as soon as we introduce localized states, we face the fact that, because of the term e^2/r_{12}, the ionization energy and the electron affinity for the state are not equal. Therefore it is probably best in many cases to think of the states as singly occupied rather than doubly occupied; impurity-conduction is treated in this way in Chapter 6. In fact, the introduction of many-body theory to the subject of this book has hardly begun, and references to such effects here are speculative.

The last four chapters contain a detailed description of the properties of a number of non-crystalline semiconductors, together with an attempt to describe them in terms of the models put forward in this book.

THEORY OF ELECTRONS IN A NON-CRYSTALLINE MEDIUM

2.1. Introduction

2.2. Localized states

2.3. The Kubo–Greenwood formula

2.4. Vanishing of the conductivity when states are localized; the ω^2 law

2.5. Situations in which states are localized in one range of energies and not localized in another

2.6. Many-body effects and magnetic susceptibility

2.7. The density of states

    2.7.1. Random distribution of centres in space

    2.7.2. Liquids, glasses, and amorphous solids

2.8. Conductors and insulators

2.9. Temperature-dependent conductivity

    2.9.1. Conduction due to electrons with energies near the Fermi energy

    2.9.2. Amorphous semiconductors; the mobility shoulder

    2.9.3. Thermoelectric power

2.10. Hopping conduction for alternating currents

    2.10.1. Debye-type energy loss for hopping conduction

2.11. Optical interband transitions in semiconductors

2.12. The Hall effect

2.13. One-dimensional problems

2.1. Introduction

THIS chapter introduces some of the theoretical concepts and formulae appropriate to the discussion of electronic processes in non-crystalline materials, particularly electrical conduction and optical absorption. Except where otherwise stated, the discussion will be in terms of the same approximation as that normally used in the band theory of crystalline materials, the interaction e^2/r_{12} between electrons being neglected except in so far as it can be included in the averaged Hartree–Fock field.

As we stated in Chapter 1, there is one concept that is applicable equally to both crystalline and non-crystalline materials. This is the density of electronic states, which is denoted by $N(E)$ and is defined so that $N(E) \, \mathrm{d}E$ is the number of eigenstates in unit volume for an electron in the system with given spin direction and with energy between E and $E + \mathrm{d}E$. Whatever the nature of the eigenstates, this density function must exist. Then at a temperature T the number of electrons in the energy range dE is, for each spin direction,

$$N(E)f(E)\ \mathrm{d}E,$$

where $f(E)$ is the Fermi distribution function

$$f(E) = 1/\{e^{(E-\zeta)/kT}+1\}.$$

The Fermi energy ζ is a function of T and tends to a limiting value E_F as $T \to 0$, E_F separating occupied from non-occupied states.

For the form of $N(E)$, there are two possibilities, as we emphasized in Chapter 1. One is that the scattering of the electrons by each atom is weak, in which case the electrons are described by wave functions each having a fairly well-defined wave number k. The mean free path L is then large and the uncertainty Δk in k, given by the relation $L\,\Delta k \sim 1$, is such that $\Delta k/k \ll 1$. In this case, the energy E of each electron is to a first approximation a parabolic function of k, so that

$$E = \hbar^2 k^2/2m;$$

the Fermi surface is spherical, and the density of states for the electrons is given for each spin direction by the free-electron formula

$$N(E) = 4\pi k^2/8\pi^3(\mathrm{d}E/\mathrm{d}k)$$

$$= km/2\pi^2\hbar^2. \qquad (2.1)$$

These conditions are normally satisfied in liquid metals and will be discussed in the next chapter, where it will be seen that m is not necessarily the free-electron mass.

The other possibility is that the interaction is strong, so that $\Delta k/k \sim 1$. In this case, the mean free path is short ($kL \sim 1$); it cannot be less than this, as Ioffe and Regel first emphasized (1960). As we shall see later in this chapter, there is another possibility when the interaction is strong, namely that states are localized. This case is illustrated in Fig. 2.1.

In either case a density of states $N(E)$ that is a continuous function of E remains a valid concept, but *if and only if* $\Delta k/k \sim 1$ are large deviations from the free-electron form possible. Some of these forms are illustrated in Fig. 2.1, and we shall see later that the forms of Fig. 2.1(b), (c), and (d) all imply $\Delta k/k \sim 1$ (or localization) in the regions where the deviation of $N(E)$ from the free-electron value is large. Reasons for assuming that these forms can occur are discussed in later sections.

In this chapter, we discuss the mathematical formalism appropriate to the calculation of the electrical properties when $\Delta k/k \sim 1$, or when $a\,\Delta k \sim 1$, a being the distance between atoms. The case of long mean free paths, appropriate to liquid metals, is treated in Chapter 3, and

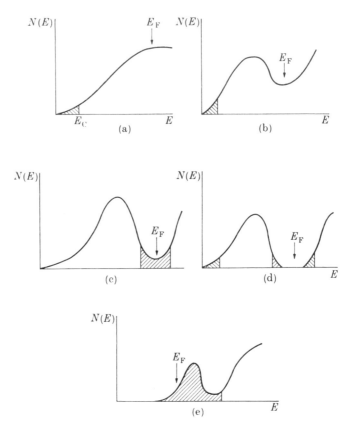

FIG. 2.1. Density of states in non-crystalline materials (schematic). E_F is the Fermi energy at the absolute zero of temperature; localized states are shaded. (a) Liquid or amorphous metal. (b) Semi-metal. (c) Semi-metal with deep pseudogap. (d) Insulator or intrinsic semiconductor. (e) Impurity band in heavily compensated n-type semiconductor.

here the Boltzmann formalism is applicable. When, however, the mean free path is short, a different approach is necessary; this is to evaluate the optical absorption due to all electrons with energies up to E by the elementary methods of quantum mechanics, and thus deduce $\sigma(\omega)$, the conductivity at frequency ω. We calculate this for a rigid system at $T = 0$, and for states filled up to a Fermi energy E; we

denote the result by $\sigma_E(\omega)$. This is related to the absorption coefficient α by the equation

$$\alpha = 4\pi\sigma_E(\omega)/n_0, \tag{2.2}$$

where n_0 is the real part of the refractive index.

For the d.c. conductivity at zero temperature for a system with
states filled up to an energy E, we write

$$\sigma_E(0) = \lim_{\omega \to 0} \sigma_E(\omega). \tag{2.3}$$

This will be called the Kubo–Greenwood formula (Greenwood 1958),
and its derivation, as we shall see, is elementary. It turns out to be an
important concept for our understanding of localized states.

2.2. Localized states

In this section we discuss further the concept of localized states,
and approach it by considering the d.c. conductivity of a system with
states filled up to a limiting value E_F. At low temperatures we may
distinguish two limiting cases:

(a) Situations in which the conductivity is determined by the
properties of electrons with energies near E_F. This is so in metals,
crystalline or liquid; it is also the case in impurity-conduction at
low temperatures (Chapter 6) whether or not the motion of electrons
is by thermally activated hopping.

(b) Situations where the mobility of electrons with energies near
the Fermi energy E_F is zero or negligibly small, or in which $N(E)$ is
zero there. The current is then carried by excited electrons, as in an
intrinsic semiconductor, or as in an extrinsic semiconductor if impurity-conduction is absent.

Examples of the two kinds of conduction are discussed in this chapter, but for the moment we shall confine ourselves to case (a). We
have already indicated that a range of energies may exist in which
$N(E)$ is finite but states are localized, and the mobility of an electron
with such an energy is zero at $T = 0$. $\sigma_E(0)$ vanishes for these energies.
The vanishing of $\sigma_E(0)$ can serve as a definition of localization for
electrons with energy E. Other definitions of localization are possible.
One is that all eigenfunctions of the one-electron Schrödinger equation
decay exponentially in space outside regions in which the eigenfunction
is localized, as in Fig. 2.3. More strictly, we should say that any eigenfunctions that do not decay in this way are so rare as to contribute a
term to $\sigma_E(0)$ that tends to zero when the number N of atoms tends

to infinity. Or alternatively we can say, following Anderson (1958), that states are localized if an electron with energy $E \pm dE$ placed in a volume l^3, large enough to satisfy the uncertainty principle, will not diffuse away. We believe all definitions to be equivalent.

In case (b), that of an intrinsic semiconductor, the concept of localization is important too; we shall see that for non-localized states $\sigma_E(0)$ can then be interpreted as $eN(E)kT\mu$, where μ is the mobility for carriers with energy E, always with neglect of the effects of interaction with phonons. If states are localized, μ vanishes at $T = 0$. At finite temperatures the mobility is essentially due to inter-action with phonons and is several orders of magnitude smaller than for non-localized (extended) states.

There is one particular point that we should emphasize about these statements, which will be elaborated later in this chapter. This is that for any model of a non-crystalline system, for instance a liquid, a great many configurations are possible; we call the totality of all such configurations an *ensemble*. Any quantity deduced from quantum mechanics that is to be compared with experiment should be averaged over all configurations of the ensemble. The result of doing this to $\sigma_E(0)$ will be written $\langle \sigma_E(0) \rangle$. We say that states with energy E are localized if

$$\langle \sigma_E(0) \rangle = 0.$$

This does not mean that σ vanishes for all configurations of the ensemble; for instance, one possible configuration of a liquid is that of a perfect crystal, and for this no states will be localized in the sense described above. But we assert that, for an assembly of N atoms, a range of electron energies may exist such that the number of con-figurations for which σ does not vanish tends to zero as $N \to \infty$. In other words, the expectation value of σ tends to zero. Thus our defini-tion of localization is that, for a Fermi gas of non-interacting electrons with Fermi energy E,

$$\lim_{N \to \infty} \langle \sigma_E(0) \rangle = 0.$$

2.3. The Kubo–Greenwood formula

We shall now deduce formulae for the quantities $\sigma(\omega)$ and $\sigma(0)$ introduced in the last section. Suppose that the eigenfunctions for an electron with energy E in the non-periodic field, with any appropriate boundary conditions, are $\psi_E(x, y, z)$, and that these are normalized to give one electron in a volume Ω. Suppose that an alternating field

$F \cos \omega t$ acts on an electron so that the potential energy is $exF \cos \omega t$. Then the chance per unit time that an electron makes a transition from a state with energy E to any of the states with energy $E + \hbar \omega$ is

$$\tfrac{1}{4} e^2 F^2 (2\pi/\hbar) \, |x_{E+\hbar\omega,E}|^2_{av} \, \Omega N(E+\hbar\omega). \qquad (2.4)$$

The matrix element $x_{E',E}$ is defined by

$$x_{E',E} = \int \psi_{E'}^* x \psi_E \, d^3x,$$

and the suffix 'av' represents an average over all states having energy near $E' = E + \hbar \omega$. It is convenient to write

$$x_{E+\hbar\omega,E} = \frac{\hbar}{m\omega} D_{E+\hbar\omega,E}, \qquad (2.5)$$

where

$$D_{E',E} = \int \psi_{E'}^* \frac{\partial}{\partial x} (\psi_E) \, d^3x.$$

Thus (2.4) becomes

$$(\pi e^2 \hbar \Omega / 2m^2 \omega^2) F^2 \, |D|^2_{av} \, N(E+\hbar\omega). \qquad (2.6)$$

We now introduce the conductivity for frequency ω, written $\sigma(\omega)$ and defined so that $\sigma(\omega)\tfrac{1}{2}F^2$ is the mean rate of loss of energy per unit volume. To obtain this, we must multiply eqn (2.6) by $N(E)f(E) \, dE$, the number of occupied states per unit volume in the energy range dE; by $\{1 - f(E+\hbar\omega)\}$, the chance that a state with energy $E + \hbar \omega$ is unoccupied; by $\hbar \omega$, the energy absorbed in each quantum jump; and by 2 for the two spin directions. We find, integrating over all energies,

$$\sigma(\omega) = \frac{2\pi e^2 \hbar^2 \Omega}{m^2 \omega} \int [f(E)\{1 - f(E+\hbar\omega)\} - $$
$$- f(E+\hbar\omega)\{1 - f(E)\}] \, |D|^2_{av} \, N(E)N(E+\hbar\omega) \, dE. \qquad (2.7)$$

The second term in the square brackets gives the energy emitted in downward jumps. $|D|^2$ is now averaged over all initial and final states. The quantity in the square brackets simplifies to

$$f(E) - f(E+\hbar\omega),$$

so eqn (2.7) reduces to

$$\sigma(\omega) = \frac{2\pi e^2 \hbar^3 \Omega}{m^2} \int \frac{\{f(E) - f(E+\hbar\omega)\} \, |D|^2_{av} \, N(E)N(E+\hbar\omega)}{\hbar\omega} \, dE. \qquad (2.8)$$

When $T = 0$ formula (2.8) reduces to

$$\sigma(\omega) = \frac{2\pi e^2\hbar^3\Omega}{m^2} \int \frac{|D|^2_{\mathrm{av}}\, N(E)N(E+\hbar\omega)}{\hbar\omega}\, \mathrm{d}E. \qquad (2.9)$$

The lower limit of integration is $E_{\mathrm{F}}-\hbar\omega$, this being the lowest energy of an electron that can absorb a quantum; the upper limit is E_{F}.

To obtain the d.c. conductivity we take the limit of $\sigma(\omega)$ when $\omega \to 0$. At $T = 0$, this depends only on the values of the quantities in the integral when $E = E_{\mathrm{F}}$. We define $\sigma_E(0)$ by

$$\sigma_E(0) = (2\pi e^2\hbar^3\Omega/m^2)\, |D_E|^2_{\mathrm{av}}\, \{N(E)\}^2, \qquad (2.10)$$

where

$$D_E = \int \psi^*_{E'}\, \frac{\partial}{\partial x}\, \psi_E\, \mathrm{d}^3x \qquad (E = E').$$

The 'av' represents an average over all states E and all states E' such that $E = E'$, so that at $T = 0$ the conductivity $\sigma(0)$ is given by

$$\sigma(0) = \{\sigma_E(0)\}_{E=E_{\mathrm{F}}}.$$

At a finite temperature,

$$\sigma(0) = -\int \sigma_E(0)\, \frac{\mathrm{d}f}{\mathrm{d}E}\, \mathrm{d}E. \qquad (2.11)$$

We call this the Kubo–Greenwood formula.

It is now necessary to show that, if the scattering is weak and the mean free path L long, these formulae lead to the expression deduced from the Boltzmann treatment, namely

$$\sigma = ne^2\tau/m$$
$$= S_{\mathrm{F}}e^2L/12\pi^3\hbar, \qquad (2.12)$$

where S_{F} is the area $(4\pi k^2_{\mathrm{F}})$ of the Fermi surface. The method is due to Mott (1970). We suppose that the free-electron model is applicable, and that a mean free path exists such that $k_{\mathrm{F}}L \gg 1$. Then we define the mean free path such that the phase of ψ loses all memory of its value in a distance L. If we define a volume v equal to that of a sphere with radius L, so that

$$v = 4\pi L^3/3,$$

the phases of the wave functions in these volumes will be uncorrelated. Thus, if δ is defined by

$$\delta = \int^v \psi^*_{k'}\, \frac{\partial}{\partial x}\, \psi_k\, \mathrm{d}^3x, \qquad (2.13)$$

then D is equal to the sum of Ω/v contributions, each equal to δ but with random signs. We may thus write

$$D = (\Omega/v)^{\frac{1}{2}}\delta.$$

To evaluate δ we write

$$\delta = k \int^v \frac{\exp\{i(\mathbf{k'} - \mathbf{k}) \cdot \mathbf{r}\}}{\Omega} \, d^3x,$$

and setting

$$|\mathbf{k} - \mathbf{k'}| = 2k \sin \tfrac{1}{2}\theta \simeq k\theta,$$

where θ is the scattering angle, we approximate by writing

$$\delta = kv/\Omega \qquad \text{if } kL\theta < 1,$$
$$= 0 \qquad\qquad \text{otherwise.}$$

Thus

$$|D|^2_{\mathrm{av}} = (\Omega/v)(k^2 v^2/\Omega^2) \int^{1/kL} \frac{2\pi\theta}{4\pi} \, d\theta$$
$$= \pi L/3\Omega.$$

Substituting from (2.1) for $N(E)$ we see that

$$\sigma = e^2 k^2 L/6\pi^2 \hbar,$$

which is the same as (2.12) apart from a factor of 2. The derivation of the correct numerical constant by so crude a method could not be expected.

The mean free path depends on the scattering mechanism, and methods of calculating it will be discussed in the next chapter. Edwards (1958), taking weak-scattering potentials, also derived the Boltzmann formula starting from the Kubo–Greenwood formalism. He proved directly that formula (1.2), with $I(\theta)$ given by the Born approximation, follows from formula (2.10).

An extension of this method to the conductivity at frequency ω should yield the Drude formula

$$\sigma(\omega) = \sigma(0)/(1 + \omega^2\tau^2) \qquad (\tau = L/u), \qquad (2.14)$$

which thus appears as due to optical transitions in which the k-selection rule is violated, made possible by the finite mean free path and consequent uncertainty in k. We shall not derive this formula, but point out that, if k_1 and k_2 are the wave vectors before and after the process, the method given above is valid only if $(k_1 - k_2)L \ll 1$. Also

$$k_1 - k_2 \simeq (dk/dE)\hbar\omega = \omega/u,$$

where u is the velocity at the Fermi surface, so the derivation breaks down when $\omega\tau \sim 1$. If $\omega\tau \gg 1$, the integral (2.13) for δ must be multiplied by $1/(k_1 - k_2)L$, which shows why the factor $\omega^2\tau^2$ appears in the denominator of the Drude formula.

2.4. Vanishing of the conductivity when states are localized; the ω^2 law

In the last section we have used the Kubo–Greenwood formula (2.10) to derive the conductivity for the case characteristic of a metal,

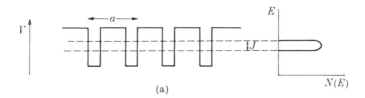

(a)

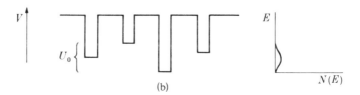

(b)

FIG. 2.2. (a) Potential wells for a crystalline lattice. (b) Potential wells for the Anderson lattice. The density of states is shown in both cases.

namely that in which the density of states is finite at the Fermi energy and $kL \gg 1$. We consider now the opposite case; that in which the potential-energy function $V(x, y, z)$ is no longer a small perturbation in the Schrödinger equation

$$\nabla^2\psi + \frac{2m}{\hbar^2}(E - V)\psi = 0.$$

The extreme case is the *tight-binding approximation*, in which a crystalline array of potential wells produces a narrow band of levels, as in Fig. 2.2(a). Applications could be to the d band of a transition metal or to donors producing a metallic impurity band in a semi-conductor (Chapter 6). We suppose that the wells are so far apart that the overlap between the atomic wave functions $\phi(r)$ on adjacent wells is small. If the suffix 'n' describes the nth well and $\mathbf{R}_n$ its lattice site, the Bloch wave function for an electron in the crystal is

$$\psi_k(x, y, z) = \sum_n \exp(i\mathbf{k} \cdot \mathbf{R}_n)\phi(\mathbf{r} - \mathbf{R}_n). \qquad (2.15)$$

We take the functions ϕ to be spherically symmetrical (s functions). If then W_0 is the energy level for an electron in a single well, the energies for an electron in a simple cubic lattice corresponding to the wave functions (2.15) are

$$E = W_0 + W_k,$$

where

$$W_k = -2I(\cos k_x a + \cos k_y a + \cos k_z a).$$

Here, I is the overlap integral given by

$$I = \int \phi^*(r - a_n) H \phi(r - a_{n+1}) \, \mathrm{d}^3 x, \qquad (2.16)$$

where H is the Hamiltonian. The overlap integral occurs many times in this book. Its exact form depends on the shape of the wells, but for our purpose it will be sufficient to write it

$$I = \mathrm{e}^{-\alpha R} I_0. \qquad (2.17)$$

Here α is defined so that $\mathrm{e}^{-\alpha r}$ is the rate at which the wave function on a single well falls off with distance $(\alpha = (2mW_0)^{\frac{1}{2}}/\hbar)$; $I_0 \simeq \alpha^3 v_0 D_0$, where D_0 is the depth of each well and v_0 the volume in which the potential energy in each well differs from zero. R is the distance between a well and its nearest neighbour ($R = a$ for the simple cubic lattice).

The effective mass m^* at the bottom of a band is

$$m^* = \hbar^2/2Ia^2, \qquad (2.18)$$

and the band width J is

$$J = 2zI,$$

where z is the coordination number.

Our problem is to consider what happens to this band of energies when the potential-energy function is non-periodic. A non-periodic potential can be formed in two ways:

(a) By the displacement of each centre by a random amount, as for instance by lattice vibrations, or by the destroying of the long-range order (lateral disorder).

(b) By the addition of a random potential energy $\frac{1}{2}U$ to each well, in such a way that the energy level W_0 for an electron in the well is changed to $W_0 + \frac{1}{2}U$. We write

$$\langle U^2 \rangle = U_0^2,$$

so that U_0 gives a measure of the disorder. The resulting potential energy V is illustrated in Fig. 2.2(b); we shall call it the *Anderson potential* (Anderson 1958). It will be treated further in this section, and case (a) will be deferred till § 2.7.1.

If U_0 is small, its effect will be to introduce a mean free path L. This can be estimated from formula (2.4) (the Born approximation). We find, using the 'golden rule', that

$$\frac{1}{L} = \frac{2\pi}{\hbar}(\tfrac{1}{2}U_0)^2 \frac{a^3 N(E)}{u} \tag{2.19}$$

where E and the velocity u are to be taken at the Fermi energy, and a^3 is the atomic volume. Using formula (2.1) for $N(E)$, we may write this as

$$1/L = 4\pi (m/2\pi\hbar^2)^2 a^3 (\tfrac{1}{2}U_0)^2, \tag{2.20}$$

which is the formula obtainable by the usual methods of collision theory (Mott and Massey 1965 p. 86), or alternatively

$$a/L = (U_0/I)^2/16\pi. \tag{2.21}$$

We make use of this formula later.

We have already referred to the rule of Ioffe and Regel that a mean free path for which $kL < 1$ is impossible. In the middle of the band, $ka \sim 1$, and for our case the rule becomes that a is the minimum possible mean free path. Under such conditions the sign of the (real) wave function ψ will vary in a random way from well to well. The type of wave function expected is illustrated in Fig. 2.3(a). Formula (2.21) suggests that this may happen when U_0/I reaches the value ~ 7, or U_0/J the value $7/12$ when $z = 6$.

To see what happens when U_0 exceeds this value, we consider a pair of wells at a distance R from each other with energies shifted from the mean by amounts U_a, U_b. As is well known, the two wave functions for a pair of electrons in these states are

$$\psi_1 = A\phi_a + B\phi_b,$$
$$\psi_2 = B\phi_a - A\phi_b.$$

The values of A, B, and the energies E_1, E_2 can be found by minimizing the energy integral; the results are rather complicated (see, for instance, Miller and Abrahams 1961), and we need quote only the following limiting cases:

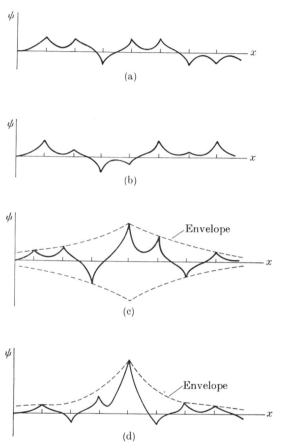

FIG. 2.3. Form of the wave function in the Anderson model: (a) when $L \sim a$; (b) when states are just non-localized $(E \gtrsim E_C)$; (c) when states are just localized $(E \lesssim E_C)$; (d) strong localization.

(a) If $|U_a - U_b| \ll I$, then $A \sim B$ and $E_1 - E_2 \simeq 2I$. It cannot be less than $2I$.

(b) If $|U_a - U_b| \gg I$, then

$$A/B \simeq |U_a - U_b|/2I. \qquad (2.22)$$

Wave functions for the two cases, and also a plot of $E_1 - E_2$ as a function of $|U_a - U_b|$, are shown in Fig. 2.4.

If we turn again to the infinite array of wells, the form of ψ for a pair suggests that there should be random fluctuations of the amplitude (as well as of the phase) of ψ in going from well to well, and that as U_0/J increases, these fluctuations get larger (Fig. 2.3(b)). This undoubtedly occurs. However, if U_0/J is very large, one would expect intuitively that the wave functions for each isolated well would be little perturbed by all the other wells, and so would fall off

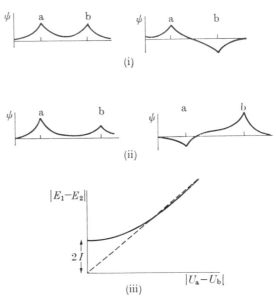

FIG. 2.4. Wave functions of odd and even parity for a pair of wells. (i) $U_a = U_b$. (ii) $U_a < U_b$ and $U_b - U_a \gg 2I$. (iii) Plot of the difference in the energies of the two states.

exponentially with distance, as in Fig. 2.3(c) and 2.3(d). The important questions are: does this in fact occur, and if so at what value of U_0/J? And also, if U_0/J is large enough, does it happen for all wave functions of the system or only for some?

The first approach to this problem is contained in Anderson's important paper, 'Absence of diffusion in certain random lattices', published in 1958. For more recent discussions of Anderson's work see Ziman (1969), Anderson (1970), and Thouless (1970). Anderson takes the potential of Fig. 2.2(b), and asks the following question. Suppose at time $t = 0$ an electron is placed on one of the wells. What happens then as $t \to \infty$? Is there a finite probability that the electron will have diffused to large distances, at the absolute zero of temperature, or does the change that an electron will be found at a large distance r vary as

$\exp(-2\alpha r)$, in which case there is no diffusion? Anderson finds that there is no diffusion if U_0/J is greater than a constant that depends on the coordination number z, and which for $z = 6$ is about 5 (see caption to Fig. 2.5). This means that if $U_0/J > 5$ all the wave functions for an electron in the system are of the type shown in Fig. 2.3(c), decaying exponentially with distance r from some well n. The initial state is of the form

$$\sum a_m \psi_m,$$

and the coefficient a_m will fall off exponentially with distance between wells m and n.

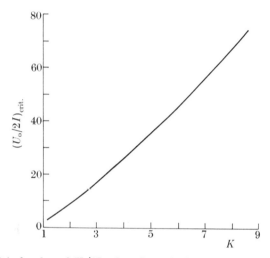

FIG. 2.5. Critical value of $U_0/2I$ taken from Anderson (1958). In Anderson's paper K is the connectivity. The relationship with the coordination number z according to Anderson is that $K = 4\cdot5$ for the simple cubic lattice. In the discussions of this book we have assumed K proportional to z. If values for K due to Domb (1970) are used, the critical values should be $4\cdot0$ for the diamond lattice, $5\cdot5$ for the simple cubic, $6\cdot4$ for the body-centred cubic, and $7\cdot5$ for the face-centred cubic.

Another and perhaps clearer way of expressing the Anderson condition is to take for the initial state an electron localized in a large volume of radius Δx, the energy being defined as closely as allowed by the uncertainty principle. Then if E is taken at the centre of the band, there will be no diffusion if the condition is satisfied; if not the amplitude will tend to zero as the time t increases.

The critical value of U_0/J depends weakly on the coordination number z. Anderson's plot of $U_0/2I$ is reproduced in Fig. 2.5. U_0/J has the value $\sim$5 for $z = 6$; evidence to be presented later suggests that for a random distribution of centres this value is in fair agreement with experiment.

Some more recent work on Anderson localization (Mott 1967, 1970) has concentrated on the quantity $\sigma(0)$. If there is no diffusion, the conductivity σ too must vanish for all energies in the band. One can also investigate σ_E for any energy E in the band, and ask if σ_E vanishes or not. To obtain a meaningful result, one must investigate the average of σ_E, which we write $\langle \sigma_E(0) \rangle$, over all configurations of the ensemble, that is for all values of U_i for each well i such that $\langle U^2 \rangle = U_0^2$. Clearly, for some configurations, namely those for which all or most values of U are small, σ will not vanish. The question at issue is whether, for an infinite number of wells, such states make a finite contribution to $\langle \sigma \rangle$ or a contribution that tends to zero exponentially for large N. The problem has been investigated in detail by Mott (1970). The method used is to evaluate the conductivity at frequency ω, $\sigma(\omega)$, and to show that for all configurations, except a proportion that gives a vanishing contribution as $N \to \infty$, $\langle \sigma(\omega) \rangle$ behaves like ω^2 for small ω. $\langle \sigma(0) \rangle$, therefore, vanishes.

As a preliminary we consider two fairly distant wells, a and b, for which U_a and U_b are nearly equal. The wave function will be of the type illustrated in Fig. 2.4(i), so long as for any well, denoted by c, lying in between, $|U_c - U_a| \gg |U_b - U_a|$. We want to know what contribution these two wells a, b make to $\langle \sigma(\omega) \rangle$. If the lower state is occupied and the upper one empty, and if the two states differ in energy by $\hbar \omega$, the chance per unit time that a field $F \cos \omega t$ will cause a transition from one to the other is (compare eqn (2.4))

$$\tfrac{1}{4} F^2 (2\pi e^2 / \hbar) \, |x_{ab}|^2 \, n(E_b).$$

Here $n(E) \, \mathrm{d}E$ is the probability, in the ensemble average, that E, the energy of an electron in a well, lies in the range $\mathrm{d}E$. $n(E)$ is of order $1/U_0$. If therefore there are N centres per unit volume, and if states are filled up to an energy E_F, and if also $\hbar \omega / U_0 \ll 1$, then the conductivity $\langle \sigma(\omega) \rangle$ is given by

$$\frac{\pi e^2}{\hbar} (\hbar \omega)^2 \{n(E_F)\}^2 N^2 \int |x|^2 \, 4\pi R^2 \, \mathrm{d}R,$$

where x is to be evaluated at $E = E_F$, and R is the distance between any two wells. The lower limit of the integral is given by the condition that, for small values of $\hbar \omega$, the two wells must be sufficiently far apart for the resonance energy $2I (= 2I_0 \exp(-\alpha R))$ to be not greater than $\hbar\omega$. This minimum distance, which we denote by R_ω, is thus given by

$$R_\omega = (1/\alpha)\ln(2I_0/\hbar\omega). \tag{2.23}$$

At these distances, when B/A (eqn (2.22)) is not small, x_{ab} is of order R, though for larger distances, when $B/A \sim 2I/|U_a - U_b|$, x_{ab} falls off exponentially with distance. So significant contributions to the integral come from the volume between spheres of radii R_ω and $R_\omega + \alpha^{-1}$. We find therefore that

$$\langle\sigma(\omega)\rangle \simeq (4\pi^2 e^2/\hbar)(\hbar\omega)^2 N^2 n^2 4\pi R_\omega^4/\alpha. \tag{2.24}$$

Since $Nn = N(E)$, the density of states, this may be written

$$\langle\sigma(\omega)\rangle \simeq (\pi e^2/\hbar)\{N(E_F)\}^2 \alpha^{-5}(\hbar\omega)^2\{\ln(I_0/\hbar\omega)\}^4. \tag{2.25}$$

This is the form that the Kubo–Greenwood formula (2.11) takes for localized states. It tends to zero with ω. The matrix elements D in (2.9) *all* tend to zero, as may be seen from eqn (2.5), since x tends to a finite value.

To make this argument rigorous, the effect of all the other wells on the two under consideration must be examined. It must be shown that the number of configurations of the ensemble for which the two wave functions are not localized in the sense of Fig. 2.3 corresponds to a fraction of the whole that tends to zero when N tends to infinity. This question has been examined by Mott (1970). The presence of all the other wells does, of course, always affect the rate at which the wave functions decay in space, so α in eqn (2.17) will not have the value for an isolated well. In particular, α should tend to zero as U_0/J tends to the critical Anderson value, where diffusion begins.

Formula (2.25) can conveniently be written, with $N(E_F) = N/U_0$,

$$\langle\sigma(\omega)\rangle = (\pi^2 e^2/\hbar)N^2(\hbar\omega/U_0)^2\alpha^{-5}\{\ln(I_0/\hbar\omega)\}^4. \tag{2.26}$$

There should be no variation of σ with temperature until kT becomes comparable with U_0. Tanaka and Fan (1963) were the first to obtain an ω^2 law with a model of this kind; they considered the case when $kT > U_0$. If this is so our formulae should be multiplied by U_0/kT. Further reference to this formula is given in § 2.11 and in Chapter 6.

The important deduction from this work is that $\langle\sigma(0)\rangle$ vanishes if U_0/J is large enough. Of course, $\sigma(0)$ does not vanish for all configurations of the ensemble, but only for a proportion that tends to unity as $N \to \infty$. Assuming that the results of the Anderson model apply to real materials, therefore, one might expect 'conducting channels' due to statistical fluctuations through a thin film, and a dependence of resistivity on film thickness as in Fig. 2.6.

There has been a great deal of discussion in the literature of the validity of the Anderson approach (see Mott 1970; Anderson 1970). Other quite different discussions have been given (Edwards 1970; Cohen 1970; Neustadter and Coopersmith 1969). The last authors calculate the mobility of an electron in a system of randomly located hard-core scatterers, and find a sharp drop in the mobility at a critical density.

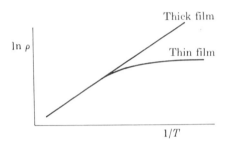

FIG. 2.6. Resistivity ρ as a function of $1/T$ for thick and thin films (schematic).

2.5. Situations in which states are localized in one range of energies and not localized in another

This can occur for an electron with the potential energy illustrated in Fig. 2.2(b), if the Anderson criterion is not satisfied, and in many other cases to be discussed below. $\langle \sigma_E(0) \rangle$ will then be finite for values of the energy E in the middle of the band, but may be zero towards its extremities if the density of states drops there, as can be shown by the argument of the last section (see Mott 1967, 1970). In this case, a critical energy E_C must separate the two regions; this is defined so that

$$\begin{aligned}\langle \sigma_E(0) \rangle &= 0 \qquad (E < E_c) \\ &\neq 0 \qquad (E > E_c)\end{aligned}\Bigg\}. \tag{2.27}$$

This is illustrated for a density of states resulting from the Anderson potential in Fig. 2.7. Other examples will be given later in this book.

Anything that we can say about the behaviour of $\langle \sigma \rangle$ and the wave functions in the neighbourhood of the energy E_C is somewhat speculative. Mott (1969a, 1970) has suggested that for values of E slightly less than E_C the wave function is as in Fig. 2.3(c); a wave function on any well will have random signs and amplitudes, but its envelope, shown by the dotted line, falls away exponentially as $e^{-\alpha'r}$, and $\alpha' \to 0$ as $E \to E_C$. For such wave functions, each localized orbital will overlap many others. If states are localized, an electron can move only by hopping from one state to another, exchanging energy with a phonon in the process. The rate-determining processes will of course be those in which an electron *receives* energy from phonons. An argument that will be used elsewhere in this book is that, if states are distant from each other in space, the overlap of orbitals is small, so the hopping probability should be small; on the other

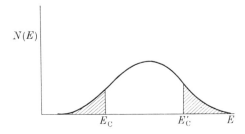

Fig. 2.7. Density of states in the Anderson model, when states are non-localized in the centre of the band. Localized states are shown shaded. E_C, E'_C separate the ranges of energy where states are localized and non-localized.

hand, the further an electron can tunnel, the more states it has to choose from, and the greater the chance of finding another state with nearly the same energy. We conjecture, therefore, that as $E \to E_C$ from below, the activation energy W for hopping tends to zero as a multiple of $U_0\alpha'^3$. The energy is shown schematically in Fig. 2.8(b). We return to this argument in § 2.9.

For values of E slightly greater than E_C, the wave functions should, we believe, appear as in Fig. 2.3(b); again the sign of the wave function on each well is random, but the wave function extends through the lattice. We call such a wave function *extended*. If the wave function is indeed of this form, the value of $\langle \sigma(0) \rangle$ is finite. There will therefore be a discontinuity in $\langle \sigma_E(0) \rangle$ at $E = E_C$, as shown in Fig. 2.8(a). There will be no discontinuities in $\sigma(\omega)$, or in the conductivity at finite values of T; the behaviour shown in Fig. 2.8(a) by the dotted line is to be expected. Examples of this kind of behaviour will be shown in various parts of this book.

It must be emphasized that no formal proof that $\langle \sigma(0) \rangle$ shows this discontinuity has been given, and some authors have thought otherwise (Cohen 1970). The matter is discussed by Mott (1970); we believe that experimental evidence in its favour, which will be discussed in this book, is strong.

Figure 2.9 shows the behaviour of the conductivity according to this model for values of E_F above and below the critical value E_C. Examples taken from the study of impurity-conduction are given in Chapter 6.

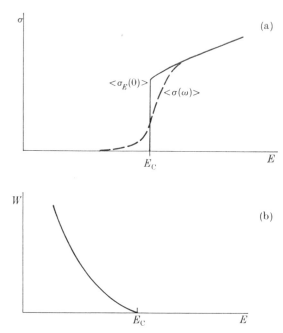

FIG. 2.8. (a) The conductivity $\langle \sigma_E(0) \rangle$ as a function of E when $T = 0$ in the Anderson model. The dotted line shows $\langle \sigma(\omega) \rangle$ for small ω or $\langle \sigma(0) \rangle$ for small T. (b) The hopping activation energy W as a function of E.

A numerical estimate of $\langle \sigma(0) \rangle$ when E is just above E_C will now be given. A rather surprising result of the model is that, as we shall see below, the value of the disorder parameter U_0 for which $L \sim a$ is considerably less than that required for localization. This means that for values of E near to E_C there will be strong fluctuations in the amplitude as well as in the phase of ψ from well to well. In the analysis below we neglect these, which may lead to a certain error.

We start from formula (2.10), and suppose that there is a random phase relationship between the wave functions in each well. Then

$$D = N^{\frac{1}{2}}\delta,$$

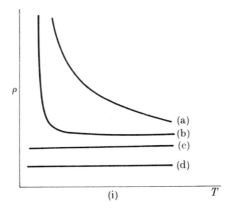

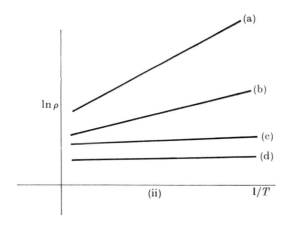

Fig. 2.9. Dependence of the conductivity on temperature in the Anderson model: (i) plotted against T; (ii) plotted logarithmically against $1/T$. (a) and (b) are for E_F in the range of energies where states are localized ($E < E_C$), (c) and (d) for $E > E_C$.

where $N \; (= \Omega/a^3)$ is the number of wells in the volume Ω, and

$$\delta = \int \psi_1 (\partial/\partial x) \psi_2 \; \mathrm{d}^3 x,$$

the integration being over a single well. The difficulty in the problem is the estimation of δ. We shall assume that it has the same value as for the periodic lattice (that is, for $U_0 = 0$). It is then similar in magnitude to the current vector, so that (see p. 58)

$$\delta \simeq (m/m^*) ka^3/\Omega, \tag{2.28}$$

where m^* is the effective mass for the periodic lattice and k is the wave number. Thus

$$|D|^2 = \frac{\Omega}{a^3}\left(\frac{m}{m^*}\right)^2 \frac{k^2 a^6}{\Omega^2}.$$

For k we take π/a, so that

$$|D|^2 \simeq (m/m^*)^2 \pi^2 a/\Omega.$$

Substituting in eqn (2.10), we find

$$\sigma_E(0) = (2\pi^3 e^2 \hbar^3 a/m^{*2})\{N(E_F)\}^2. \tag{2.29}$$

If we write $\hbar^2/2m^*a^2 = I$ and $N(E) = 1/a^3 U_0$, this becomes

$$\sigma_E(0) = (8\pi^3 e^2/\hbar a)(I/U_0)^2. \tag{2.30}$$

For the value of U_0 at which the Anderson transition occurs,

$$U_0 \sim 5J = 60I$$

for coordination number 6. This means that, for a value of E in the middle of the band, the value of the conductivity when metallic conduction first appears is

$$\sigma_0 = 0{\cdot}06e^2/\hbar a. \tag{2.31}$$

(This is for coordination number $z = 6$; for other values of the co-ordination number it should be multiplied by $(6/z)^2$.) For $a = 4$ Å σ_0 is about 350 Ω^{-1} cm^{-1}.

Mott (1970) has argued that eqn (2.31) gives the minimum metallic conductivity also in all cases where E just exceeds E_C, if we write, instead of a, the distance a_E between localized states, so that

$$\sigma_0 = 0{\cdot}06e^2/\hbar a_E. \tag{2.31a}$$

This quantity a_E can be defined as follows. We suppose that the spread in the energies of the wells, U_0, is the same in the tail of the band as elsewhere; any drop in the density of states is due to an increase in the mean distance between wells deep enough to contribute states to the tail. Thus we can write

$$N(E) = 1/a_E^3 U_0. \tag{2.32}$$

which gives a measure of a_E.

If a_E is defined in this way, an estimate of the values E_C of E for which localization occurs can be obtained. This is (Mott 1970)

$$\alpha(a_E - a) = \ln(5J/U_0). \tag{2.33}$$

When localization occurs in the middle of the band, the right-hand side of this equation is zero. If for instance $J = U_0$, then

$$a_E = a + \alpha^{-1} \ln 5$$

and $N(E_C)$ can be read off from eqn (2.32).

The many approximations used in the derivation of σ_0 given above do not of course give reliable values. But there is a good deal

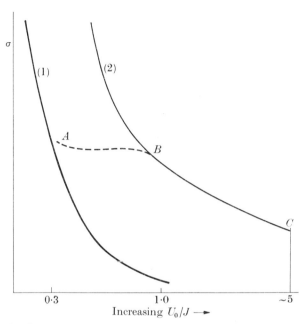

Fig. 2.10. Conductivity in the Anderson model at $T = 0$ as a function of U_0/J. (1) is the Born approximation, (2) the formula (2.30), AB the intermediate region.

of evidence, which we review in this book, that a minimum metallic conductivity of the order predicted is observed. The matter is discussed further in § 2.7 and Chapter 6.

There is a considerable range of the parameter I/U_0 for which $L \sim a$. An elementary calculation shows that, when the Born approximation is valid, for states in the middle of an Anderson band

$$\sigma = \frac{16\pi}{3} \frac{e^2}{\hbar a} \left(\frac{I}{U_0} \right)^2, \tag{2.34}$$

and $L/a = 16\pi(I/U_0)^2$. For $U_0/I \geqslant \sqrt{(16\pi)} \sim 7$, we expect σ to remain constant as U_0/I increases until, as we see from eqn (2.30), $U_0/I \sim \sqrt{(8\pi^3)} \sim 16$; thereafter σ will drop with $(I/U_0)^2$ until localization sets in. The kind of behaviour expected is shown in Fig. 2.10.

In § 3.17 we describe how n.m.r. measurements in certain liquids can distinguish between the three regions.

A further point of interest is that the Drude formula is not expected to be valid when $L \sim a$. The quantity τ in eqn (2.14) should in any case be very small; but the derivation given here shows that this formula should be applicable only when $L \gg a$. The conductivity $\langle \sigma(\omega) \rangle$ for non-localized states will depend on a mean of $N(E)$ and $N(E + \hbar\omega)$ over all possible transitions, and is as likely to increase with ω as to decrease (compare § 3.15 and § 7.6.5).

2.6. Many-body effects and magnetic susceptibility

The Anderson model, described in the last section, is directly applicable to impurity-conduction, and this phenomenon is described in Chapter 6. The greater part of this book, however, is based on the assumption that certain of the concepts derived from the model, notably those of localized states, the energy E_C, and the minimum metallic conductivity $\sigma_0 = 0 \cdot 06 e^2 / \hbar a_E$, can be applied to amorphous and liquid semiconductors. Before describing these more general problems, however, we must enquire to what extent the Hartree–Fock approximation of non-interacting electrons is adequate to describe the concepts that we have introduced.

In the Hartree–Fock approximation, the energies of the states obtained from the one-electron Schrödinger equation do not depend on whether the state is doubly or singly occupied. For metals and in general for non-localized wave functions, this approximation is satisfactory. As soon as localized states appear, however, it is not; owing to the Coulomb repulsion e^2 / r_{12} between electrons, the energy required to remove the first electron from a doubly occupied state is less than that to remove the second. It is necessary to suppose that the energy of a state depends on whether it is doubly or singly occupied. In other words, the electron affinity and the ionization potential are not equal.

In our discussion of impurity-conduction in Chapter 6, the localization is strong; the difference between the ionization potential, denoted by ε_1, and the electron affinity, denoted by $\varepsilon_1 - \varepsilon_2$, is large. In this case therefore we have only singly occupied centres. These make a contribution to the paramagnetism, though if the wave functions on the centres overlap there will be coupling between them, presumably antiferromagnetic, about which little is known.

If localization is weak, as in Fig. 2.3(c), the difference between the electron affinity and the ionization potential ought to be small. The number of states that are singly occupied will be small, and there will be strong coupling between their spins. No detailed investigations have been made of the magnetic properties of such a system, but as the localization gets weaker we should expect a gradual appearance of Pauli spin paramagnetism independent of temperature. Some speculations are reviewed in § 6.9.

A further important point may be made about localized states. Whether a state is occupied by an electron or is empty will affect the energy levels, and hence the occupation number, of surrounding states owing to the Coulomb field, and also the spins of electrons in the surrounding states because of exchange forces. The consequences of these many-body effects on transport processes have yet to be worked out.

2.7. The density of states

Up to this point we have considered the simplest possible non-periodic potential, namely the Anderson model of a crystalline array of wells of random depth. We shall now apply the concepts introduced to other systems. We begin with the density of states. We have already seen that, using the model of non-interacting electrons, the concept of the density of states $N(E)$ is valid for non-crystalline as for crystalline materials. In the last section we have seen that, if states are localized, the wave functions are not the same for the two spin directions; but, averaged over a large number of atoms, the density of states will be the same. We have seen also that over some ranges of energy the wave functions are localized and over other ranges they are not. In this section we shall discuss the density of states, the factors that affect it, and give some further consideration to the conditions under which the states are localized. Few definite proofs exist; we shall summarize what can be conjectured, either from theoretical work based on approximations or from experimental observations.

2.7.1. Random distribution of centres in space

One of the simplest problems is that of a random array of centres in each of which the atomic function is s-like. This differs from Anderson's model in that there is no random potential; instead, the sites are distributed at random in space. The case of weak scattering, or that in which the centres are close together, is treated in Chapter

3, which deals with liquid metals; the approach in this section is again based on a tight-binding approximation. An application would be to the impurity band of semiconductors with no compensation and hence no random potential—though, unless the concentration is well on the metallic side of the metal–non-metal transition (Chapters 5, 6), a treatment neglecting the correlation term e^2/r_{12} will give misleading results.

Lifshitz (1964) has discussed this problem by separating the centres into pairs in such a way that the distance between the atoms in each pair is as small as possible compared with the average distance between the pairs. The result of such a treatment shows:

(a) That the band is widened, the width being the maximum separation between the states of odd and even parity on a pair of atoms.

(b) That if the mean distance between atoms is great enough, the density of states will show a minimum in the middle (Fig. 2.11). The

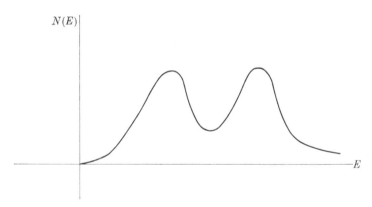

FIG. 2.11. Density of states in an impurity band according to Lifshitz.

reason is as follows. If E is the energy of an electron in any isolated state, the energy of an electron in the field of a pair of atoms will have the form

$$E \pm I,$$

where I is the overlap energy integral (as in H_2^+) for the two atoms. It is argued that, if the mean distance is great enough, this effect will lower the density of states in the centre. Wolf, Losee, Cullen, and Compton (1971) have made observations of $N(E_F)$ in an impurity band of p-type silicon by a barrier-tunnelling technique and found evidence for a minimum in the density of states that could be interpreted in this way.[†]

Mott (1969a) has given a qualitative discussion of the condition for localization in this case. He finds that, if the wave functions fall off as $\exp(-\alpha r)$, αR must be greater than about 8, where R^{-3} is the number of centres per unit volume. This may be of little practical importance; if the band contains one electron per atom, it will become insulating because of the term e^2/r_{12} before localization due to disorder sets in (Chapter 5); if the number of electrons is less than one per atom, as in a semiconductor as a consequence of compensation, a random field is set up (Chapter 6).

The density of states and condition for localization when a random potential is applied to each centre have already been discussed. No attempt has yet been made to treat the combined effect of random distribution and random potential energy, though the latter is probably the more important.

2.7.2. Liquids, glasses, and amorphous solids

From the theoretical point of view these present more difficult problems than does an impurity band, because the only information that we usually have about their structure is the pair distribution function (Chapter 3), which is sufficient to determine $N(E)$ only if the scattering by each atom is weak. Calculations of $N(E)$ under these conditions (i.e. for liquid metals) are described in Chapter 3. In addition, there have been extensive calculations of the tail at the bottom edge of an s band (Fig. 2.12(a)), caused by thermal fluctuations in the density (Lifshitz 1964; Halperin and Lax 1966; Zittartz and Langer 1966). Mott (1967) has pointed out that such fluctuations will give rise to a few deep potential wells in crystals as well as in liquids, and that states in these will be localized.

The conjecture that at the extremities of the conduction (or valence) band of amorphous or liquid semiconductors there exists a range of localized states, which is nothing to do with thermal fluctuations, was made by Fröhlich (1947) and by Banyai (1964).[‡] This is

---

[†] An alternative explanation is that for values of R approaching the metal–non-metal transition the density of states near the Fermi energy must be small for one electron per centre, and thus in the middle of the band; in § 6.13 the magnetoresistance of heavily doped semiconductors is interpreted in this way (Wulf et al. 1971).

[‡] It must be emphasized that these are traps, normally empty, not donors as postulated by Gubanov (1963).

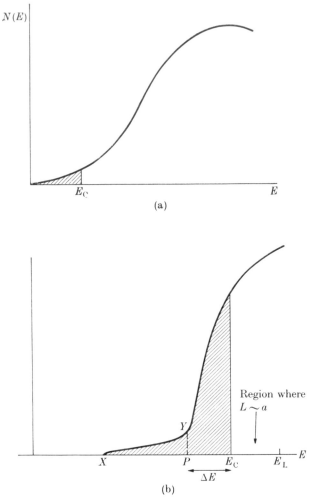

Fig. 2.12. Density of states in the conduction band. (a) Case where the wave functions are s-like at the bottom of the band (e.g. liquid argon). (b) Suggested form when states are p-like or d-like, as in germanium or a glass. XY is the tail, due to fluctuations in density; the region of localized states between P and E_C may be wide (~ 0.2 eV). Between E_C and E_L the wavelength $\lambda \sim a$.

now generally accepted; perhaps the most direct evidence for it comes from measurements of the drift mobility of injected carriers. Experiments on the drift mobility in amorphous silicon and in amorphous selenium are reviewed in Chapters 8 and 10. Mott (1969a) has pointed out that we may expect a difference between conduction bands where the wave functions are s-like on the individual atoms at the bottom of the band (liquid metals, liquid argon, or alkali halides), and those in which they are p-like or d-like (germanium, chalcogenides). In the former case, we start in the crystalline state with a *spherical* surface of constant energy; in the non-crystalline state, if the mean free path is long enough for a surface of constant energy to be defined, it must be spherical. So there is no qualitative difference between the wave functions for the crystal and the non-crystal. The mean free path can be calculated by perturbation theory, as in Chapter 3.

If the wave functions do not have this symmetry, as in the conduction and valence bands of germanium for example, the effective mass m^* in the crystal depends on direction, and the energy surfaces are not spherical. If the mean free path L in the non-crystalline state is long enough for the effective mass m^* to be defined, m^* must be independent of direction. To produce this change, the interaction with the lattice must be strong near the bottom of the band, so that *either* the mean free path will be short *or* localization will occur. Fig. 2.12 contrasts the two cases. For s states, as for instance in the conduction band of liquid argon, there is simply a small thermal tail of localized states; in all other cases we expect a region of localized states and an energy E_C separating localized and non-localized states, and E_C could have a value such that the density of states $N(E_C)$ is already quite high. There may also be a tail of localized states due to fluctuations of density or coordination number. In this book we shall make the assumption that an energy E_C of this kind does exist in the conduction band of amorphous materials, and a corresponding energy E_V for the valence band. We shall also use formulae of type (2.29) to estimate $\sigma(E_C)$ at the non-localized side of E_C, and deduce from it the mobility in semiconductors. This is an assumption that needs further theoretical verification, but there is plenty of evidence that it works.

The arguments leading to this somewhat speculative conclusion are (Mott 1970):

(a) In the crystalline state, near the extremity of a band where the states are not s-like, the Schrödinger equation has solutions of the form $e^{ikx} u(x)$ *and* of the form $e^{\pm \gamma x} u(x) \sin(kx + \eta)$.

(b) In the amorphous state, it is suggested that we can set up Wannier-type functions using all eigenstates in some fairly wide range of ΔE. By minimizing the total energy we determine the location of these states in space; on account of the term $\exp(\pm \gamma x)$ in the crystalline wave functions we should expect their wave functions to decay exponentially with distance.

(c) We can then apply the Anderson criterion in the form

$$a_E^3 N(E)B = \tfrac{1}{5};\qquad (2.35)$$

B is here of the order of the band width. If the left-hand side is less than 5, these Wannier states are the eigenstates. If not, we must combine them into extended functions.†

An energy E_C thus exists in such a band, and its position is given by

$$a_E^3 N(E_C)B \sim \tfrac{1}{5}.$$

For energies on the localized side of E_C, conduction is by thermally activated hopping. For energies on the non-localized side, we expect eqn (2.31) to be valid for the conductivity, with a_E perhaps about twice the interatomic distance.

Mott (1969a) has also given arguments to suggest that in a valence or conduction band, when the wave functions are not s-like, the density of states near the limit of the band is linear in E, apart from the effect of structural defects. The argument is as follows. Suppose we are dealing with p states. It is then *assumed* that the orientation of the nodal plane passing through each atom varies in a random way from atom to atom. If we now consider two atoms, and a state such that the two nodes are both perpendicular to the line joining them, the integral $\int \psi^* H \psi \, d^3x$ over these two atoms will have the minimum possible value. We suppose this gives an approximation to the energy of a localized state. If the two nodes are both oriented with their normals in a solid angle $d\omega$ at angles to the line joining the atoms, the number of configurations for which this is so will be

$$d\omega_1 \, d\omega_2 = \sin\theta_1 \, d\theta_1 \sin\theta_2 \, d\theta_2$$

and the energy is proportional to $\theta_1^2 + \theta_2^2$. Writing $\theta_1^2 = x$, $\theta_2^2 = y$ we note that the number of configurations with energies E, $E + dE$ is the area between the lines $x + y = E$, $x + y = E + dE$, which is proportional to $E \, dE$.

2.8. Conductors and insulators

In the Bloch–Wilson theory of crystalline solids, the allowed energies for an electron are divided into bands. In an insulator or intrinsic semiconductor, a fully occupied valence band does not

---

† A somewhat different model has been used by Stern (1971) to make quantitative estimates for silicon; he finds that E_C is between 0·1 and 0·2 eV from the band edge. A similar estimate for the valence band of chalcogenides was made by Mott (1970).

overlap an empty conduction band. There is a band of forbidden
energies, in which the density of states is zero, and the Fermi energy
lies in this gap. In a semi-metal there is a small overlap, and the
density of states can be low at the Fermi energy (Fig. 2.13).

The problem of calculating the density of states in a non-crystalline
material under conditions when a gap is expected has not been solved.
We believe however that in many cases the density of states is

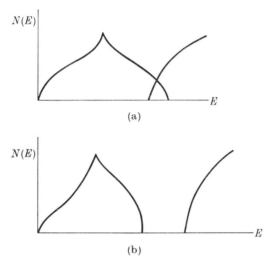

Fig. 2.13. Density of states in a divalent crystalline material. (a) Metal or semi-metal,
with overlapping bands. (b) Semiconductor.

determined mainly by the actual potential of the atom and its
nearest neighbours, as it would be in the tight-binding approximation, and not, except in minor detail, by the structure. We therefore envisage a valence band, and a conduction band, both of which
have tails, which may or may not overlap with each other. When
they overlap (Fig. 2.14), the density of states shows a minimum,
which we call a *pseudogap*.

It is perhaps necessary to emphasize that in non-crystalline *transparent* materials such as glass or water the density of states must
show a real gap, not a pseudogap, and the gap has very few, if any,
localized states in it. Since most treatments of non-metallic materials
ascribe the gap to the crystalline structure, there has been some
speculation about how a gap can occur (Ziman 1970; Klima and
McGill 1971). In the tight-binding approximation, however, the gap
does not depend essentially on long-range order; if E_1, E_2 are the

energies of the atomic states from which bands are formed, the gap
cannot be less than

$$(E_2 - E_1) - z(J_1 + J_2),$$

where z is the (maximum) coordination number, and J_1, J_2 the
maximum overlap integrals in the two bands. Such a treatment would
certainly be appropriate for a liquid rare gas. For an amorphous
covalent material such as Si calculations by Weaire (1971) and Heine
(1971) show that a gap must appear if there are no dangling bonds.

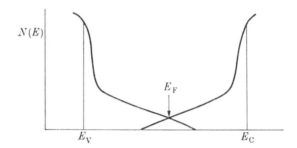

FIG. 2.14. Density of states in valence and conduction bands of an amorphous non-
metal, with overlapping tails.

We now ask whether, when $N(E_F) \neq 0$, a material is an insulator or
conductor. According to the Bloch–Wilson theory of non-interacting
electrons, insulating behaviour can occur in a crystal only if $N(E_F)$
vanishes as in Fig. 2.13. In non-crystalline materials, however, the
situation is different. In the last section we have given arguments to
suggest that states in the tails of conduction or valence bands are
localized, and it is not a great extrapolation to suggest that this can
also happen when the tails of two bands overlap and $N(E_F)$ is small.

We introduce the hypothesis, then, that if a pseudogap is deep
enough the states there are localized. If so, a material will be non-
conducting at $T = 0$ even if $N(E_F)$ is not zero. An insulator, in our
model, is a material for which *either* $N(E_F)$ vanishes *or* states are
localized at E_F. We have to ask how deep the pseudogap must be for
states to be localized. Equation (2.35) could be used. In Chapter 3
this is expressed in a rather different form, as follows. If we define a
factor g by

$$g = N(E_F)/N(E_F)_{\text{free}},$$

then for localization g is of the order 0·3. We return to this problem in Chapter 3.

We thus have three possibilities if E_F lies in the pseudogap:

(a) $g > 0·3$. The behaviour is then metallic, in the sense that σ tends to a finite value as $T \to 0$. This case is discussed further in Chapter 3; the minimum metallic value of σ seems to be about the same as for the Anderson model, namely $\sim 350 \ \Omega^{-1} \ \text{cm}^{-1}$.

(b) $g < 0·3$, but not too small. Conduction at low temperatures is then by thermally activated hopping, but at higher temperatures carriers will be excited to non-localized states (§ 2.9).

(c) g small or zero. The tunnelling factor $\exp(-2\alpha R)$ between localized states will make thermally activated hopping improbable, so that the main part of the current is carried by electrons excited into the conduction band (or holes in the valence bands). The material is then an intrinsic semiconductor. Unless g is actually zero, however, process (b), similar to impurity-conduction, will be predominant at very low temperatures.

For an understanding of the conductivity, therefore, it is important to know in what ways the density of states differs from that of the crystal. This will of course depend on the coordination number and can change drastically if that changes. For instance, amorphous germanium, which is a semiconductor, preserves the coordination number 4 characteristic of the crystal and retains an energy gap, but liquid germanium with a higher coordination number is a metal. There is, moreover, another way in which many amorphous materials (e.g. chalcogenides, germanium) differ from the crystals. As the Leningrad school, particularly Kolomiets, emphasized first, their conductivities are relatively insensitive to impurities; unlike the crystals, glasses and many amorphous films cannot be doped. This will be brought out in the chapters dealing with these materials. The explanation due to various authors (Mott 1967; Haisty and Krebs 1969a, b) is that a glassy substance can rearrange itself so that all available electrons are taken up in bonds. Thus phosphorus in crystalline germanium is placed as in Fig. 2.15(b), the fifth electron being loosely bound. In amorphous germanium it is suggested that a phosphorus atom would be surrounded by *five* germanium atoms (Fig. 2.15(a)). As we shall see in the next chapter, this kind of structure may break down at high temperatures in the liquid state; the coordination number then increases and the material becomes metallic.

There is some experimental evidence that this is a correct model for the amorphous alloy $Te_{39}Ge_{11}$. Betts, Bienenstock, and Ovshinsky (1970) have determined the radial distribution function of several alloys including this one and have concluded that Te–Te chains are cross-linked by a Ge atom which thus has four Te neighbours. Their

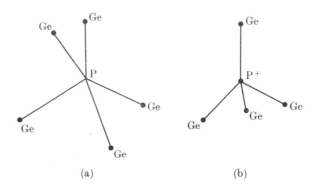

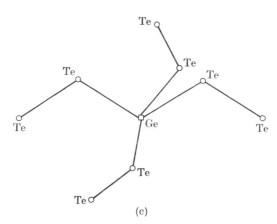

FIG. 2.15. Suggested position of phosphorus atom in (a) amorphous and (b) crystalline germanium; (c) shows the configuration in Ge–Te according to Adler *et al.* (1970).

model is shown in Fig. 2.15(c). Adler, Cohen, Fagen, and Thompson (1970) have interpreted n.m.r. results of Senturia, Hewes, and Adler (1970) and come to a similar conclusion.

Thus in glassy substances we do not expect an impurity band due to impurities such as that illustrated in Fig. 2.1(e). On the other hand there is some evidence that many glassy substances have *deep* bands of localized levels of similar type, caused by structural defects, lying near the middle of the band gap. This comes from estimates of the density of states at the Fermi level, and will be reviewed below and in Chapter 7. A possible hypothesis is that dangling bonds produce acceptors, and interstitial metal atoms a smaller number of donors.

Not all amorphous materials behave in this way. Thus the conductivity of amorphous Mg_3Bi_2 is very sensitive to excess of one constituent (compare § 3.16.2). Glasses containing vanadium ions V^{5+} and V^{4+} are conductors; the electron on the V^{4+} is not taken up in bonding. On the other hand, glasses containing Cu^+ and Cu^{2+} can apparently exist in a conducting and a non-conducting state (Drake and Scanlan 1970; see also Chapter 6), and this may be associated with a rearrangement of the glass so that the hole in Cu^{2+} *is* taken up in a bond.

2.9. Temperature-dependent conductivity

As we emphasized at the beginning of this chapter and in the last section, for non-crystalline as for crystalline materials we can divide conduction mechanisms into two classes:

(a) That in which the current depends on the mobility of electrons with energies at or near the Fermi energy. This class includes metals and highly doped crystalline semiconductors, in which the conductivity tends to a finite value at low temperatures. It also includes various cases of hopping conduction such as impurity-conduction in crystalline semiconductors and low-temperature conduction in amorphous materials, which we believe is a similar process (defect conduction) due to the structural defects mentioned above.

(b) That in which the conductivity $\sigma_E(0)$ for $E \sim E_F$ is small compared with the contribution of electrons excited into the conduction band. As in case (a), carriers may move by a hopping or non-hopping mechanism as discussed in § 2.9.2.

2.9.1. Conduction due to electrons with energies near the Fermi energy

For conduction in class (a), if states are localized, we start with the assumption that the probability p that an electron jumps from one localized state to a given different state with higher energy contains the following factors:

(a) The Boltzmann factor $\exp(-W/kT)$, where W is the difference between the energies of the two states.

(b) A factor ν_{ph} depending on the phonon spectrum. If $W/\hbar$ is larger than the maximum phonon frequency ω_{max}, then to a good approximation $\nu_{\text{ph}} \sim \omega_{\text{max}}$ and is thus in the range 10^{12}–10^{13} s⁻¹. In other cases ν_{ph} can have values over a wide range (§ 4.3), though $\sim 10^{12}$ s⁻¹ turns out to be appropriate to impurity-conduction in germanium.

(c) A factor depending on the overlap of the wave functions. If the overlap is small, because the localized states are far apart, this factor should be $\exp(-2\alpha R)$ as in impurity-conduction. If there is considerable overlap the factor will be of order unity (compare § 4.7, particularly the discussion of the adiabatic approximation).

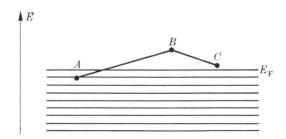

FIG. 2.16. The mechanism of hopping conduction. Two hops are shown, from A to B and from B to C.

Only electrons with energies within a range of order kT at the Fermi energy need be considered as taking part in the conduction process. Those with lower energies will *on the average* need more activation to hop to an empty state. The number of such electrons is $N(E_F)kT$. Thus the diffusion coefficient is†

$$pR^2 N(E_F)kT,$$

and the conductivity by Einstein's relationship is

$$\sigma \simeq (e^2/kT)pR^2 N(E_F)kT \qquad (2.36)$$

$$\simeq e^2 pR^2 N(E_F),$$

where

$$p = \nu_{\text{ph}}\, e^{-2\alpha R - W/kT}.$$

R is here the distance covered by each hop (Fig. 2.16).

We consider next the quantity W, the mean activation energy for hopping. This will be inversely proportional to the density of states.

† Note that p is the probability per unit time that an electron will hop to a *particular* atom; otherwise a factor $\frac{1}{6}$ must be introduced. The last two factors in (2.36) give the proportion of the electrons able to move.

For strong localization, as in impurity-conduction, the electron will not move further than to the nearest neighbour; thus

$$W \sim 1/R^3 N(E). \tag{2.37}$$

If localization is weak, so that $1/\alpha'$ defined in § 2.6 is greater than the distance R between centres,

$$W \sim \alpha'^3/N(E), \tag{2.38}$$

and in this case, since the electron has a wide choice of centres to which it can hop, we should multiply p by a factor

$$\phi \sim 1/\alpha'^3 R^3 \gg 1,$$

as has already been pointed out in § 2.5. If E_F lies at an interval ΔE from E_C, it is a reasonable hypothesis that

$$\alpha' \sim \sqrt{\{(2m \, \Delta E)/\hbar^2\}},$$

so that

$$W \sim \{2m \, \Delta E/\hbar^2\}^{\frac{3}{2}}/N(E). \tag{2.39}$$

The behaviour of W is therefore expected to be as already illustrated in Fig. 2.8(b), i.e. varying as $(\Delta E)^{\frac{3}{2}}$.

At low temperatures W will not remain constant. It is constant only if the factor $\exp(-2\alpha'R)$ is sufficiently small to ensure that an electron will always jump to the nearest centre. At low temperatures the electron will have a higher probability of jumping to a more distant centre, because with more centres from which to choose the energy difference can be smaller. We can use the following analysis (Mott 1968a). At distances less than R from a given atom, the number of states with energies between W and ΔW is given by

$$(4\pi/3)R^3 N(W) \, \mathrm{d}W.$$

It follows that, if R is large, the average spacing ΔW between the energies of states near the Fermi energy is given by

$$\Delta W = 3/4\pi R^3 N(E_F). \tag{2.40}$$

In considering hopping for carriers with energies near E_F, then, we can consider two ranges of T:

(a) The high-temperature range. Here the factor $\exp(-2\alpha R)$ will ensure that the electron jumps only a small distance and thus to one of the nearest centres. In the Anderson model, W is thus of the order of the band width, but will vary with the Fermi energy. According to the calculations of Miller and Abrahams (1960, 1961; and Chapter 6)

it will be a minimum when the band is half filled. The activation energy
is independent of temperature.

(b) The low-temperature region. Here W is given by eqn (2.40),
and the jump frequency is

$$\nu_{\text{ph}}\exp[-2\alpha R - \{(4\pi/3)R^3 N(E_{\text{F}})kT\}^{-1}].$$

The most probable jumps come from a value of R such that

$$2\alpha = 9/4\pi R^4 N(E_{\text{F}})kT,$$

which gives a jump frequency of the form

$$\nu_{\text{ph}}\exp(-B/T^{\frac{1}{4}}), \qquad B \simeq 2\cdot1\{\alpha^3/kN(E_{\text{F}})\}^{\frac{1}{4}}. \tag{2.41}$$

Thus we expect the log of the conductivity to vary as $1/T^{\frac{1}{4}}$. Examples
of this behaviour are shown in Chapters 6 and 8 for both amorphous
and crystalline materials (with a random distribution of centres).
It has also been observed in amorphous carbon by Adkins, Freake,
and Hamilton (1970).

We turn now to the situation where the states at E_{F} are non-
localized (extended) and $\langle\sigma\rangle$ at $T = 0$ is finite. There are several
systems in which this occurs. We mention here conduction in degenerate impurity bands in crystalline semiconductors and the work of
Cutler and Leavy (1964) on Ce_2S_3 (Chapter 6). The experimental
evidence is that when the states are just delocalized the conductivity
has about the same value† (2·31) as that calculated for the Anderson
model, namely $\langle\sigma\rangle_{E=E_{\text{C}}} \sim 0\cdot06\ e^2/\hbar a_E$. We do not have a theoretical
model which makes it certain that this is to be expected, and, since
in the Anderson model the value depends somewhat on the coordination number, we should in any case not expect exact agreement.
However, if we make this assumption, in systems like the two
mentioned above where it is possible to change the electron concentration so that E_{F} moves from a region where states are localized
to one where they are not, and thus to cross a critical energy E_{C}, we
expect at $T = 0$ a discontinuous change in $\langle\sigma\rangle$ to the finite value
given above. At temperatures such that kT is of the order of the
hopping energy W, we expect also a rapid change, since below E_{C} the
conductivity depends on the phonon frequency term ν_{ph}. This problem
is discussed further in Chapter 6; the closely analogous problem of
the mobility shoulder is discussed in the next section.

† This is quite striking, especially in view of the fact that a_E differs by a factor of
about 15 in the two examples cited here.

Finally, we have assumed throughout this chapter that the correlation term e^2/r_{12} does not affect the results in any significant way. As we shall see in Chapter 5, for low densities of the electron gas a kind of localization can occur that is nothing to do with disorder. We defer until Chapter 5 further discussion of these effects.

2.9.2. Amorphous semiconductors; the mobility shoulder

We consider now the case when $\langle \sigma_E \rangle$ is negligible at $E = E_F$ and current is carried by electrons (or holes) excited into the conduction (or valence) band. Here we introduce the mobility μ and emphasize the important point that the localized and non-localized energy states in the band can both carry current. The question is, which makes the major contribution?

Let us consider first the contribution made by carriers with extended wave functions. The contribution to the conductivity is, by equation (2.11),

$$\sigma = -\int \langle \sigma_E(0) \rangle \frac{\partial f}{\partial E} \, dE,$$

and since for a semiconductor $f = e^{-(E-E_F)/kT}$, this gives

$$\sigma = \sigma_0 \exp\{-(E_C - E_F)/kT\}, \tag{2.42}$$

where

$$\sigma_0 = \langle \sigma(0) \rangle_{E=E_C},$$

σ_0 is just the quantity we have calculated already, of order 350 Ω^{-1} cm^{-1} for $z = 6$. The mobility can be deduced only if $N(E_C)$ is known. Since the number of electrons with energies above E_C is

$$N(E_C)kT \exp\{-(E_C - E_F)/kT\},$$

the mobility μ_{ext} at E_C is

$$\{\langle \sigma(0) \rangle / eN(E)kT\}_{E=E_C}.$$

To obtain an order of magnitude, we take the band width $B = \hbar^2/mR^2$, which gives a value of ~ 1 eV, and then assume that $N(E_C)$ is $0 \cdot 2/R^3 B$, the factor $0 \cdot 2$ being chosen to put E_C a few tenths of an eV above the band edge. We then find $\mu_{ext} = 0 \cdot 3e\hbar/mkT \sim 12$ cm^2 V^{-1} s^{-1} at room temperature, but other values are possible. This formula enables us to write the mobility in a form appropriate to diffusive motion,

$$\mu_{ext} = \tfrac{1}{6} e \nu_{el} R^2 / kT, \tag{2.43}$$

where ν_{el}, an electronic frequency, depends on the value of $N(E_C)$ assumed, but will be of order given by

$$\nu_{el} \sim 2\hbar^2/mR^2 \sim 3 \times 10^{15} \, \text{s}^{-1}.$$

For an alternative derivation of a formula of type (2.43), see Cohen (1970).

For $E \lesssim E_C$, conduction will be by hopping, and we may write, neglecting the term $e^{-2\alpha R}$,

$$\mu_{\text{hop}} = \tfrac{1}{6}\nu_{\text{ph}}(eR^2/kT)\exp(-W/kT), \tag{2.44}$$

where ν_{ph} is the phonon frequency discussed in Chapter 4, not greater than of order $10^{12} \, \text{s}^{-1}$. Near E_C we may assume $W \lesssim kT$. Thus a drop in the mobility by a factor $\sim 10^3$ is expected as the energy E goes through the value E_C (or E_V for the valence band). This drop in the mobility has been called the mobility shoulder, and was first described by Cohen.† If then ΔE in Fig. 2.12 is less than about $5kT$, we should expect current at room temperature to be carried by electrons (or holes) in *extended* states.

Now, as Stuke (1969, 1970a, b) first emphasized, for many semi-conducting glasses the plot of $\ln \sigma$ against $1/T$ gives a good straight line over a considerable range of temperature; we may write

$$\sigma = Ce^{-E/kT}, \tag{2.45}$$

and C is often in the range 10^3–$10^4 \, \Omega^{-1} \, \text{cm}^{-1}$. The evidence is reviewed in Chapter 7. To explain this behaviour, it must be assumed that the Fermi energy is pinned at its zero-temperature value E_F. This might be because the material is a true intrinsic semiconductor and the curves of the densities of states in the conduction and valence bands have the same functional forms near their limits, or alternatively (§ 2.10) because there is a high density of states, perhaps due to structural defects, near the middle of the band gap. It must also be assumed that the carriers are excited to the mobility shoulder of Fig. 2.17. The conductivity is then of the form (2.42). If $E_C - E_F$ varies linearly with temperature, so that we can write

$$E_C - E_F = E(0) - \gamma T,$$

then a linear plot of $\ln \sigma$ as a function of $1/T$ is still obtained of the form (2.45) with

$$E = E(0),$$

† At a conference in 1968; see Mott (1969a, c); Cohen, Fritzsche, and Ovshinsky (1969).

and

$$C = \sigma_0 e^{\gamma/k},$$
$$\sigma_0 = \langle \sigma(0) \rangle_{E=E_C}.$$

If the drop in the mobility is about 1000 at the mobility edge and the current is carried by electrons in extended states at room

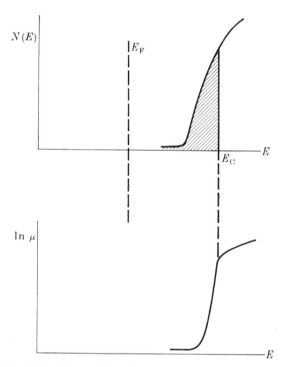

FIG. 2.17. The mobility shoulder, showing the rapid drop in mobility as E drops below E_C.

temperatures, then, as we have seen, ΔE, the range of energies over which states are localized, cannot be greater than about 0·2 V.

We should, in fact, expect three terms in the conductivity over the whole temperature range:

$$\sigma = C\exp(-E/kT) + C_1\exp(-E_1/kT) + C_2\exp(-E_2/kT). \quad (2.46)$$

Here $C \sim 10^3 \ \Omega^{-1} \ \text{cm}^{-1}$ and has already been discussed; the second term is due to electrons excited to the band edge, and for this $C_1 \sim 1 \ \Omega^{-1} \ \text{cm}^{-1}$ and $E_1 = E - \Delta E + \Delta W$; the last term is due to hopping conduction by electrons with energies near E_F, so $C_2 \ll C_1$ and $E_2 \ll E_1$; at very low temperatures $\exp(-E_2/kT)$ should be replaced by $\exp(-\text{const.}\,T^{-\frac{1}{4}})$. Figure 7.7 shows schematically the behaviour expected, and some examples are given in later chapters.

The quantity γ is of considerable importance. It can in principle be determined from the change of the optical band gap with temperature or from measurements of the thermopower (Chapter 7). It may be due partly to thermal expansion, but in materials in which the gap is due to structure, whether crystalline or amorphous, the gap may change with increasing T even at constant volume. We discuss this point further in Chapter 3.

It is perhaps worth noting that a value of C independent of T can occur also in crystalline semiconductors. The number of electrons in a conduction or valence band is, for such materials,

$$2(2\pi m^* kT/\hbar^2)^{\frac{3}{2}} e^{-E/kT}$$

per unit volume; the mobility μ is $e\tau/m^*$. For τ we can write L/v; $\frac{3}{2} m^* v^2 = kT$ and $L \sim a(J/kT)$ where J is a few eV. Thus for lattice scattering

$$\mu = eaJ/m^{*\frac{1}{2}}(kT)^{\frac{3}{2}}.$$

The term in the conductivity is therefore of the form

$$C = (2\pi)^{\frac{3}{2}} e^2 aJ m/h^3$$

and does not contain T. Furthermore, it is of the same order as for amorphous semiconductors for carriers at the mobility shoulder. This similarity is fortuitous: a larger effective density of states in the mobility shoulder is approximately cancelled by a reduced mobility.

It should be emphasized that the mobility $\mu(E_C)$ that can be deduced from σ_0 in equation (2.43) is not the same as the drift mobility determined when electrons or holes are injected into amorphous materials. Experiments on the drift mobility are discussed in Chapter 7. If electrons are injected into a high-resistance material, and if the deep traps are few and have little effect, then hopping from one localized state is to be expected at low temperatures, while at higher temperatures the mobility is trap-controlled.

A theoretical estimate of the range of energies ΔE would be of interest. Mott (1970) has suggested that in chalcogenide glasses, selenium, tellurium, and other materials in which π orbitals form the valence band, we can take $U_0 \sim J$ in formula (2.33). This gives a value for ΔE for order 0·1 eV.

2.9.3. Thermoelectric power

In this section we summarize the formulae needed for the interpretation of the thermoelectric power. This can be expressed in terms of σ_E; in § 2.2 we have defined this quantity for a disordered lattice at zero temperatures and have shown that at a finite temperature

$$\sigma = -\int \sigma_E \frac{\partial f}{\partial E}\, \mathrm{d}E.$$

We can also generalize this equation when conduction is by hopping; if p is the probability per unit time that an electron jumps to another site, then we can write

$$\sigma_E = e^2 p R^2 \{N(E_{\mathrm{F}})\},$$

and the formula above reduces to eqn (2.36).

The thermoelectric power S is then given by (Cutler and Mott 1969)

$$S\sigma = \frac{k}{e}\int \sigma_E \frac{E-E_{\mathrm{F}}}{kT}\frac{\partial f}{\partial E}\, \mathrm{d}E. \tag{2.47}$$

The proof is as follows. If F is the field, then the current $\mathrm{d}j$ due to electrons with energies between E and $E+\mathrm{d}E$ is given by

$$\mathrm{d}j = -\sigma_E(\partial f/\partial E)F\, \mathrm{d}E.$$

The free energy carried by this current is $-(E-E_{\mathrm{F}})\, \mathrm{d}j/e$, which becomes

$$\frac{1}{e}\frac{\partial f}{\partial E}\,\sigma_E(E-E_{\mathrm{F}})F\, \mathrm{d}E.$$

Integrating this equation we obtain the total electronic heat transport, which is equal to $j\Pi$, where Π is the Peltier coefficient, so that

$$\Pi j = \frac{F}{e}\int \sigma_E \frac{\partial f}{\partial E}\,(E-E_{\mathrm{F}})\, \mathrm{d}E.$$

Since $S = \Pi/T$, formula (2.47) follows.

From this we may easily deduce the following formulae. If the mobility is such that the current is determined by electrons with energies in the neighbourhood of E_{F}, we obtain the formula familiar for metals,

$$S = \frac{\pi^2}{3}\frac{k^2 T}{e}\left\{\frac{\mathrm{d}(\ln \sigma)}{\mathrm{d}E}\right\}_{E=E_{\mathrm{F}}}, \tag{2.48}$$

whether conduction is by hopping or not. In the hopping case, if σ is of the form $\sigma_3 \exp(-W/kT)$, S will be given by

$$S = \frac{\pi^2}{3} \frac{k}{e} \left\{ kT \frac{d(\ln \sigma)}{dE} - \frac{dW}{dE} \right\}_{E=E_F}. \tag{2.49}$$

Applications of this formula to cerium sulphide (Chapter 6), to amorphous Mg–Bi (Chapter 3), and to glasses containing transition-metal ions (Chapter 6) are discussed later. These formulae, it must be emphasized, are valid only if $kT \ll E_F$.

If the gas is non-degenerate in a parabolic band,

$$S = -(k/e)\tfrac{3}{2}\ln T + \text{const}. \tag{2.50}$$

If kT is greater than the band width,

$$S = (k/e)\ln\{c/(1-c)\}, \tag{2.51}$$

where c is the ratio of the number of electrons to the number of atoms. Formula (2.51) is due to Heikes and Ure (1961). It is in agreement with experiment for glasses containing vanadium ions V^{4+} and V^{5+} (Chapter 6).

For semiconductors in which a mean free path L can be defined, we obtain the usual formula

$$S = \frac{k}{e}\left(\frac{E_C - E_F}{kT} + \frac{5}{2} + r\right),$$

where $r = d(\ln \tau)/d(\ln E)$ and τ is the time of relaxation. For amorphous semiconductors, if σ_E is treated as zero up to E_C and for $E > E_C$ behaves like $\sigma_0 + \alpha E$, then a short calculation (Cutler and Mott, 1969, eqn (11)) shows that

$$S = \frac{k}{e}\left(\frac{E_C - E_F}{kT} + 1 + \text{ terms of order } T\right). \tag{2.52}$$

In many forms of conduction in non-crystalline materials, such as impurity-conduction in a degenerate band, the mean free path is of the order of the distance between the atoms, and the conductivity should depend on E primarily as $\{N(E_F)\}^2$ (formula (3.16)). We expect therefore that a good expression for the thermopower would be

$$S \simeq \frac{2\pi^2}{3} \frac{k^2 T}{e} \frac{d\{\ln N(E)\}}{dE}. \tag{2.53}$$

Thus a half-filled impurity band should give a zero or small value of the thermopower. In the hopping case, eqn (2.49), since σ_0 is proportional to $\{N(E)\}$, the first term in eqn (2.49) should have a similar form. Thus the thermopower due to impurity conduction in donors should be p-type if the compensation K is less than $\sim\frac{1}{2}$ (Chapter 6). A change of sign of the thermopower at low temperatures is a common phenomenon and can be interpreted as a change in the mechanism from charge transport by excited carriers (whether in extended or localized states) to conductivity due to electrons in some kind of defect band. Examples are given in Chapters 6, 7, and 8.

2.10. Hopping conduction for alternating currents

We have already discussed for zero temperature the quantity $\sigma(\omega)$, which is the conductivity at frequency ω. This has been calculated using the formalism appropriate for optical transitions between occupied and empty states in the material. At low frequencies it is usual to derive $\sigma(\omega)$ by quite different methods, starting from the Boltzmann equation. For instance, if the current is carried by electrons in non-localized states, the conductivity at frequency ω is given by the Drude equation

$$\sigma(\omega) = (Ne^2\tau/m)/(1+\omega^2\tau^2), \tag{2.54}$$

where N is the (effective) number of free electrons per unit volume and τ the time of relaxation. It has to be emphasized that, so long as energy exchange with phonons does not play an essential role (as it does in hopping), formula (2.54) must be a consequence of the Kubo–Greenwood formula (2.10). We have also seen that the Drude equation is valid only if $kL \gg 1$; it should certainly not be applied to free carriers near the critical energy E_C (Mott 1970). We return to this problem in §3.15.

When states are localized, conduction is by hopping, and $\sigma(\omega)$ tends to zero with T; and we have already seen that at the absolute zero $\sigma(\omega)$ varies as ω^2 if the density of states is finite at E_F.

A variation of σ with ω is expected if the conductivity of the material is inhomogeneous on a macroscopic scale. For instance, if the material of bulk conductivity σ_0 contains barriers with conductivity σ_B occupying a fraction f of the volume, an elementary analysis shows that, for $\omega < 16\pi^2\sigma_0\sigma_B$, the conductivity is proportional to σ_B, for $\omega > \sigma_0$ the conductivity is σ_0, and between these limits it increases as ω^2. A review of such mechanisms is given by Volger (1960).

2.10.1. Debye-type energy loss for hopping conduction

In this section we show how to calculate the conductivity and loss angle that results from thermally activated hopping from one localized state to another. This is an example of the Debye theory of energy loss, of which an outline is as follows (Fröhlich 1958).

Suppose a material contains n sites per unit volume, at each of which a dipole D has two alternative positions with energies W_1, W_2, so that

$$\Delta W = W_1 - W_2.$$

If the dipole is inclined at an angle θ to a field F, the polarization produced by the field can be calculated to be

$$\{F D^2 \overline{\cos^2\theta} / kT\} / (1 + e^{\Delta W/kT}),$$

and $\overline{\cos^2\theta}$ averaged over all directions is equal to $\tfrac{1}{3}$. Then Debye's analysis shows that, if τ is the mean time for a transition from the upper to the lower state,

$$\sigma(\omega) = \frac{nD^2}{3kT} \frac{1}{1 + \exp(\Delta W/kT)} \frac{\omega^2 \tau}{1 + \omega^2 \tau^2}. \tag{2.55}$$

In amorphous materials we have to deal with situations in which $\sigma(\omega)$ must be averaged over a range of values of ΔW. If, near $\Delta W = 0$, there are $N(W)\,dW$ pairs with ΔW in the range dW, then since

$$\int_0^1 (1+x)^{-1}\,dx = \ln 2,$$

we find

$$\sigma(\omega) = 0{\cdot}2nN(W)D^2\omega^2\tau/(1+\omega^2\tau^2). \tag{2.56}$$

We may also have to average over τ. Suppose the relaxation process involves an electron surmounting a barrier of height U, so that

$$1/\tau = \nu_{\text{ph}}\exp(-U/kT),$$

and $B(U)\,dU$ is the number of barriers of height between U and $U+dU$. Then

$$d\tau/\tau = dU/kT,$$

so that the average of $\omega^2\tau/(1+\omega^2\tau^2)$ is

$$kT\omega^2\int B(U)\frac{1}{1+\omega^2\tau^2}\,d\tau.$$

If $B(U)$ is constant this gives

$$\tfrac{1}{2}\pi kT B(U)\omega,$$

so

$$\sigma(\omega) \simeq 0\cdot 3 n N(W) B(U) D^2 k T \omega. \tag{2.57}$$

The conductivity is proportional to T and to ω.

Most processes in which σ is averaged over a range of values of τ give a value of $\sigma(\omega)$ that is approximately proportional to ω. For non-crystalline materials, the most important such process is thermally activated hopping of electrons between pairs of localized states. The contribution to the d.c. conduction of this process has already been discussed, and is the subject matter of Chapter 6. If two centres are distant R apart, with energies differing by ΔW, the contribution to σ is given by eqn (2.56) with $D = eR$; if this is averaged over all ΔW, it gives eqn (2.57). τ is now the mean time for phonon-assisted tunnelling:

$$1/\tau = \nu_{\mathrm{ph}} e^{-2\alpha R}.$$

Significant contributions to the conductivity will be made for centres with energies separated by $\sim kT$ or less from the Fermi energy, so if there are n centres per unit volume,

$$\sigma(\omega) = 0\cdot 2 n^2 D^2 \{N(W)\}^2 k T \int \frac{\omega^2 \tau}{1+\omega^2\tau^2} \, 4\pi R^2 \, \mathrm{d}R.$$

Writing

$$\mathrm{d}\tau/\tau - 2\alpha \, \mathrm{d}R,$$

we see that most of the integral comes from the critical radius R_ω, where $\omega\tau \sim 1$, defined by

$$R_\omega = (1/2\alpha)\ln(\nu_{\mathrm{ph}}/\omega). \tag{2.58}$$

Thus

$$\sigma(\omega) = \frac{4\pi}{3} \, (\ln 2) \, e^2 k T n^2 \{N(W)\}^2 \alpha^{-5} \{\ln(\nu_{\mathrm{ph}}/\omega)\}^4 \omega, \tag{2.59}$$

which may be written

$$\sigma(\omega) \simeq 2\cdot 5 e^2 (n/U_0)^2 \omega k T \alpha^{-5} \{\ln(\nu_{\mathrm{ph}}/\omega)\}^4. \tag{2.60}$$

It should be noted that this formula is deduced subject to two assumptions:

(a) That $kT \ll E_{\mathrm{F}}$. The well-known treatment of Pollak and Geballe (1961) treated impurity-conduction with very low compensation, so in this case eqn (2.60) is not valid. We must multiply (2.60) by E_{F}/kT, and $\sigma(\omega)$ is then independent of T, apart from any dependence of ν_{ph} on T (Chapter 4).

5

(b) That the resonance energy I of centres distance R_ω apart is less than kT. Pollak (1964) has given a discussion of the very low-temperature case when this is not so; $\sigma(\omega)$ will always tend to zero with T.

In impurity-conduction in germanium ν_{ph} is of the order 10^{12} s^{-1}, and then the factor $\{\ln(\nu/\omega)\}^4$ varies as $\omega^{-0.2}$ for frequencies in the neighbourhood of 10^4 Hz, so $\sigma \sim \omega^{0.8}$, a form of behaviour which is often observed. On the other hand, much smaller or larger values of ν_{ph} are possible (§ 4.2), so smaller powers of ω can occur.

It is interesting to compare formula (2.60) with (2.25), the conductivity (proportional to ω^2) due to optical transitions; one would expect the second formula ($\sigma \sim \omega^2$) to be predominant at high frequencies. The two contributions are equal when

$$\frac{kT}{\hbar\omega} = \left\{\frac{\ln(I_0/\hbar\omega)}{\ln(\nu_{ph}/\omega)}\right\}^4 .$$

The transition temperature is very sensitive to ν_{ph}; the problem is discussed further in Chapter 4.

It will be noted that the Pollak term varying as $\omega^{0.8}$ and the optical term are both proportional to $(N/U_0)^2$, namely the square of the density of states at the Fermi level. Pollak (1971b) has compared his formula with results for various conducting glasses, and high values of (N/U_0) of the order 5×10^{19} cm^{-3} eV^{-1} are obtained, as they are from other evidence (Fritzsche 1969). This has led Davis and Mott (1970) to suppose that many glasses contain a defect band, due perhaps to dangling bonds, near the middle of the band gap. We emphasize that the tails to the conduction and valence bands proposed by Cohen, Fritzsche, and Ovshinsky (1969) are supposed to be traps, with wave functions derived from those of the conduction and valence bands, and caused by fluctuating fields or varying density or composition (Srinivasan and Cohen 1970). If a peak in the density of states exists, it must be due to some more specific defect, such as a dangling bond. The matter is discussed further in Chapter 7.

2.11. Optical interband transitions in semiconductors

For states near to the energies E_C or E_V, whether localized or not, we can assume that $\Delta k/k \sim 1$, so that the normal selection rules for interband optical transitions are broken down. This is not necessarily so for absorption of quanta of somewhat greater energies. The effect of this on the absorption spectrum of germanium is discussed in Chapter 8.

Interband transitions near the absorption edge, where $\Delta k/k \sim 1$ and the selection rules break down, have been discussed by Tauc (1970a), by Davis and Mott (1970), and Hindley (1970). The method of § 2.5 can be applied to formula (2.9). If the integrand in (2.9) is evaluated between two states at $E = E_V$ and $E = E_C$ over a range $\mathrm{d}\omega$, then the contribution to $\sigma(\omega)$ is $(\mathrm{d}\omega/\omega)\sigma_{\mathrm{opt}}$, where σ_{opt} is exactly the minimum metallic conductivity σ_0 calculated in § 2.5 ($\sim$350 Ω^{-1} cm^{-1}), except that the matrix elements D, which now correspond to interband transitions, should be of order $\pi/a\Omega^{\frac{1}{2}}$ rather than $\pi(m/m^*)/a\Omega^{\frac{1}{2}}$ (compare equation (2.28)). We conclude that, as regards orders of magnitude at any rate, $\sigma_{\mathrm{opt}} \sim \sigma_0$. Davis and Mott interpret absorption spectra of many conducting glasses by assuming:

(a) That the probability of transitions between localized states is low.

(b) That the density of states near the tail is linear in E. They conclude that

$$\sigma(\omega) = \sigma_0(\hbar\omega - E_0)^2/\hbar\omega \,\Delta E, \qquad (2.61)$$

where ΔE is the width of the region of localized states shown in Fig. 2.11. This formula is applied in Chapter 7 and subsequent chapters.

2.12. The Hall effect

For hopping conduction, whether due to Anderson localization or to polaron formation, there have been extensive calculations of the Hall effect (Holstein 1961; Friedman and Holstein 1963; Firsov 1964; Schnakenberg 1965). These calculations suggest that the Hall mobility μ_H should be greater than the conductivity mobility μ_0 with a lower activation energy. The argument in its simplest form is as follows. The transverse mobility μ_{xy} responsible for the Hall effect is due to the quantum-mechanical interference of transition amplitudes via alternative paths. Now, as shown in detail by Holstein and Friedman (1968), this requires a thermal fluctuation that makes at least three sites energetically coincident; the minimum energy required for this in excess of the binding energy we define as η_3. On the other hand, the ordinary conductivity mobility μ_{xx} in the presence of an applied electric field requires only a two-site coincidence, with energy denoted by η_2. Thus

$$\mu_H = \mu_{xy}/\mu_{xx} \sim \exp\{-(\eta_3 - \eta_2)/kT\}.$$

The probability for the three-site coincidence is of course smaller than that for a two-site coincidence, $\eta_3 > \eta_2$. On the other hand, it is larger than for two uncorrelated two-site coincidences, $\eta_3 < 2\eta_2$. The reason is that in the vicinity of a two-site coincidence the probability of the coincidence of the third site is greater than random. Detailed calculation gives $\eta_3 = 4\eta_2/3$. Thus,

$$\mu_H \sim \exp\left(-\tfrac{1}{3}\eta_2/kT\right), \tag{2.62}$$

and

$$R_H nec = \frac{\mu_H}{\mu_0} \propto \exp\left(\frac{2\eta_2}{3kT}\right). \tag{2.63}$$

The above applies to the classical limit $(kT \gg \hbar\omega)$, in which the lattice motion may be treated classically. It also applies in the limit in which the overlap of atomic wave functions on neighbouring sites is sufficiently small (the non-adiabatic régime in the case of small-polaron formation; compare Chapter 4). For larger values of the overlap (adiabatic régime; Emin and Holstein 1969), it is still true that the activation energy of the Hall mobility is less than that of the conductivity mobility; in fact it can in some cases approach zero. However, the magnitude of the Hall mobility may be comparable with or even less than that of the conductivity mobility.

The Hall effect has been observed for polaron hopping (Chapter 4), but attempts to observe it in hopping impurity-conduction have so far failed (Amitay and Pollak 1966). Cutler and Leavy (1964) however have observed it in CeS, and eqn (2.63) is approximately valid (Chapter 6).

Under conditions when the mean free path is short but conduction is by hopping no generally accepted theory exists.[†] The experimental evidence suggests:

(a) That when $kL \sim 1$ the Hall mobility in semiconductors is one or two orders of magnitude less than the conductivity mobility.

(b) That the Hall effect has often the same sign as for electrons, even if the current is carried by holes in a valence band.

(c) That when the current is carried by electrons at the Fermi energy, R_H is sometimes greater than $1/nec$.

Some of the evidence is as follows. R_H is 2–3 times this value for liquid tellurium if we assume six electrons per atom (Chapter 3). In impurity-condition for 'metallic' concentrations, the Hall co-

† See discussions by Banyai and Aldea (1966), Allgaier (1969), Böer and Haislip (1970), Böer (1970).

efficient is also not far from the value expected from the number of electrons deduced from the Hall effect at high temperatures (Chapter 6), though it does not have an abnormal sign. In liquid tellurium–thallium alloys extensively investigated by Cutler and by Enderby (Chapter 3), on the tellurium-rich side of the composition $TeTl_2$ the thermopower is p-type and the conductivity greater than $100 \ \Omega^{-1} \ cm^{-1}$, so metallic conductivity in a nearly full band is indicated. But the Hall coefficient is negative and the number of carriers deduced from it is too small, if the number of holes is supposed to be proportional to the Te content in excess of $TeTl_2$.

Turning to phenomena in which the current is carried by excited carriers, we find that in many chalcogenide glasses the thermoelectric power shows that conduction is p-type, and the considerations of the last sections show that the mobility of carriers in extended states is of order $10 \ \Omega^{-1} \ cm^2 \ V^{-1} \ s^{-1}$. However, measurements show that the Hall effect is negative with mobilities of order $0 \cdot 1 \ cm^2 \ V^{-1} \ s^{-1}$ (Male 1967; see also Chapter 7).†

Volger (1960) has given a formula for the Hall constant R_H in a material where the conductivity is due to barriers. His formula is

$$R_H = R_{H1} + c(l_2/l_1)^2 R_{H2}$$

where R_{H1} is the Hall constant of the bulk material, R_{H2} of the material of which the barriers are made up, and l_1, l_2 are the linear dimensions of the two regions.

2.13. One-dimensional problems

The problem of an electron moving in one dimension in the kind of non-periodic field discussed in this chapter has had up till now no

† *Note added in proof*. Friedman (1971) has applied the methods developed by Holstein and Friedman (1968) for thermally activated hopping to the case considered here, namely no thermal activation but a random change in the phase of the wave function from site to site. He finds that the Hall coefficient is normally negative, even for p-type materials, and that for a semiconductor

$$\mu_H/\mu_0 \sim kT/I \sim 10^{-2},$$

where I is defined by eqn (2.16). This is because μ_H at a mobility shoulder does not involve the temperature, while μ_0 is proportional to $1/T$. When the current is due to electrons with energies near E_F, there is no such large discrepancy. The Hall coefficient is proportional to $1/N(E_F)$, and when a pseudogap exists a good approximation is

$$R_H = C/necg,$$

where g is defined on p. 36 and C is probably about $0 \cdot 75$, Straub, Roth, Bernard, Goldstein, and Mulhern (1968) proposed this formula (with $C = 1$) for highly doped semiconductors, though they did not give a derivation. A similar correction to the normal Hall formula for metals was proposed by Ziman (1967b) using quite different considerations not based specifically on a short mean free path.

practical applications. It was, however, one of the first problems in this subject to be investigated, both for its inherent interest and for the information it was expected to give on the properties of liquids. The one-dimensional problem has very different properties from the three-dimensional problem, however; some of these have been described by Mott (1967), and a critical review has been given by Halperin (1967). Only a brief account will be given here.

Early papers (James and Ginzbarg 1953; Landauer and Helland 1954; Lax and Phillips 1958; Frisch and Lloyd 1960) deal with the density of states, a quantity accessible to machine calculation. If ψ_ν is any solution of the Schrödinger equation defined in the range $0 < x < l$ with cyclic boundary conditions, the quantum number ν may be taken to denote the number of zeros. If we write

$$k = 2\pi\nu/l,$$

then the density of states is given by

$$N(E) = l/2\pi(\mathrm{d}E/\mathrm{d}k).$$

A minimum (pseudogap) will replace an energy gap for an array of scatterers separated by a distance $a \pm \delta$ if the quantities have (for instance) a Gaussian distribution. The question of whether a gap can even exist in a random lattice was discussed by Landauer and Helland (1954), by Makinson and Roberts (1962), and by Halperin (1967). The result appears to be that a gap can exist if limits are set on the magnitude of δ, but that if no limits are set, as for instance with a Gaussian distribution, $N(E)/l$ will not become zero for infinite l anywhere. A similar theorem may well be true in three dimensions.

Finally we come to the question of localization. Mott and Twose (1961), using a random Kronig–Penney model, first gave arguments to suggest that *all* states in the one-dimensional lattice were localized. Borland (1963) considered a random array of scatterers, and proved for this model that, considering all configurations of the ensemble, the expectation fraction of the number of states that are not localized tends to zero as $l \to \infty$. Halperin (1967) has examined in detail the mathematical rigour of the argument. By a localized wave function is meant one that decays exponentially in space. This surprising result is valid for all energies of the electron and for all strengths of the scattering potential, however weak.

It must follow from the same argument as for the three-dimensional case that $\langle \sigma_E(0) \rangle$ vanishes for all values of E in the limit when $E = 0$. This is considered by Halperin (1967 p. 173) to be not rigorously proved, because Borland's argument fails to establish that the rate of decay of the exponential wave function is independent of l and does not tend to zero as $l \to \infty$. It seems intuitively likely that localized wave functions do not depend on what happens a long way away, so it is very probable that $\langle \sigma_E(0) \rangle$ always vanishes.

Landauer (1970) has given a treatment of the conductivity for a finite one-dimensional array, and finds that it is finite but tends to zero exponentially with l. Cohen (1970) and Economou and Cohen (1970) come to the same conclusion. This behaviour, we believe, should be shown also in three dimensions when states are localized (§ 2.4).

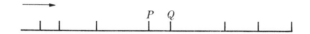

FIG. 2.18. A random array of scatterers in one dimension.

The remainder of this section will show in an elementary and non-rigorous way how these results arise. Consider a wave e^{ikx} falling on the random array of scatterers illustrated in Fig. 2.18; by familiar methods a mean free path L can be calculated, and at a distance of some multiples of L the wave function should be

$$A e^{ikx} + B e^{-ikx},$$

with $|A| \sim |B|$. But conservation of current gives

$$|A|^2 - |B|^2 = 1.$$

If $|A|$ and $|B|$ are nearly equal, this is only possible if $|A|$ and $|B|$ are large. This suggests that the solution of the equation that varies as e^{ikx} to the left of the array *increases* exponentially with x as $e^{x/L}$.

We now look at real solutions of the form $\sin(kx+\eta)$ to the left of the array. In general, such a solution will increase with x, but Borland's analysis shows that there is one value of η for which ψ decreases exponentially. The solution then corresponds to a beam of electrons incident on the array and totally reflected, just as they would be at a potential step.

Localized states are obtained as follows. In a given interval PQ of an infinite one-dimensional lattice, any solution will have the form $\sin(kx+\eta)$. We can choose η uniquely so that ψ will decay exponentially for values of x to the right of PQ; let the value be η_1. We can choose also η so that ψ decreases exponentially for decreasing values of x to the left of PQ; let the value be η_2. In general $\eta_1 \sim \eta_2$. But quantized values of the energy E exist such that $\eta_1 = \eta_2$. The two solutions fit together, and we have a bounded solution with ψ continuous everywhere. This is the localized eigenstate that we require, the localization being in the neighbourhood of PQ.

Note added in proof. A better approximation might be to write instead of (2.28)

$$\delta^2 = \tfrac{1}{3}\{(m/m^*)k_{\mathrm{F}}a^3/\Omega\}^2;$$

the factor $\tfrac{1}{3}$ comes from averaging $\mathbf{k}^2$ over all directions. If the free-electron formula (2.1) is then used for $N(E)$, the conductivity for a free-electron gas when $L \sim a$ agrees with (2.12) except that the factor $12\pi^3$ is replaced by $24\pi^2$.

LIQUID METALS, SEMI-METALS, AND SEMICONDUCTORS

3.1. Introduction
3.2. Scattering of electrons by a random distribution of centres: degenerate semiconductors
3.3. Resistivity of liquid metals; Ziman's theory
3.4. The absolute magnitude of the resistivity
3.5. Resistivity of liquid alloys
3.6. Thermoelectric power
3.7. Hall effect
3.8. Density of states
3.9. Knight shift
3.10. Change in the magnetic susceptibility on melting
3.11. X-ray emission spectra
3.12. Amorphous metallic films; grain boundaries

3.13. Injected electrons in liquid rare gases
3.14. Effect of the density of states on the conductivity
3.15. Optical properties
3.16. Liquid and amorphous semimetals
  3.16.1. Mercury at low densities.
  3.16.2. Amorphous Mg–Bi alloys.
3.17. Liquid semiconductors and semimetals
  3.17.1. Semiconductors in class (d); selenium
  3.17.2. Tellurium
  3.17.3. Tellurium–selenium liquid alloys
  3.17.4. Liquid alloys of tellurium with metallic elements

3.1. Introduction

THIS chapter is concerned in the first place with liquid metals. The discussion will, however, include other systems, such as amorphous metal films, electrons injected into liquid rare gases, and highly doped semiconductors, where the scattering by each centre is comparatively weak and the mean free path can be long. In Chapter 2 we examined situations in which it is natural to start with the tight-binding approximation and a narrow band width, so that the effect of the atoms is not to be treated as a small perturbation; we then found that in non-crystalline substances under certain conditions the wave functions are localized, and that the conductivity is therefore due to thermally activated hopping. As the band width is broadened, or the disorder or random fields become smaller, a situation is reached in which the wave functions at the Fermi energy are no longer localized, but 'extended' so that the conductivity remains finite at $T = 0$. We gave some estimates of the magnitude of the conductivity when this has just occurred. In this chapter we shall start from the opposite limiting case. The wave functions of the electrons will be described by plane waves, and the scattering by the atoms will be treated as small. As the scattering by the atoms increases, it will be important to see if these two descriptions of conduction give results that fit together for the intermediate region.

The effect of an atom on the wave functions of a conduction electron in a metal is not, of course, ever small. In sodium for instance the wave functions will have two spherical nodal surfaces round each atom, as in a 3s atomic wave function. The possibility of treating the resistance of liquid metals by perturbation theory depends on the use of pseudopotentials, or model potentials in which the condition that ψ must be orthogonal to the wave functions of the inner shells, which leads to the spherical nodes, is replaced by the addition of a repulsive core to the potential. This can be chosen to give correctly the energies of the atomic states, or the phase shifts. If the phase shifts are small, perturbation theory can be used. If not, the phase shifts could be used in principle to give the scattering by each atom, but numerical results would then depend on the application of multiple-scattering theory. In spite of extensive theoretical work (Lax 1951, 1952; Phariseau and Ziman 1963; Beeby 1964; Ballentine 1965: Rubio 1969), there does not exist as far as we know a numerical calculation of the effect on the resistivity of the multiple-scattering term.

We next emphasize that, for *crystalline* materials, the use of perturbation theory to calculate the resistivity does not depend on replacing the true potential by a pseudopotential. We start with a periodic field in which the potential energy of an electron is $V(x, y, z)$. The solutions of the Schrödinger equation are of the Bloch form, $e^{ikx}u_k(x, y, z)$, and near the Fermi surface, for instance in semi-metals, these and the corresponding surfaces of constant energy may bear no relationship at all to those for free electrons. But the scattering of electrons, and hence the electrical resistivity, is due to phonons. The scattering potential is thus of the form

$$\sum_n (\mathbf{a}_n \cdot \operatorname{grad} V_n),$$

where V_n is the potential in the atom n and $\mathbf{a}_n$ the displacement of the atom due to the phonon under consideration. This displacement, except at very high temperatures, is small. The matrix element that determines the scattering from state k to state k' is

$$\sum_n \mathbf{a}_n \cdot \int \psi_{k'}^* \operatorname{grad} V_n \psi_k \, \mathrm{d}^3 x. \tag{3.1}$$

If the functions V are replaced by pseudopotentials, and the wave functions ψ by plane waves, and if we assume a 'muffin-tin' potential such that V vanishes on the boundaries of the atomic cell, then eqn (3.1) can be replaced by

$$\sum_n \mathbf{a}_n \cdot \int V_n \; \mathrm{grad}(\psi_{k'}^* \psi_k) \; \mathrm{d}^3x = \sum_n (\mathbf{a}_n \cdot \mathbf{q}) \int V_n \mathrm{e}^{i(\mathbf{q} \cdot \mathbf{r})} \; \mathrm{d}^3x,$$

where

$$\mathbf{q} = \mathbf{k}' - \mathbf{k}.$$

If, and only if, the potential is small, so that ψ_k can be replaced by $\mathrm{e}^{i(\mathbf{k} \cdot \mathbf{r})}$, we can express the resistance in terms of the matrix elements of V_n. This is the case with which we are concerned in this chapter.

In much theoretical work on liquid metals, as also in the theory of the resistance of disordered alloys, the change in the energy of the electron when it is scattered is neglected. It is not necessary to do this, as the work of Greene and Kohn (1965; see § 3.4) on liquid sodium has shown, and in alloys this neglect may lead to errors (see § 4.2). In the next section we shall make this approximation, which probably leads to very small errors in liquid metals.

3.2. Scattering of electrons by a random distribution of centres: degenerate semiconductors

A degenerate electron gas with scattering by a random distribution of centres is the simplest example of the theory; this model could apply in principle to a degenerate gas of electrons scattered by n-type centres in a highly doped semiconductor. We can ascribe to each centre a differential cross-section for scattering $I(\theta)$; $I(\theta) \, \mathrm{d}\omega$ is the effective area for scattering by a centre through an angle θ into a solid angle $\mathrm{d}\omega$. For the conductivity σ we can write

$$\sigma = ne^2\tau/m. \tag{3.2}$$

Here n is the number of electrons per unit volume, and the time of relaxation τ is given by

$$\frac{1}{\tau} = N_c v \int_0^{\pi} I(\theta)(1 - \cos \theta) 2\pi \sin \theta \; \mathrm{d}\theta. \tag{3.3}$$

N_c is the number of centres per unit volume and v the velocity of electrons at the Fermi energy. This formula, though used in calculations of the resistance of disordered alloys since Nordheim's paper of 1931, had not been derived rigorously until Edwards (1958) obtained it from the Kubo–Greenwood formula (compare § 2.3).

If the potential energy $V(r)$ of an electron in the field of a centre is small, $I(\theta)$ can be obtained from the Born approximation by writing

$$I(\theta) = |f(\theta)|^2,$$

where

$$f(\theta) = \frac{m}{2\pi\hbar^2} \int V(r)e^{i(\mathbf{q}\cdot\mathbf{r})} \, d^3x,$$

where as before $\mathbf{q} = \mathbf{k}' - \mathbf{k}$ and $\mathbf{k}$, $\mathbf{k}'$ are the wave vectors before and after a collision. This can be evaluated to give

$$f(\theta) = \frac{2m}{\hbar^2} \int\limits_0^\infty V(r)\frac{\sin\{2kr \sin(\tfrac{1}{2}\theta)\}r^2 \, dr}{2kr \sin(\tfrac{1}{2}\theta)}. \tag{3.4}$$

In the application of these formulae to a highly doped semiconductor, the potential energy, which must be added to the lattice potential, should be that of a screened Coulomb field, and may be written

$$V(r) = -(e^2/\kappa r)\exp(-\gamma r). \tag{3.5}$$

Here κ is a background dielectric constant. This is a true potential and not a pseudopotential, and since the potential is not strong enough to produce nodes in the wave function, it is likely that the Born approximation may be fairly good. The theory has been extensively reviewed (Mott and Twose 1961; Katz 1965; Mott 1967 § 7.8; Krieger and Strauss 1968; Meeks and Krieger 1969). For doped silicon and germanium the results can be summarized as follows:

(a) For high concentrations, using the formula (see § 3.14)

$$\sigma = Se^2L/12\pi^3\hbar, \tag{3.6}$$

where S is the area of the Fermi surface, and deducing the mean free path L from comparison with experiment, one finds that L is of the order of the distance between centres. Therefore the scattering is not weak, and the use of the Born approximation (3.4) is suspect. It leads to values of L about twice those observed.

(b) For lower concentrations n of electrons per unit volume, the observed conductivity decreases more rapidly with n than the calculations predict, and near the metal–non-metal transition (Chapter 5) the discrepancy may amount to 10, the apparent mean free path dropping below the distance between centres. While this may be due to faults in the Born approximation, a discrepancy of this kind is found in other systems (liquid caesium at high temperatures and low densities, sodium dissolved in liquid ammonia); in Chapter 5 it is suggested that the effect is due to the approach to the metal–non-metal transition. This should introduce a factor g^2 into eqn (3.6), g being the ratio of the actual density of states to the free-electron value, as discussed in the last chapter and in § 3.14. Another related factor that may contribute to a discrepancy is the possible existence of magnetic moments on the centres (Chapter 6).

The Hall mobility of such systems is discussed in Chapter 6; it is normally about the same as the conductivity mobility.

Katz, Koenig, and Lopez (1965) report a T^2 term in the electrical resistance of n-type degenerate germanium, which they ascribe to electron–electron scattering (Baber 1937; for a review see Ziman 1960; Mott 1964; also Hartman 1969 for measurements of the effect in certain semi-metals, e.g. Bi). The T^2 term depends on the many-valley nature of the conduction band and disappears when the energies of the valleys are separated by stressing the crystal.

In compound semiconductors with high static dielectric constants the potential (3.5) might be expected to be very weak and the mobility consequently high. Allgaier and Scanlon (1958) and Allgaier and Houston (1962) in their work on PbS, PbSe, and PbTe find mobilities as high as 8×10^5 cm^2 V^{-1} s^{-1}. Other examples will be discussed in Chapter 6.

3.3. Resistivity of liquid metals; Ziman's theory†

When the scattering centres are the atoms of a liquid metal (or amorphous metal film), the atoms are not distributed completely at random; the amplitude scattered by two atoms at a vector distance **R** from each other is

$$\{1+\exp(i\mathbf{q}.\mathbf{R})\}f(\theta), \tag{3.7}$$

where **q** as before is $\mathbf{k}-\mathbf{k}'$. Thus if we neglect multiple scattering the conductivity is given by eqn (3.6) where

$$\frac{1}{L} = \frac{1}{v\tau} = N\int S(\mathbf{q})(1-\cos\theta)I(\theta)2\pi\sin\theta\,\mathrm{d}\theta. \tag{3.8}$$

Here N is the number of atoms per cm^3 and $S(q)$ is the structure factor, given by

$$S(q) = N^{-1}\int\{1+\exp(i\mathbf{q}.\mathbf{R})\}^2 P(R)\,\mathrm{d}^3X.$$

† Ziman (1961, 1967b); for a review, see Faber (1971).

$P(R)$ is here the pair distribution function, $P(R)$ d^3X being the probability that another atom is in the volume d^3X at a distance R from the given atom. Using the Born approximation for $f(\theta)$ we can write for the resistivity ρ, following Faber and Ziman (1965),

$$\rho = \frac{3\pi}{\hbar e^2 v_{\mathrm{F}}^2 \Omega} \int_0^{2k_{\mathrm{F}}} \frac{|v(q)|^2 S(q) q^3 \, \mathrm{d}q}{4k_{\mathrm{F}}^4}, \tag{3.9}$$

where

$$v(q) = \int V(r) e^{\mathrm{i}(\mathbf{q} \cdot \mathbf{r})} \, \mathrm{d}^3x/\Omega,$$

and the integral is over the volume Ω.

Figure 3.1 shows schematically the behaviour of $S(q)$ and $v(q)$. The possibility of applying perturbation theory depends on the fact that $v(q)$ is small in the region where $S(q)$ is large.

The theory of the scattering of the electrons in a liquid metal is thus identical with that used for the scattering of X-rays or neutrons in a

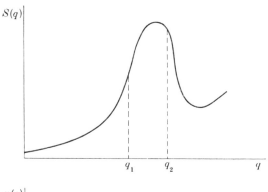

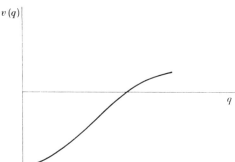

FIG. 3.1. The structure factor $S(q)$ and pseudopotential $v(q)$ for a liquid metal. q_1 and q_2 show the values of $2k$ for monovalent and divalent metals.

liquid. The first suggestion that the resistivity of liquid metals could be calculated in this way was made by Krishnan and Bhatia (1945) and Bhatia and Krishnan (1948). Ziman (1961) put forward the idea again, using for $V(r)$ the atomic pseudopotential, and made a detailed comparison with experiment. One of the most successful applications

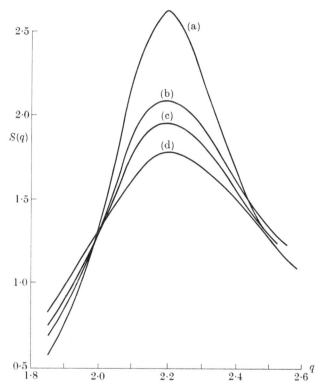

FIG. 3.2. The function $S(q)$ for liquid lead determined from neutron scattering at different temperatures. (a) 340°C; (b) 600°C; (c) 780°C; (d) 1100°C (North, Enderby, and Egelstaff 1968).

of Ziman's theory is to the temperature dependence of the resistivity, also discussed by Bhatia and Krishnan, which explains the difference between monovalent and divalent metals in terms of the observed behaviour of the structure factor $S(q)$.

Figure 3.2, deduced by North, Enderby, and Egelstaff (1968) from their neutron-scattering measurements, shows $S(q)$ for liquid lead at various temperatures. It will be seen that for monovalent metals the resistivity is determined by the left-hand side of the peak, and indeed since $v(q)$ has a zero near $q = 2k_F$ (Fig. 3.1), probably well below the maximum in $S(q)$. It is observed† that the resistivity of monovalent liquid metals at constant volume is proportional to the absolute temperature;† this suggests that $S(q)$ is also proportional to T over the range in which $|v(q)|^2$ is significant. For very low q, the structure factor $S(q)$ will be given by the Ornstein–Zernike formula

$$S(q) = kT/\beta\Omega_0, \tag{3.10}$$

where β is the bulk modulus and Ω_0 the atomic volume. This represents the contribution from macroscopic fluctuations of density and will be true for liquids or solids. But the formula should not be true near $q = 2k_F$, even for monovalent metals, and Fig. 3.2 shows that it is not. There has been a good deal of controversy as to whether, with experimental values of $S(q)$, the linear dependence of ρ on T can be explained. Greenfield (1966) and Wiser and Greenfield (1966) deduce for liquid sodium from observed values of $S(q)$ that the calculated value of $d(\ln \rho)/dT$ is half the observed value. We think that the observed linear dependence of ρ on T must depend on the fact that for real monovalent metals $|v(q)|^2$ vanishes near $q = 2k_F$ (see § 3.4).

3.4. The absolute magnitude of the resistivity

Table 3.1 (partly from Cusack 1963) shows some values of the mean free paths in metals deduced from the free-electron formula

$$\sigma = ne^2 L/\hbar k_F, \qquad k_F = mv_F/\hbar = (3\pi^2 n)^{\frac{1}{3}},$$

where n is taken to be the number of valence electrons per unit volume and m is taken to be the free-electron mass. It will be observed that $kL \gg 1$ for most of the normal metals, though not for tellurium and some liquid alloys. To most of the liquid metals, therefore, the Ziman perturbation theory should be applicable. It should however be mentioned that the use of the Born approximation is not beyond criticism; $v(q)$ is necessarily equal to $\frac{2}{3}E_F$ at $q = 0$, which is not small. L is large only because $S(q)$ is small for small q, as we shall see below.

The difficulty in using the theory to obtain numerical values of the conductivity σ derives from uncertainties in both $S(q)$ and (particularly) $v(q)$, as well as doubts about the validity of the Born approximation. Figure 3.3 shows some values of $v(q)$ calculated by Animalu and Heine (1965). All curves show a zero in the neighbourhood of the maximum of

---

† See, for example, Lien and Sivertsen (1969), who observe for Na and K a linear dependence on T at constant volume over a temperature range of about 200 K.

TABLE 3.1

	Li	Na	Cu	Zn	Hg	Pb	Bi	Te	PbTe	HgTe
Valence	1	1	1	2	2	4	5	6	5	4
$L(\text{Å})$	45	157	34	13	7	6	4	0·9	0·5	0·3
k_{F} (Å^{-1})	1·1	0·89	1·33	1·56	1·34	1·54	1·63	1·60	1·69	1·65
E_{F} (eV)	4·6	3·0	6·6	9·2	6·9	9·0	10·0	9·7	10·9	10·3

$S(q)$ and this makes the conductivity very sensitive to the position of $v(q)$, as is shown particularly by the calculations of Ashcroft and Lekner (1966), who use various forms of $v(q)$.

The zero in $v(q)$ means, of course, that the scattering vanishes at a certain angle of scattering θ, the scattering amplitude due to s-type and p-type phase shifts being of the form $A + B \cos \theta$. In the Born approximation, A and B are real, but not if exact phase shifts are taken, and the success of the theory in obtaining a fair approximation to the resistivity suggests therefore that the Born approximation is sufficient and the phase shifts really are small.† On the other hand, the phase

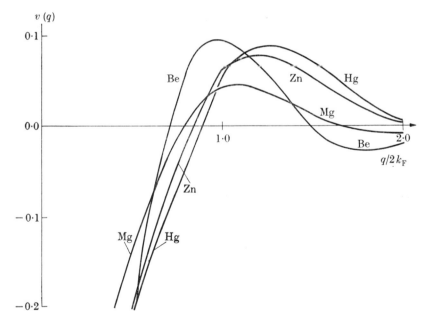

FIG. 3.3. Pseudopotentials $v(q)$ for certain metals in Rydbergs (Animalu and Heine 1965).

† For some calculated values for alkali metals, see Ashcroft (1966).

shifts η_l for a single atom should satisfy the Friedel sum rule

$$\frac{2}{\pi} \sum (2l+1)\eta_l = z,$$

where z is the valency, an equation that can be used to derive the relationship (if all η_l are treated as small)

$$v(0) = \tfrac{2}{3}E_{\mathrm{F}}$$

(Harrison 1966; Heine 1970). It may be emphasized (Heine 1970) that it would not be correct to take exact phase shifts, calculate $I(\theta)$, and put the result in equation (3.8); the scattering at small angles is never small because of the Friedel rule, and multiple-scattering theory would give comparable corrections. Perturbation theory works because $S(q)$ is small for small q, and $v(q)$ small for large q.

The same considerations enable a distinction to be made between monovalent and polyvalent metals. In monovalent metals, $S(q)$ is small nearly up to $q = 2k_{\mathrm{F}}$, so the resistance is small compared with that which would be produced if the atoms were distributed at random. In polyvalent metals the two quantities are comparable.

The attempts to obtain detailed agreement between theory and experiment are reviewed by Faber (1971). We may mention particularly the calculations of the resistivity of crystalline and liquid sodium carried out by Greene and Kohn (1965), and by Hasegawa (1964).† Both authors find that both in the solid and liquid the calculated resistance is about one-half of that observed. Darby and March (1964) however obtain fair agreement for the solid by taking into account the variation of elastic constants with volume, which is large.

3.5. Resistivity of liquid alloys

Ziman's theory has been extended to liquid alloys by Faber and Ziman (1965; see also Faber 1967). In order to give a complete description, for a binary alloy the three separate pair correlation functions $S_{11}(q)$, $S_{22}(q)$, and $S_{12}(q)$ are needed, giving the Fourier transforms of the probability that an atom of type 1 or 2 is at a given distance from another atom of its own kind or of the opposite kind. The analysis of Faber and Ziman is based on the assumption that these

---

† These authors use a dynamic structure factor, obtainable from neutron diffraction, which takes into account the fact that in the liquid as in the solid the collisions are inelastic. It is not clear how important this correlation is.

quantities are identical, and for many alloy systems the assumption gives a good description of the observations. The theory gives for a concentration c of one component a resistivity $\rho = \rho' \pm \rho''$, where

$$\rho' = (3\pi N/\hbar e^2 \Omega v_F^2)\langle(1-c)S\,|v_1(q)|^2 + cS\,|v_2(q)|^2\rangle,$$
$$\rho'' = (3\pi N/\hbar e^2 \Omega v_F^2)\langle c(1-c)(1-S)\,|v_1(q)-v_2(q)|^2\rangle.$$

The sign $\langle\ \rangle$ denotes an average heavily weighted towards large

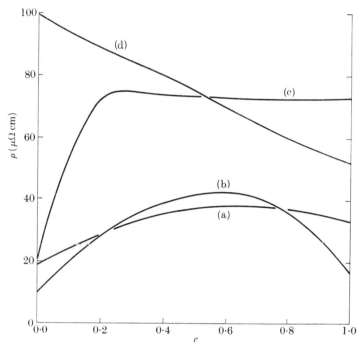

FIG. 3.4. Resistivity of liquid alloys as a function of concentration: (a) Ag–Au at 1200°C; (b) Na–K at 100°C; (c) Cu–Sn at 1200°C; (d) Pb–Sn at 400°C (Faber and Ziman 1965).

$q\ (q \lesssim 2k_F)$. It will be seen that the second term is likely to be small for polyvalent metals because $S \sim 1$ over the important range of scattering. Thus ρ' makes the major contribution, and the scattered intensities from atoms 1 and 2 must be added together. Figure 3.4 (from Faber and Ziman) shows that this is so for Pb–Sn. On the other hand, for monovalent metals $S \ll 1$, and ρ'' makes the major contribution. The interference between waves scattered by different atoms is important, just as in crystalline alloys, and curves such as those shown for Ag–Au and Na–K are obtained.

A theoretical account of the curve reproduced for Cu–Sn needs a determination of the three separate partial structure factors, which can be obtained from a combination of X-ray and neutron diffraction (Enderby, North, and Egelstaff 1966). Enderby and Howe (1968) have shown that good agreement with experiment can be obtained when this is done.

Mercury alloys (amalgams) normally show the behaviour shown in Fig. 3.5, the resistivity dropping sharply with concentration; the

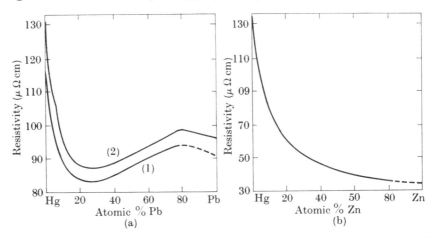

Fig. 3.5. Resistivity of some liquid amalgams, as a function of composition: (a) Hg–Zn; (b) Hg–Pb (Adams and Kravitz 1961).

evidence is summarized by Mott (1966), though his suggested explanation is perhaps not correct. At the time of writing, no fully accepted explanation is available, but Evans (1970) has proposed that because of the proximity of the full 5d band to the Fermi surface there is an abnormally large d phase shift, and that the value of this is very sensitive to energy. The result is that $v(q)$ is negative everywhere and does not change sign, in contrast with the behaviour shown in Fig. 3.3. For a divalent metal, $S(q)$ can be greater than unity in an important range of q (Fig. 3.1), so ρ'' can be negative. If $v_1(q)$ and $v_2(q)$ have opposite signs in this range of q, ρ will drop very rapidly with c.

3.6. Thermoelectric power

As we emphasized in Chapter 2, for materials in which the conductivity is determined by electrons with energies near E_F, we may use the 'metallic' formula for the thermoelectric power, which we write in the form

$$S = (\pi^2/3)(k/e)(kT/E_F)\xi,$$

where

$$\xi = \{d(\ln \sigma)/d(\ln E)\}_{E=E_F}.$$

Ziman (1961) and Bradley, Faber, Wilson, and Ziman (1962) applied this formula to liquid metals using equation (3.9) for σ; they found

$$\xi = 3 - 2\eta, \tag{3.11}$$

where

$$\eta = \{|v(q)|^2 S(q)\}_{q=2k_F}/\langle v^2 S(q)\rangle,$$

and the symbol $\langle \ \rangle$ denotes as before an average over q that is defined in their papers. For most metals, comparison with experiment gives values of η close to unity, so the thermopower is negative (n-type). This is because the scattering amplitude $v(q)$ for most liquid metals has a zero near $2k_F$; in other words, the probability of scattering through an angle 180° is small and decreases with E. This is not necessarily so, for instance for scattering by Na^+ ions in a $Na–NH_3$ solution, and in §§ 3.14, 3.15, and in Chapter 5, we shall discuss cases when ξ is negative.†

Formula (3.11) cannot give a value of ξ greater than 3; for mercury the experimental value of ξ is 5, and Bradley et al. and subsequent workers (Faber 1971) ascribe this to a breakdown of the assumption that the scattering potential $v(q)$ is independent of energy; Evans (1970) ascribes this to the d phase shift.

If the mean free path has its minimum value ($k_F L \sim 1$ so that $L \sim a$) and σ is of the form (see § 3.14)

$$\sigma = Se^2g^2a/12\pi^3\hbar,$$

where S is the Fermi surface area and $g = N(E_F)/N(E_F)_{free}$, then the only terms which vary with E are S and g^2. Under these conditions we expect (compare § 2.9.3)

$$\xi = 2[d\{\ln N(E)\}/d\{\ln E\}]_{E=E_F},$$

so that the density of states determines the thermopower. This situation is discussed more fully in § 3.14.

3.7. Hall effect

For most liquid metals, measurements of the Hall coefficient R_H, when interpreted by the use of the formula

$$R_H = 1/nec, \tag{3.12}$$

† In solids too the nearly-free-electron model can give a value of the thermopower of either sign (Robinson 1967).

give a value of n, the number of electrons per unit volume, equal to the actual number if all valence electrons are free. Some results are shown in Table 3.2†; it will be seen that there are deviations for some metals with short mean free path. The reason for this is not known, and indeed we have no quantitative theory applicable to the case when $k_F L \sim 1$ (see § 2.13). However the recent work of Friedman (1971) discussed

TABLE 3.2

Values of n_0/z deduced from the Hall effect in liquid metals

Metal	z	n_0/z; $n_0 = n \times$ atomic volume
Na	1	0·98
Cu	1	1·00
Ag	1	1·02, 1·97
Au	1	1·00
Zn	2	1·01, 1·01, 1·00, 1·00
Cd	2	0·99, 0·98, 0·96, 1·04
Hg	2	0·99, 0·98, 1·00, 1·00, 1·00, 0·98, 0·96, 1·20, 1·22
Al	3	1·00
Ga	3	0·97, 0·99, 1·00, 1·04
In	3	0·93, 1·00, 0·98, 1·04, 0·95, 0·80
Tl	3	0·96, 0·76
Ge	4	1·00
Sn	4	1·00, 1·00, 1·00, 1·00, 0·98, 1·07
Pb	4	0·88, 0·88, 0·88, 0·73, 0·38
Sb	5	0·92, 1·14
Bi	5	0·95, 0·95, 0·69, 0·60
Te	6	3·3 (decreases on heating)

on p. 55 gives a qualitative description of how values of R_H greater than (3.12) can arise, as for tellurium, and the discussion of § 2.13 suggests that this is a general property of many liquids for which the mean free path is short.

3.8. Density of states

In second-order perturbation theory, the energy of an electron with wave number k is

$$E = E_k + v(0) + \frac{\Omega}{8\pi^3} \int \frac{|v(q)|^2 S(q) \, d^3q}{E_k - E_{k+q}}, \qquad (3.13)$$

where

$$E_k = \hbar^2 k^2 / 2m.$$

† From Faber (1971), which gives references; see also Appendix (p. 401).

The density of states for a liquid or amorphous material can be evaluated using the formula (cf. eqn 2.1)

$$N(E) = 4\pi k^2/8\pi^3(\mathrm{d}E/\mathrm{d}k)$$

(Faber 1967). These formulae are not exact, because one cannot treat the changes in E that result from the term $|v(q)|^2$ without at the same time treating the scattering. Edwards (1961, 1962) and Faber (1971) treat the two together.

If E is known as a function of k, the density of states can be calculated, and in this way a number of authors have discussed the changes in the density of states due to the last term in eqn (3.13) (for references see Ballentine 1966; Mott 1967). For actual liquid metals we believe the effect to be small. We emphasize again that significant deviations from free-electron behaviour are to be expected if—and only if—$\Delta k/k \sim 1$. This case will be considered in § 3.14.

The term $v(0)$, if $v(q)$ is a function only of q, will add a constant term to E. But it must be remembered that the use of a *small* potential $v(q)$ results from the substitution of a small pseudopotential for a large potential, and this may not always be possible. A useful approximation is to make $v(0)$ and $v(q)$ functions of E. We have already seen that the thermoelectric power of liquid mercury demands that $v(q)$ should decrease with E. Animalu and Heine (1965) derive an energy-dependent pseudo-potential for this metal with $v(0)$ *decreasing* with E, so that the effective mass is less than $\sim 0.7m$.

In general it is useful to distinguish, as many workers have done, between terms that depend on the structure, and thus on $S(q)\,|v(q)|^2$, and those that depend on the potential in the first order.† Thus if $V(r)$ has a resonance (a virtual bound state, see Friedel (1954), Ziman (1960)) there should be a sharp maximum in $N(E)$ at that energy, whatever the structure. In the tight-binding approximation on which the considerations of Chapter 2 are based, the positions of the bands are determined by atomic energy levels and the width of the band by a single overlap integral and by the coordination number z. The density of states depends on the potential in the first order, and could never be obtained from perturbation theory if a value of $v(q)$ independent of the energy is used.

---

† See for instance Ham (1962), who describes the effective mass in what he calls the spherical approximation.

3.9. Knight shift

Table 3.3 shows the change in the Knight shift K on melting for a number of metals. For some metals there is little change. Since K is proportional to the density of states $N(E_F)$ at the Fermi surface, this indicates that $N(E_F)$ does not change much in these metals. This does not necessarily mean that $N(E_F)$ has the free-electron value; the effect of $v(0)$ is the same in the liquid as in the solid. But it does mean that either the effect of band structure for all these solids is small, or that the term $S(q)\,|v(q)|^2$ gives the same change in $N(E_F)$ as the corresponding term in the crystal. In view of the calculations of Ballentine and others, showing that for the liquid this term is small, it seems likely that for

TABLE 3.3

Change of Knight shift K on melting (from Faber 1971).

Metal	Li	Na	Rb	Cs	Cu	Cd	Hg	In	Sn	Bi	Te
Liquid K_L	0·026	0·116	0·662	1·46	0·25	0·8	2·45	0·75	0·73	1·40	0·38
$\dfrac{10^2(K_L - K_S)}{K_L}$	0	+2	+1	−2	+5	24	0	−1	−3	80	100

these particular metals there is little band-structure effect on $N(E_F)$ in the crystal. This problem has been reviewed by Ziman (1967a). It would be particularly interesting to make the comparison for a metal where there is likely to be a large change (e.g. Be, Ca).

Ziman (1967a) has plotted the observed Knight shift of a large number of liquid metals against the free-electron density of states and shows that the values lie closely about a straight line; he argues from this that there is little deviation of the density of states from the free-electron value.

We shall discuss in § 3.17 some other cases where the density of states certainly falls below the free-electron value, and increases with T; this effect is reflected in the Knight shift.

3.10. Change in the magnetic susceptibility on melting

Measurements of this quantity provide another way in which the change in the density of states near the melting point can be estimated, assuming the electron-spin contribution to be given by the Pauli term $2\mu_B^2 N(E_F)$. The review by Cusack (1963 p. 378) shows that, while the change is large for such metals as Bi where the coordination number changes, it is small for the alkalis. Recent results by Collings (1969 and unpublished) give a change for aluminium of a few per cent only, though there is a rapid drop with temperature before the melting point (Fig. 3.6). The reason for this drop is not understood. The change for Mg is also negligible, but a decrease of 20 per cent for zinc is reported. Collings emphasizes that this may not be due to the

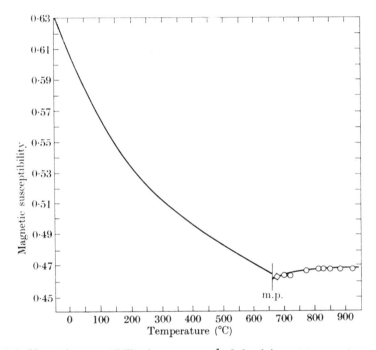

FIG. 3.6. Magnetic susceptibility in μ e.m.u. g^{-1} of aluminium at temperatures through the melting point (Collings, private communication).

Pauli spin term, which is proportional to $N(E_F)$; other terms may also change on melting (Timbie and White 1970).

3.11. X-ray emission spectra

Soft X-ray emission bands frequently show a structure. Until recently it was thought that these were due to band-structure effects and some may be. Thus the persistence of the structure shown by the L_{III} band in Al into the liquid phase (Fig. 3.7), as observed by Catterall and Trotter (1963), was cited as evidence that the term $|v(q)|^2$ produces about the same result in the liquid as in the crystalline state. However the work of Roulet, Gavoret, and Nozières (1969) now makes it clear that a peak at the Fermi limit can be caused by a many-body

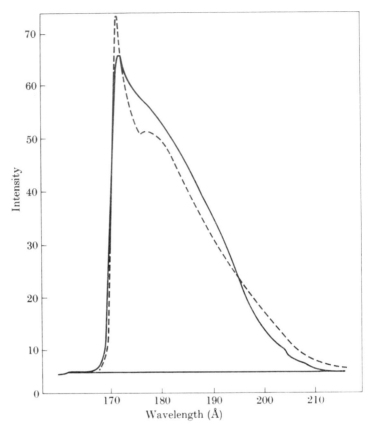

Fig. 3.7. X-ray emission bands of solid (dotted line) and liquid aluminium (Catterall and Trotter 1963).

effect, which should be the same in the liquid as in the solid. In view of these new developments it has not yet proved possible to use X-ray spectra to make firm predictions about the change of $N(E)$ on melting.

3.12. Amorphous metallic films; grain boundaries

The structure of amorphous alloy films, such as liquid-quenched Fe–P–C and Pd–Si alloys, electro-deposited Ni–P, and vapour-quenched Cu–Mg and Ag–Cu, has been reviewed by Wagner (1969). His general conclusion is that the order is somewhat greater than in the liquid, but the breadth of the diffraction lines is not dissimilar.

According to Mader, Widmer, d'Heurle, and Nowick (1963) and Mader (1965), amorphous alloys can normally be deposited on a cold substrate if there is a difference in the atomic radii of more than 10 per cent: such films are stable up to $\sim 0\cdot 3 T_M$, where T_M is the melting point. Figure 3.8 shows the same results for Cu $+50$ % Ag evaporated onto a substrate at 80K. The results show that the resistivity of the film is about half that of the liquid. References to results on amorphous bismuth films are given in Mott (1967).

As a contrast to the comparatively low resistivity of amorphous films, it is worth mentioning that Andrews, West, and Robeson (1969) have

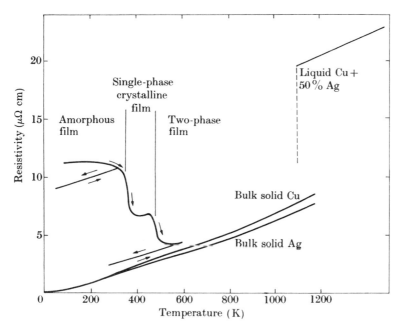

FIG. 3.8. Resistivity of amorphous films of Cu $+50$ % Ag evaporated at 80 K, showing reversible and irreversible behaviour due to annealing (Mader 1965).

measured the grain boundary contribution to the resistivity in Cu and Al and find $\sim 3 \times 10^{-12}$ Ω cm^2; Kasen (1970) finds $1\cdot 35 \times 10^{-12}$ Ω cm^2 for aluminium. Assuming the width of a grain boundary to be 3×10^{-8} cm, this corresponds to a resistivity of $\sim 10^{-4}$ Ω cm, which is about ten times the resistivity of liquid copper at the melting point. Grain boundaries therefore behave as if they are much more disordered than the liquid.

3.13. Injected electrons in liquid rare gases

A number of investigations have been made of the transport of electrons in solid and liquid rare gases. Thus Miller, Howe, and Spear

(1968) have produced carriers by pulses of 40 keV electrons and measured the drift mobility. Similar work has been carried out by Halpern, Lekner, Rice, and Gomer (1967) and by Schnyders, Rice, and Meyer (1966). The drift velocities for solid and liquid krypton at 113K are shown in Fig. 3.9. It will be seen that at low fields the mobility in the liquid is high (2000 cm² V⁻¹ s⁻¹). This corresponds to a long mean free path of several hundred atoms. There is clearly no significant trapping by localized states. We have suggested in § 2.4 that localized

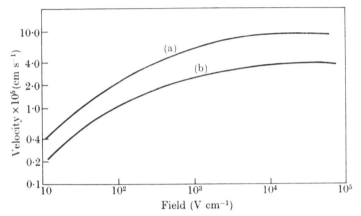

FIG. 3.9. Drift velocities of electrons in (a) solid and (b) liquid krypton as a function of field (Miller, Howe, and Spear 1968). The values of the thickness are from 185–585 μm.

states do not occur when the wave functions are s-like at the bottom of a band.†

For the liquid as for the solid the concept of a *deformation potential* can be used to calculate the mobility. If E_0 is the change in potential at the bottom of the conduction band for unit expansion, we should expect for the mean free path L

$$\frac{1}{L} = N \int S(q) l^2 (1 - \cos \theta) 2\pi \sin \theta \, d\theta,$$

where $l = \Omega_0 m E_0 / 2\pi\hbar^2$; the quantity l is called the scattering length. For $S(q)$ we can take the Ornstein–Zernike formula (3.10), so that $1/L = 4\pi l^2 kT/\beta$, where β is the bulk modulus. The mobility μ is $e\tau/m\{= eL/\sqrt{(mkT)}\}$, which may be written

$$\mu = \frac{e\beta}{4\pi l^2 kT} \frac{1}{\sqrt{(mkT)}}. \tag{3.14}$$

† A hole injected into a rare gas (say Ar) can form a kind of polaron, i.e. a molecule Ar₂⁺, which has low mobility.

A striking feature of the results shown in Fig. 3.9 is that the mobilities for liquid and solid are in the ratio of the bulk moduli β for the two states, so l and m appear to be the same in liquid and solid. This is further evidence that, for a band built up mainly from s orbitals, there is little change in the band structure on melting.

The effective mass in the solid is about $0 \cdot 5m$ for solid argon, so it must be emphasized that in liquid argon we are very far from the nearly-free-electron approximation. If we started from eqn (3.13) in a calculation of $N(E)$, we would have to assume a large dependence of $v(0)$ on E. The high value of the mobility depends on the smallness of $S(q)$. The scattering length is comparable with a. Discussions of the detailed behaviour of l have been given by Lekner (1967, 1968); an interesting result is that l goes through a zero as the gas expands.

In liquid rare gases there is strong evidence for exciton states (see Raz and Jortner 1970). Since the bottom of the conduction band is so little distorted this is not surprising. In situations where a substantial range of localized states exists at the extremities of the bands, it is doubtful whether exciton line spectra can be observed, although excitonic states must still exist (Davis and Mott 1970).

3.14. Effect of the density of states on the conductivity

The usual formula for the conductivity of a free-electron gas is

$$\sigma = ne^2\tau/m^*,$$

where n is the number of electrons per unit volume and τ the time of relaxation. It is convenient to express this in terms of the mean free path L; if v is the velocity of an electron at the Fermi surface and k_F the wave number,

$$\tau = L/v = m^*L/\hbar k_F,$$

and

$$n = (8\pi/3)(k_F/2\pi)^3,$$

so that

$$\sigma = S_F e^2 L/12\pi^3\hbar, \tag{3.15}$$

where S_F is the Fermi surface area $4\pi k_F^2$. The importance of formula (3.15) is that it shows that, so long as the energy is given by the free-electron formula $E = \hbar^2 k^2/2m^*$, or more generally if it is independent of direction, the conductivity for given L is independent of the effective mass m^* and thus of the density of states at $E = E_F$. This conclusion is correct so long as the mean free path is long ($k_F L > 1$). We have, however, to reconcile it with formulae (2.10), (2.29) which show

$\{N(E)\}^2$ in the formulae for the conductivity. In these formulae, if $m^* > m$, then m^* cancels out, for the following reason. The matrix element D (eqn (2.29)) contains m^* in the denominator; thus whether L is greater than or is comparable with a, the quantity D is inversely proportional to m^*. Conversely, the free-electron density of states (eqn (2.1)) is proportional to m^*. Thus m^* cancels out.

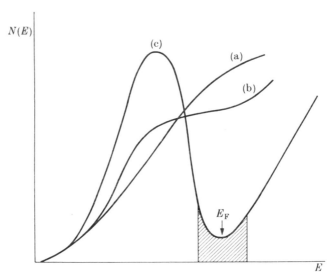

FIG. 3.10. A weak pseudogap in the density of states; the line (a) is the free-electron curve, (b) and (c) represent increasing distances between atoms. Localized states are shaded. E_F is the Fermi energy for a divalent metal.

The situation is different when $N(E)$ drops below the free-electron value because of a pseudogap, such as would arise if the distance between atoms were increased for a divalent metal. The density of states envisaged is illustrated in Fig. 3.10. As in Chapter 2, we suppose that for energies in the pseudogap a relatively small number of Wannier-type orbitals can be set up, which may combine to form either extended or localized functions. The effective mass is not a meaningful concept, since $\Delta k/k \sim 1$, and our matrix element δ (eqn (2.28)) can be taken to be $\sim (a^3/\Omega)/a$. As in Chapter 2, we introduce the ratio

$$g = \{N(E)/N(E)_{\text{free}}\}_{E=E_F},$$

and in this case $g < 1$. Thus the considerations of Chapter 2 suggest that we should write

$$\sigma = S_F e^2 L g^2 / 12 \pi^3 \hbar. \qquad (3.16)$$

We believe this is correct when $g < 1$, if by L is meant the distance in which phase memory is lost. But an interesting result due to Edwards (1962; see also Faber 1971) shows that, unless $kL \sim 1$, the introduction of the factor g makes no difference to the calculated value of σ. If L is calculated by first-order perturbation theory, taking into account the change in the density of states due to the pseudopotential $v(q)$, the result is

$$L = L_{\text{Ziman}}/g^2,$$

where L_{Ziman} is given by eqn (3.7), and is the mean free path calculated on the assumption that $N(E) = N(E)_{\text{free}}$. The factor g^2, therefore, cancels out.

On the other hand, when L drops to the smallest value it can have, namely the distance a between atoms, the perturbation calculation of the mean free path is no longer valid, and then we may write

$$\sigma = S_{\text{F}}e^2ag^2/12\pi^3\hbar. \qquad (3.17)$$

Since

$$S_{\text{F}} = 4\pi k^2 = 4\pi(3\pi^2)^{\frac{2}{3}}/a^2,$$

for one electron per atom this gives

$$\sigma \simeq e^2g^2/3a\hbar. \qquad (3.18)$$

If $a \sim 3$ Å and $g = 1$, $\sigma = 1500 \ \Omega^{-1} \text{cm}^{-1}$. For a divalent metal, we must multiply by $2^{\frac{2}{3}}$, giving $\sigma = 2500 \ \Omega^{-1} \text{cm}^{-1}$.

The quantity (3.18) is proportional to g^2 as g decreases. We have seen in Chapter 2 that localization occurs when $\sigma \sim 0 \cdot 06e^2/a\hbar$, for the Anderson model, so if this formula is assumed to be of more general applicability, the condition for localization becomes $g^2 \simeq 0 \cdot 2$ (i.e. $g \simeq 0 \cdot 45$).

These formulae show why we expect that the use of formula (3.15) to deduce the mean free path from observed conductivities can lead to values as small as $0 \cdot 04a$. When such a procedure leads to values of L/a considerably less than unity, as for liquid tellurium, we believe this to be due to the neglect of the factor g^2.

3.15. Optical properties

The Drude formula

$$\sigma(\omega) = \sigma(0)/(1 + \omega^2\tau^2),$$

where $\tau(= L/v_{\text{F}})$ is the time of relaxation, is satisfied well for most liquid metals; discrepancies, particularly those due to a d band not too far below the Fermi energy, are discussed by Faber (1966, 1971), as is the fact that the factor g of the last section cancels out of the formula, for finite ω as for $\omega = 0$. We expect deviations from the formula only if $kL \sim 1$ and if g is, say, 0·5 or less. In such a case, however, τ would be in the range 10^{-15}–10^{-16} s, and we have given reasons in Chapter 2 for believing that the factor $(1 + \omega^2\tau^2)$ is then not present. The results

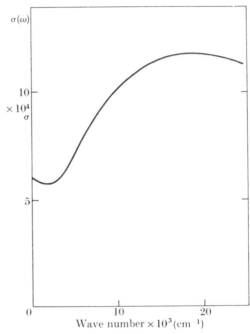

FIG. 3.11. The dependence on frequency of the conductivity $\sigma(\omega)$ in $\Omega^{-1}\,\mathrm{cm}^{-1}$ of liquid tellurium (Hodgson 1963).

of Hodgson (1963) on the absorption coefficient of liquid tellurium (Fig. 3.11) were quoted by Mott (1967) as an example of what might happen in this case, if the density of states is finite at $E = E_{\mathrm{F}}$ but sufficiently small for the term $\{N(E_{\mathrm{F}})\}^2$ in the d.c. conductivity (§2.11) to depress $\sigma(0)$ well below the value of $\sigma(\omega)$ for transitions across the pseudogap. The case of tellurium is discussed further in § 3.17.

3.16. Liquid and amorphous semi-metals

3.16.1. Mercury at low densities

We turn now to an examination of liquid and amorphous systems in which a deep pseudogap is likely to exist, so that either $k_{\mathrm{F}}L \sim 1$ or states are localized there.

In mercury, the mean free path at room temperature and pressure is already short ($\sim$7 Å). The pressure coefficient of resistance is large and negative, and the increase of resistivity with temperature (Postill, Ross, and Cusack 1967) is mainly due to thermal expansion. With rising temperature, until the mean free path drops to values such that

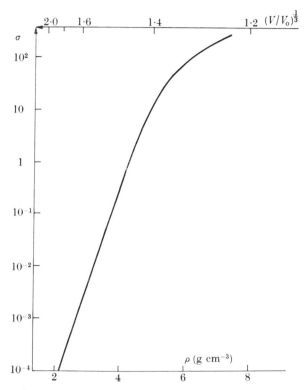

FIG. 3.12. Specific conductivity σ of mercury in $\Omega^{-1}\,\mathrm{cm}^{-1}$ at 1550°C as a function of density (Hensel and Franck 1968). V is the volume and V_0 the molar volume.

$k_F L \sim 1$, this can be accounted for by the Ziman theory, particularly in view of the cancellation of the term g^2 discussed in the last section. But as for any other divalent metal, we expect a separation of the (valence) s band and the (conduction) p band to occur for sufficient expansion, whether the material is crystalline or not; and in the latter case the separation of the two bands should be preceded by the formation of a pseudogap, as in Fig. 2.1. In this case, formula (3.17) or (3.18) should be applicable. The work of Hensel and Franck (1968) on the resistivity of mercury vapour near the critical point gives evidence of this. Figure 3.12 shows the conductivity at 1550°C as a function of volume.

7

It will be seen that the conductivity drops to a value of $\sim$200 Ω^{-1} cm^{-1} after a linear expansion of the liquid by about 30 per cent; thereafter the drop is much more rapid. It was suggested by Mott (1966) that the turnover at $\sim$200 Ω^{-1} cm^{-1} represents the minimum electrical conductivity, occurring when localization is about to set in. In Chapter 2, using the Anderson model, we found $0 \cdot 06 e^2 / \hbar a_E$ for this quantity, i.e., 350 Ω^{-1} cm^{-1} if $a_E \sim 4$ Å. Thus $\sim$200 Ω^{-1} cm^{-1} would be reasonable for mercury at these densities, where a_E should be the distance between localized states, which will be somewhat greater than the mean distance between atoms. If 200 Ω^{-1} cm^{-1} is a correct estimate, then the formula (3.17) suggests $g \sim 1/3 \cdot 5$ as the value of g for which localization sets in.

For smaller values of g, there should be a range of localized states with the Fermi energy in the middle, as in Fig. 3.10. For a solid, conduction, at any rate at low temperatures, would then be by hopping; it is doubtful if hopping will occur in a liquid, because the field of the ions is continually changing, and diffusion of the electrons at the same rate as ionic diffusion is possible. At any rate, the mobility will be low. At the temperature concerned, then, we expect the current to be carried by electrons (or holes) excited to a mobility edge.

We should expect that, as soon as a localized region is formed, E in the formula $\sigma = \sigma_0 \exp(-E/kT)$ would increase rapidly, perhaps as $\sqrt{(a - a_0)}$. Figure 3.12 shows a linear behaviour of ln σ plotted against $1/a^3$ over a considerable range; more detailed work to test this prediction would be of interest.

For low densities the conduction band becomes simply the vacuum between atoms, the valence band shrinks into the 6s^2 atomic state of mercury, and the band gap becomes the ionization energy of mercury. The conductivity–volume curve should then flatten out.

3.16.2. Amorphous magnesium–bismuth alloys

Ferrier and Herrell (1969) have studied amorphous films of this system. It was known earlier (Ilschner and Wagner 1958) that liquid alloys of Mg–Bi showed a minimum in the conductivity at the composition Mg_3Bi_2. Whether the conductivity at this composition is due to hopping cannot be determined by investigating the temperature coefficient of resistivity for the liquid, because the density of states is likely to be a function of temperature. For the evaporated films, the conductivity shows an even deeper minimum than for the liquid, as illustrated in Fig. 3.13. We may remark at once on the contrast between

this behaviour and that of the chalcogenide glasses, where the conductivity is not sensitive to composition. The concept that any additional
unpaired electrons are taken up in bonds is clearly not valid here.
Ferrier and Herrell have in fact interpreted their results in terms of a
rigid band model, with a density of states that does not depend on
composition, as is usual, for instance, in the theory of magnetic alloys

Figure 3.14 shows the temperature coefficient of the resistivity. It is
satisfactory that, on the magnesium-rich side, this changes sign where
$\sigma \sim 10^3 \ \Omega^{-1} \ \mathrm{cm}^{-1}$, which is about the value we expect when the Fermi

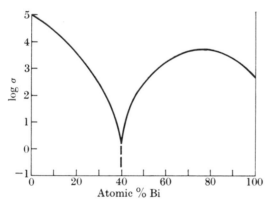

FIG. 3.13. Logarithm of the conductivity (in $\Omega^{-1} \ \mathrm{cm}^{-1}$) as a function of composition for
amorphous evaporated films of Mg–Bi (Ferrier and Herrell 1969).

energy E_F lies just on the non-localized side of E_C. On the bismuth-rich
side the temperature coefficient of resistance does not change sign, but
the values of the conductivity are too high for hopping to be probable.
A small positive temperature coefficient of resistivity does not *necessarily*
mean hopping. If the conductivity is a sensitive function of the energy,
we may write for the conductivity at a temperature T

$$\sigma(T) = \sigma(0) + \tfrac{1}{6}\pi^2(kT)^2\sigma''(0) + \ldots \tag{3.19}$$

(Mott and Jones 1936 p. 177). If the scattering decreases rapidly with
energy, as it may for energies near E_C, we expect σ to increase.

Figure 3.15 shows the thermopower. Comparing this with formula
(2.53) we can deduce $d(\ln \sigma)/dE$. Since $d(\ln \sigma)/dc$, where c is the
concentration, is obtainable from the measurements (Fig. 3.13),
dE/dc is known, and hence the density of states can be deduced. The
results are shown in Fig. 3.16.

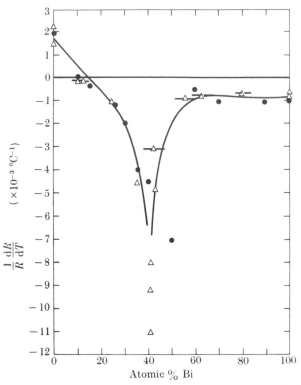

F IG. 3.14. Temperature coefficient of the resistivity of amorphous Mg–Bi (Ferrier and Herrell 1969).

3.17. Liquid semiconductors and semi-metals

The review by Ioffe and Regel (1960) and the books by Gubanov (1963) and by Glazov, Chizhevskaya, and Glagoleva (1969) were the first to treat liquid semiconductors in any detail. In our view, there is no essential difference in the theories necessary to treat electrical conduction in liquid and in solid non-crystalline materials; but liquids are in one way more complicated because the arrangement of atoms, and therefore the structure factor $S(q)$ and the density of states can and do change with temperature, while the change in $S(q)$ due to lattice vibrations in amorphous solids is probably much smaller. In non-crystalline solids we normally suppose that a large negative temperature coefficient of resistance means either thermally activated hopping or excitation to a mobility edge. For liquids this is not so. As we have seen, in most liquid metals the change in $S(q)$ with T is responsible for the dependence of resistivity on temperature, which may have either sign; this may be so *a fortiori* for semi-metals and semiconductors.

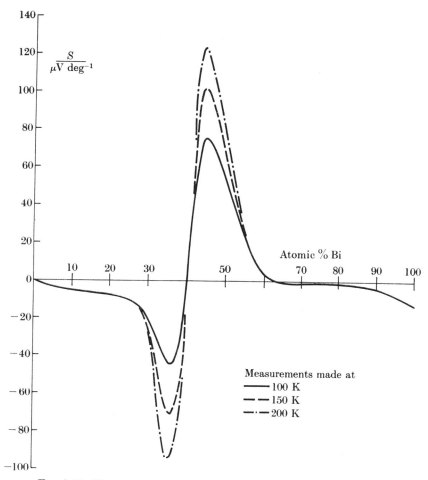

FIG. 3.15. Thermopower of amorphous Mg–Bi (Ferrier and Herrell 1969).

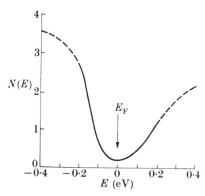

FIG. 3.16. Density of states per atom in eV^{-1} of amorphous Mg–Bi, deduced from the experimental results of Ferrier and Herrell (1969).

As for amorphous materials, we can envisage the following broad classification of liquid conductors:

(a) Typical metals, $\sigma > 5000 \ \Omega^{-1} \ cm^{-1}$; the mean free path is such that $k_F L > 1$. Ziman's theory is applicable and $d\rho/dT$ is usually positive, but negative in some divalent metals. The Hall constant is given by $R_H = 1/nec$.

(b) Liquids of intermediate type where $k_F L \sim 1$, so that the conductivity is in the range 300–$5000 \ \Omega^{-1} \ cm^{-1}$ and due to non-activated diffusive motion. Here we suppose that the conductivity is given by formula (3.17) with g in the range 0.3–1, and the thermopower as explained in § 3.6 depends on $d\{\ln N(E)\}/dE$. As the temperature is raised we may expect the pseudogap to be smeared out; a model of how this can occur is proposed for liquid tellurium–selenium alloys below. At the same time $L(\sim 1/k_F)$ remains constant, so that σ is proportional to g^2. Since the Knight shift K is proportional to g, σ is proportional to K^2. An example of this behaviour (tellurium) is shown in Fig. 3.21. When $kL \sim 1$, the work of Friedman (1971; see § 2.12) suggests that the Hall coefficient is normally negative and can be larger ($\sim 1/necg$) than the free electron value.

(c) Semi-metals or narrow-gap semiconductors, which in the liquid phase are likely to have a deep pseudogap (σ in the range 1–$100 \ \Omega^{-1} \ cm^{-1}$). In such materials there will always be two competing mechanisms for the conductivity, giving currents in parallel; these are hopping conduction by electrons with energies within $\sim kT$ of the Fermi energy, and band conduction by electrons excited to energies beyond the mobility shoulder, where the mobility is at least 100–1000 times higher. Which mechanism predominates depends on the constants involved, but only if $\sigma \sim 1 \ \Omega^{-1} \ cm^{-1}$ is the conductivity likely to be caused by the former mechanism.

In liquids, since the atoms are in constant motion so that the positions of the localized states will continually change, it is possible that, when states are (instantaneously) localized, conduction is by diffusion (as for electrons in cavities in ammonia) rather than by hopping.

(d) Semiconductors in which the (hopping) conductivity is negligible for energies near to E_F, so that the current must be carried by excited electrons with energies just above E_C, or holes just below E_V. The conductors may be intrinsic or extrinsic; in either case the conductivity due to electrons should be given by

$$\sigma = \sigma_0 \exp\{-(E_C - E_F)/kT\},$$

where σ_0 is the quantity $0.06e^2/\hbar a_E$ and $\mu_H \sim 0.1 \ cm^2 \ V^{-1} \ s^{-1}$.

We have emphasized that in liquid metals the structure factor $S(q)$ can vary with temperature, and in liquid semiconductors, where the effect of the coordination number on the density of states may be large, $N(E)$ may itself vary with temperature. For some materials, such as liquid Te–Se and some Ge–As–Te glasses, there seems to be a transition from class (d) to class (b) as the temperature is raised, resulting in a rapid increase in the conductivity to values of order $10^3 \, \Omega^{-1} \, \mathrm{cm}^{-1}$ or more. These will be discussed below.

A further point to be emphasized with reference to class (d) is the difference between conduction at the edge of a band where electrons have s-like wave functions (as in the conduction band of liquid argon) and conduction in bands where this is not so. In the former case a parabolic band form and $kL \gg 1$ is possible, in the latter case states at the bottom of the band are localized (see § 2.5).

Tables of the properties of liquid semiconductors have been published by Mott (1967), Mott and Allgaier (1967), and Allgaier (1969). The table in the Appendix has been prepared by Dr. Allgaier for this book.† It shows that practically all liquids with conductivity below $3000 \, \Omega^{-1}$ cm^{-1} have a positive value of $d\sigma/dT$. This seems to apply, therefore, to materials in class (b) as well as those in class (c); the reason in our view is that a rise in temperature fills in the pseudogap, giving a larger value of $\{N(E_{\mathrm{F}})\}^2$. The table also shows the low values of $\mu_{\mathrm{H}}(\sim 0.1)$ for a wide range of liquids with short mean free path in class (d), and this is shown in Fig. 3.17 (from Allgaier 1970).

3.17.1. Semiconductors in class (d); selenium

For such materials, if $E_{\mathrm{C}} - E_{\mathrm{F}}$ varies with temperature as $E - \gamma T$, we expect a conductivity of the form

$$\sigma = C \exp(-E/kT), \tag{3.20}$$

with $C = \sigma_0 \exp(\gamma/k)$; and for the thermopower (§ 2.9.3)

$$S = \frac{k}{e}\left\{\frac{E}{kT} - \frac{\gamma}{k} + 1\right\}. \tag{3.21}$$

Figure 3.18 for $\mathrm{As_2Se_3}$ and Fig. 3.19 for selenium, reproduced from Stuke (1970a), suggest that these materials are in this class. The magnitude of the thermopower is not as great as it ought to be, if we take E from the slope of the curves of $\ln \sigma$ against $1/T$. It is possible that this

† Liquid transition metals, although they have values of the conductivity of order $10^4 \, \Omega^{-1} \, \mathrm{cm}^{-1}$, are none the less probably in category (b), with $L \sim a$. The reason for the large conductivity is that the d band makes a large contribution to S_{F}, and when $L \sim a$ it makes a large contribution to the conductivity also (Mott 1971d).

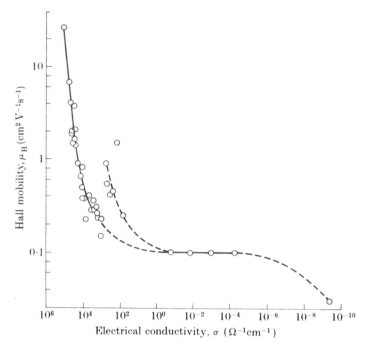

Fig. 3.17. Hall mobilities of a number of liquids plotted against conductivities (Allgaier 1970).

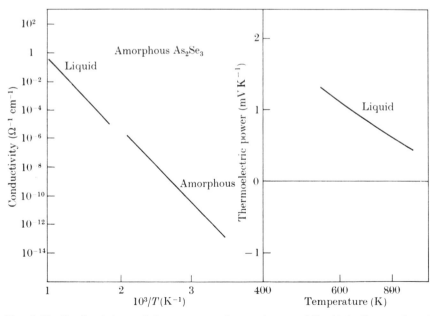

Fig. 3.18. Conductivity and thermopower of amorphous and liquid As_2Se_3 as a function of temperature (Stuke 1970a); see also Fig. 9.22.

is because both electrons and holes contribute to the current, in which case S would of course be smaller than shown by formula (3.21). This conjecture is reinforced by the observation, shown in Fig. 3.19, that S changes sign at low temperatures in Se containing a small addition of Sb or Bi. Stuke (1970b) suggests that deep donors are formed; an alternative suggestion is that these elements, by introducing cross-links between the selenium chains, widen the range of localized states in the

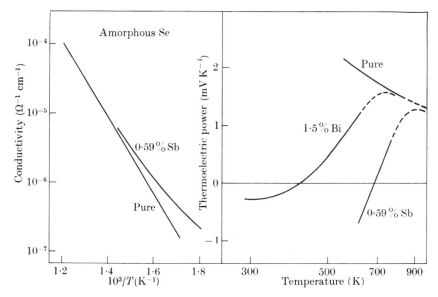

FIG. 3.19. Conductivity and thermopower of amorphous and liquid selenium as a function of temperature (Stuke 1970a); see also Fig. 10.6.

valence band, moving the bottom of the band into the forbidden gap but increasing the distance between E_F and E_V (see also p. 377).

3.17.2. Tellurium

This liquid is a semi-metal in class (b). The dependence on temperature of the Hall coefficient and conductivity of liquid tellurium are shown in Fig. 3.20. The conductivity is of order $2000 \ \Omega^{-1} \mathrm{cm}^{-1}$ and rises with temperature. This is somewhat less than the value (~ 5000 $\Omega^{-1} \mathrm{cm}^{-1}$) that we should expect with $g = 1$ (no pseudogap) and six electrons per atom, and so it seems probable that at the melting point the liquid metal has a pseudogap in the density of states with $g^2 \sim 0.4$ at the Fermi energy (Fig. 3.21), and that $g \to 1$ as the temperature rises. As we have seen in Fig. 3.11, the optical properties give evidence

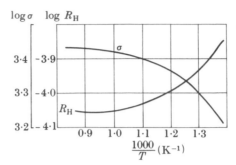

FIG. 3.20. Conductivity (σ) in $\Omega^{-1}\,cm^{-1}$ and Hall coefficient R_H in cm^3C^{-1} of liquid tellurium as a function of $1/T$ (Tièche and Zareba 1963).

for a pseudogap. Since the thermopower is positive, the Fermi energy must lie not at the minimum of the gap but displaced towards the valence band. Reasons for this behaviour are given in the next section.

Cabane and Froidevaux (1969) have measured the Knight shift in liquid tellurium as a function of T. Since the mean free path is short ($kL \sim 1$), so that in this case $\sigma \propto g^2$, the conductivity σ should be proportional to the square of the Knight shift (K); that this is so follows from these results which we have plotted as σ against K^2 in Fig. 3.22(b).

The Hall coefficient is two or three times larger than one would expect from the formula $R_H = 1/nec$, with n corresponding to six electrons per atom; it decreases however with increasing temperature,

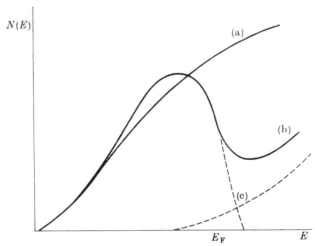

FIG. 3.21. Suggested density of states for liquid tellurium and Te–Se alloys: (a) high temperature; (b) intermediate temperature; (c) low temperature.

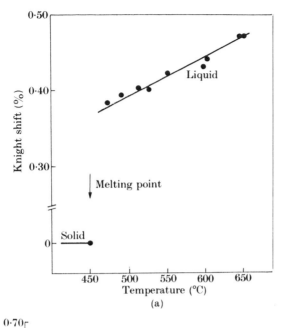

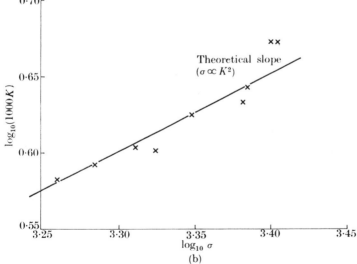

Fig. 3.22. (a) Knight shift K of liquid tellurium (Cabane and Froidevaux 1969). (b) Plot of log $(1000K)$ versus log σ, showing the linear relationship $\sigma \propto K^2$.

again suggesting the gradual establishment of normal metallic behaviour.

Urbain and Übelacker (1966) have measured the magnetic susceptibility of solid and liquid tellurium, their results being shown in Fig. 3.23. They suggest that, after the susceptibility of the ions has been subtracted, the susceptibility approaches the Pauli free-electron value for

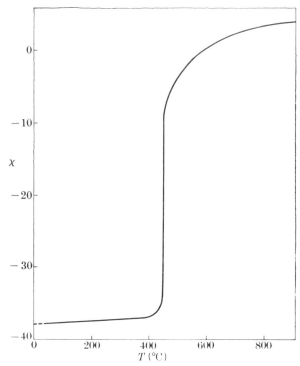

FIG. 3.23. Magnetic susceptibility χ in $cm^3 \ g^{-1}$ of solid and liquid tellurium (Urbain and Überlacker 1966). The free-electron value according to the Pauli theory is shown by the horizontal line at the top of the diagram.

six electrons per atom. We believe that this also may indicate that $N(E_F)$ gradually approaches the free-electron value ($g = 1$) as the temperature is raised.

A discussion of the structure of liquid tellurium has been given by Cabane and Friedel (1971), and the band structure has been reviewed by these authors and by Mott (1971a).

3.17.3. Tellurium–selenium liquid alloys

These have been investigated by Perron (1967), and his results for the conductivity and thermopower are shown in Figs. 3.24 and 3.25.

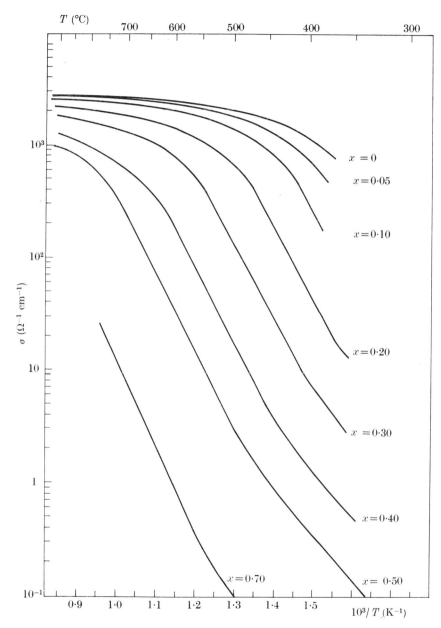

FIG. 3.24. Electrical resistivity of liquid Se–Te alloys as a function of temperature
(Perron 1967).

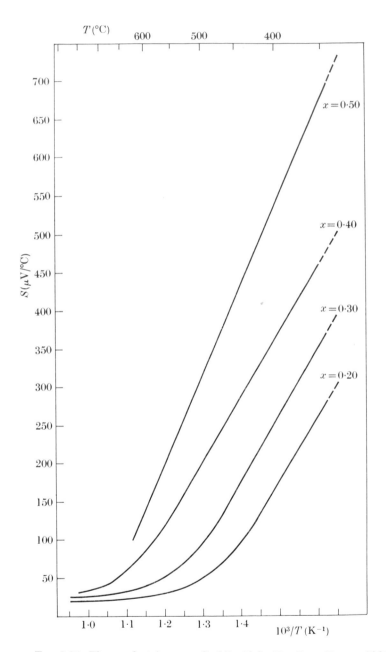

FIG. 3.25. Thermoelectric power S of liquid Se–Te alloys (Perron 1967).

In principle these results can be explained by formulae (3.20) and (3.21), the mobility gap $E_F - E_V$ diminishing and eventually disappearing as the temperature is raised. γ must therefore be very large. For values of the conductivity above 100 Ω^{-1} cm^{-1} we have to assume that the behaviour is metallic, and that σ is proportional to $\{N(E_F)\}^2$ (and thus the factor g^2), and that the pseudogap fills up as the temperature is raised.

Quantitatively, however, there are difficulties in this explanation. The sudden rise in σ (shown also by certain liquid glasses discussed in Chapter 8) is not reflected in the thermopower. The rise is believed to be associated with an increase in the coordination number (Cabane and Friedel (1971), and since it does not show up in S, it must be ascribed to a rise in σ_0. To understand this phenomenon, we need to discuss further the very rapid change in the band gap (large values of γ) that is characteristic of liquids. The matter is discussed in Chapter 7, where values of γ obtained from optical data are given. When the band gap is due to structure, both in crystals and non-crystalline materials, it normally shrinks as the temperature is raised; a large effect occurs at constant volume (§ 7.6.1) due to a decrease in the difference between the distances of nearest and next-nearest neighbours. We think that in the valence band of Te–Se and the chalcogenide glasses the range of localized states may be narrow, giving small values of σ_0, but that as the valence and conduction bands get mixed up σ_0 may rise by an order of magnitude.

3.17.4. Liquid alloys of tellurium with metallic elements

These have been extensively investigated by Cutler and Mallon (1965), Cutler and Field (1968), Enderby and Simmons (1970), Regel, Andreev, Kotov, Mamadaliev, Okuneva, Smirnov and Shadrichev (1970), and others. They show a maximum in the resistivity at a certain composition, e.g. TeTl$_2$, Te$_2$In$_3$. Cutler (1971) has given thermodynamic evidence to support the hypothesis that molecules of these compositions can form and partially dissociate as the temperature is raised; an excess of either constituent can be dissolved in the liquid formed from these molecules.

We interpret the properties of such materials in the following way. The Te^{2-} ion in the molecule (e.g. TeTl$_2$) forms a closed shell. Thus the wave functions near the bottom of the conduction band are s-like on the Te atoms. Therefore the density of states in the conduction band should be parabolic, and there will not be an extensive range of localized states

(Chapter 2). There is in fact a marked difference between the behaviour
on the Tl-rich and Te-rich sides of $TeTl_2$. Figure 3.26 shows the
resistivity ρ of these alloys as a function of composition at 800 K and
1000 K. It will be seen that for the thallium-rich alloys ρ does not
depend on T; the material has the electrical properties of a metal.

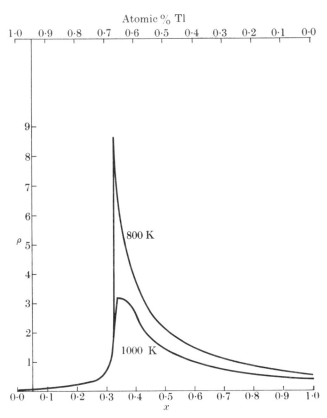

FIG. 3.26. Resistivity ρ of liquid Te–Tl alloys at 800 K and 1000 K as a function of
composition (Cutler 1971).

Cutler and Field have shown that the addition of other metals leads to
the same result, and also that the metal atom gives up *all* its valence
electrons to the degenerate gas. This is in sharp contrast with the
behaviour on the tellurium-rich side. We suggest that the reason may
be that the 'molecule' $TeTl_2$ has a dipole, and that the metal ion is
solvated. This would provide the energy required to raise the energies
of the electrons to the conduction band of liquid '$TeTl_2$'. The field
round the Tl^{3+} ion would thus be weak, and the degenerate gas should

have properties similar to those of the electrons in concentrated metal–ammonia solutions described in Chapter 5.

Figure 3.27 shows the thermoelectric power of the system as a function of concentration. The values suggest that on the Te-rich side the material is p-type. On the other hand, on both sides the Hall coefficient is found to be n-type. For the reasons given in § 2.12, we do not think that any deduction can be made from this about whether the carriers

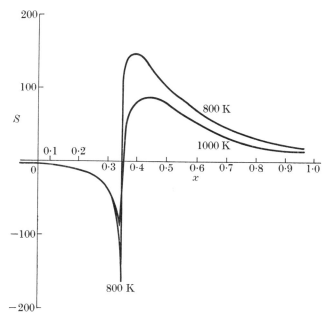

FIG. 3.27. Thermoelectric power of liquid Te–Tl as a function of concentration.

are electrons or holes. As evidence that little can be deduced from the Hall effect, Regel *et al.* (1970) have pointed out that for several materials with conductivity in the range 1–10 Ω^{-1} cm^{-1} the change in conductivity on melting is small, but the change in R_{H} is by two orders of magnitude; the example of Sb_2Se_3 is shown in Fig. 3.28. This seems to support our contention that the formula $R_{\mathrm{H}} = 1/nec$ cannot be applied to the case of short mean free path or to hopping.†

† Enderby and Collings (1970) put forward a different hypothesis, namely that the Te-rich alloys are normal metals, as the Hall effect would indicate, and that the p-type thermopower is due to some kind of resonance scattering, which increases rapidly with energy. We find this explanation difficult to accept. The conductivity of order $4 \times 10^{-3} \Omega^{-1}$ cm^{-1} is about as low as is possible for a metal; if we have to deal with a metallic conductor the mean free path must be very short and a rapid dependence on energy is unlikely.

8

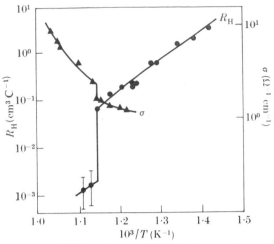

FIG. 3.28. Conductivity and Hall coefficient of Sb_2Se_3 through the melting point (Regel *et al.* 1970).

Figure 3.29 (due to Cutler and Mallon 1965) shows the dependence on temperature of the resistivity of liquid Te–Tl alloys on the tellurium-rich side of $TeTl_2$. Although there is a large change in temperature, the conductivity ($>200\ \Omega^{-1}\,cm^{-1}$) puts these materials in class (b) (metallic), and we should suppose that the conductivity is proportional to $\{N(E_F)\}^2$, which must therefore increase with T.

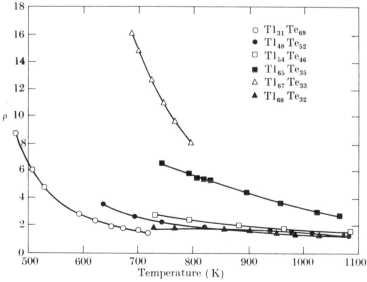

FIG. 3.29. Dependence on temperature of the resistivity of tellurium-rich Te–Tl (Cutler and Mallon 1965).

We have to ask why these materials have a thermopower which is p-type, implying that E_F is on the low-energy side of the pseudogap as in Fig. 3.21. One suggestion is that with increasing temperature the conduction band widens more than the valence band, which is made up of π orbitals that do not take part in the bonding. Another suggestion, due to Cutler, is that broken chains introduce empty orbitals and thus introduce new states into the valence band. Cutler supports this model by pointing out that at a given temperature, if it is assumed that his alloys form tellurium chains terminated by thallium, the conductivity is proportional to the number of Te–Te bonds (Cutler 1971).

The Knight shift K should provide a test of the transition between conductivities of types (a), (b), and (c). Ziman (1967b) has pointed out that for normal metals in class (a) there is a rough proportionality between $\{N(E_F)\}_{\text{free}}$ and K. In liquid semi-metals in which a pseudogap fills up as the temperature is raised, we expect the conductivity to be of type (b) or (c). In type (b), the Knight shift should be proportional to g, the conductivity to g^2, so the relationship K^2 proportional to σ should be observed (see also § 3.17.2). In two papers Warren (1970a, b) has investigated the Knight shift of liquid In_2Te_3 and Ga_2Te_3 from this point of view. Assuming g to be unity at high temperatures, he can deduce g from the value of K at lower temperatures. In this region he finds that K^2/σ is constant. Moreover, a more rapid drop in σ is observed when g drops below about $\frac{1}{3}$, which he ascribes to the onset of localization.

In the region of diffusive motion (class (b)), the nuclear relaxation rate is much greater than that given by the Korringa relation. Warren interprets the relaxation rate as depending on the time that an electron spends on each atom (in our notation $1/\nu_{\text{el}}$, Chapter 2), and thus directly related to the conductivity (see also Mott 1971a).

PHONONS AND POLARONS

4.1. Introduction
4.2. Scattering of electrons by phonons
4.3. Thermally activated hopping
4.4. The distortion of the lattice round a trapped electron
4.5. Transitions from one localized state to another in a polar lattice
4.6. Hopping at low temperatures
4.7. Polarons in crystalline materials

4.8. Motion of a polaron in a crystalline lattice
4.9. Energy required to release a charge carrier from a donor centre
4.10. Examples of hopping polarons
4.11. Thermopower due to polarons
4.12. Anderson localization of polarons
4.13. Degenerate gas of polarons
4.14. Polarons in liquids

4.1. Introduction

LATTICE vibrations (phonons) affect the electrical and optical properties of non-crystalline materials in various ways, which will be discussed under the following headings:

(a) The scattering of electrons by phonons, which makes a contribution to the electrical resistance in the same way as in a crystal.

(b) Thermally activated hopping; an electron jumping from one localized state to another that has a different energy can only do so by exchanging energy with the lattice vibrations.

(c) Polaron formation, or in the case of localized states distortion of the lattice round the centre on which the electron is localized. This can take place to some extent whether a material is polar or not, but for trapped electrons in germanium and silicon the effect is small.

(d) The effect of polaron formation on transport properties.

4.2. Scattering of electrons by phonons

We know of no theoretical treatment of the scattering of electrons by phonons in amorphous semiconductors or metals. In amorphous semiconductors, since the mean free path is probably already of the order of the lattice parameter because of disorder, the effect of phonon scattering is likely to be small, though it may be more important in non-crystalline solid metals (see Chapter 3 for a discussion of amorphous metals). It must, however, be responsible for the rate of loss of energy of an electron injected into the conduction band of a semiconductor, a quantity that is important in considering switching, photocurrents, and similar problems. It is known that an electron in an alloy when scattered by an impurity can suffer inelastic as well as elastic collisions, and the effect has been observed by Panova, Zhernov, and Kutaitsev (1968) and by Kagan and Zhernov (1966) as a pronounced maximum at 55 K in the resistivity of Mg–Pb alloys; below that temperature there are not enough electrons above the Fermi level for inelastic collisions to be significant. In a non-crystalline semiconductor an electron with energy near E_C is scattered once every 10^{-15}–10^{-16} s, and these collisions can be elastic or inelastic. The probability per unit time that an electron loses a quantum of energy $\hbar\omega$ to a phonon of angular frequency ω is normally not greater than ω ($\sim 10^{12}$ s^{-1}) unless the coupling constraint is large (Thornber and Feynman 1970). The rate of loss of energy is therefore often $\sim\hbar\omega^2$, where ω is the characteristic frequency of the lattice.

Calculations along these lines have been made by Hindley (1970). He finds that the probability that an electron will emit a phonon is of order ω, where ω is a mean phonon frequency. This is most easily seen by considering a transition from a weakly localized state of radius r to a non-localized state. The matrix element of the phonon field is of the same type as that considered in optical transitions (§ 2.11), namely

$$\int \psi_i^* \frac{\partial}{\partial x} \psi_f \, \mathrm{d}^3 x.$$

In Hindley's work, as also in § 2.5, it is considered that the phase varies in a random way from atom to atom, so that this integral contains $(r/a)^3$ terms with random sign, and is thus proportional to $(r/a)^{\frac{3}{2}}$. But the normalization factor in ψ_i is proportional to $(r/a)^{-\frac{3}{2}}$, so that r goes out from the calculation, and the same result remains valid for non-localized states.

This qualitative estimate is relevant to the problem of whether or not hot electrons can be formed in an amorphous semiconductor. We suppose electrons to be in the extended states described in Chapter 2, above the mobility shoulder. The mobility μ we take to be of the order of 10 cm^2 V^{-1} s^{-1}. The drift velocity is μF; the rate at which energy is gained is thus $e\mu F^2$ and the energy gained in a time $1/\omega$ is $e\mu F^2/\omega$. If F is measured in V cm^{-1} this is $10^{-11}F^2$ eV. Thus a field greater than 10^5 V cm^{-1} will produce, between collisions with phonons, more than the phonon energy, so at these fields the production of hot electrons is not ruled out. Moreover, since the mobility should increase with energy, as soon as hot electrons are formed they should accelerate and lead to an avalanche (see § 7.9).

4.3. Thermally activated hopping

We discuss here the process by which an electron can jump between two localized states, with energies differing by W_D, the electron exchanging this energy with the lattice vibrations. Two somewhat different cases must be considered:

(a) The energy W_D is less than $\hbar\omega_0$, where ω_0 is the highest phonon frequency of the solid.

(b) The energy W_D is greater than $\hbar\omega_0$, so that several phonons are involved.

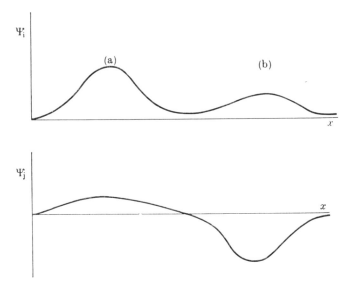

Fɪɢ. 4.1. The two orthogonal wave functions on a pair of impurity centres a and b; the energy E_a lies below E_b.

The first case is that appropriate to doped and compensated germanium and was first treated by Miller and Abrahams (1960). As regards energy exchange with phonons the treatment is elementary. We suppose Ψ_i, Ψ_j are the orthogonal wave functions on the two sites as illustrated in Fig. 4.1. We make use of the concept of the deformation potential E_1 (Bardeen and Shockley 1950), defined so that the change in the potential energy of an electron due to a dilatation η is ηE_1. We calculate the chance per unit time that an electron jumps from a state

i to a state j by using the usual formula (Chapter 2)

$$(2\pi/\hbar)\,|H_{ij}|^2 N(E), \tag{4.1}$$

where $N(E)$ is the density of states of the system in the final state and H_{ij} the matrix element of the interaction between the electron and phonon. If q is the wave number of the phonon,

$$N(E) = (1/8\pi^3)4\pi\Omega q^2\,dq/dE,$$

where Ω is the volume; and since for a phonon the energy E is given by

$$E = \hbar\omega = \hbar qs,$$

this gives

$$N(E) = (1/2\pi^2)\Omega q^2/\hbar s. \tag{4.2}$$

s is here the velocity of longitudinal sound for the value of q considered.

To determine H we consider a block of the solid of density ρ_0; the Schrödinger equation for the normal modes is

$$\frac{d^2\phi}{dX^2}+\frac{2\rho_0\Omega}{\hbar^2 q^2}(E-\tfrac{1}{2}\Omega\rho_0 s^2 X^2)\phi = 0,$$

where X is the (dimensionless) dilatation, and $\phi(X)$ the vibrational wave function. The interaction term H for a phonon of wave number q is of the form

$$XE_1 e^{i(\mathbf{q}.\mathbf{r})}$$

and, since Ψ'_i, Ψ'_j are orthogonal, we can write, if $|\mathbf{q}|\,|\mathbf{r}_i-\mathbf{r}_j|\ll 1$ in the volume occupied by the two wave functions,

$$\int \Psi_i^* e^{i(\mathbf{q}.\mathbf{r})}\Psi_j\,d^3x \simeq i\mathbf{q}\cdot\mathbf{r}_{ij}.$$

For X we may write

$$|X_{n,\,n+1}|^2 = (\hbar q/2\rho_0\Omega s)n_q,$$

where n_q is the number of phonons in the state considered. Thus the number of transitions per unit time is

$$(E_1^2 q^5/2\pi\hbar\,\rho_0 s^2)\,|r_{ij}|^2\,n_q, \tag{4.3}$$

which may be written

$$(E_1^2\omega^5/2\pi\hbar\,\rho_0 s^7)\,|r_{ij}|^2\,n_q, \tag{4.4}$$

with

$$n_q = 1/(e^{\hbar\omega/kT}-1). \tag{4.5}$$

If the two centres a, b are well separated, as in impurity-conduction for low concentrations, we may write for the two wave functions Ψ_i, Ψ_j (compare p. 18)

$$\Psi_i = \psi_a + (I/\ W_D)\psi_b,$$
$$\Psi_j = \psi_b - (I/\ W_D)\psi_a,$$

where $2I$ is the energy separation when $W_D = 0$, and W_D is written for $\hbar\omega$. I may be written in the form

$$I = I_0 e^{-\alpha R},$$

where I_0 is an energy characteristic of each well and R the distance between them.

The matrix element r_{ij} is thus

$$RI/\ W_D,$$

and the transition probability thus becomes

$$(E_1^2 W_D^3 I_0^2 R^2/2\pi\hbar^6 \rho_0 s^7)e^{-2\alpha R}n_q. \tag{4.6}$$

Formula (4.6) is not valid unless it gives, apart from n_q, a value less than ω, the phonon frequency. If this is not so, it should be replaced by ωn_q. It also depends on the assumption that $qR \ll 1$. This is not so in impurity-conduction in doped silicon and germanium, and as a consequence Miller and Abrahams assumed that

$$\int \psi_i^* e^{i(\mathbf{q}\cdot\mathbf{r})}\psi_j \ d^3x \approx I/W_D,$$

so eqn (4.6) becomes

$$(E_1^2 W_D I_0^2/2\pi\hbar^4 \rho_0 s^5)e^{-2\alpha R}n_q. \tag{4.7}$$

The term in the brackets is of the order 10^{12} s^{-1} for these phenomena, but this is accidental, and is not because the vibrational frequency has this value.

If W_D is larger than the maximum phonon energy $\hbar\omega$, more than one phonon is required for the transition to occur. We do not know of any treatment of hopping conduction when $W_D > \hbar\omega$, but for strongly localized states, particularly in polar semiconductors, the distortion of the lattice round the localized state leads to an additional term in the activation energy for hopping, and multiphonon processes must be considered. We shall describe the nature of this distortion in the next section.

Analogous to the use of multiphonon theory to calculate hopping between two localized states is Kubo's (1952) calculation of the factor C

in the probability per unit time, $C\exp(-E/kT)$, for the ionization of a centre in which an electron is bound with energy E.

4.4. The distortion of the lattice round a trapped electron

An electron in a donor centre in silicon or germanium is described by a wave function with a large radius, and the distortion of the lattice by the electron is expected to be small and is usually neglected. This is not so for electrons in deep traps, particularly in polar lattices, for instance at anion vacancies. Thus in F centres in alkali halides the removal of an electron from the centre leads to a movement of the surrounding ions that releases a considerable amount of energy (Mott and Gurney 1940 p. 116). In general we can say that when a localized state is such that the electron (or hole) is confined to the neighbourhood of a very few atoms, it will not be justifiable to neglect the distortion.

A simple and convenient way of introducing the theory of these effects is to consider the energy of a diatomic molecule as a function of some configurational coordinate q, which might be the distance between the nuclei (Fig. 4.2); if the minimum of the energy is taken to be at $q = 0$, we may write the energy as Aq^2 for small values of q. If an electron (or hole) is placed on the molecule, the energy relative to some arbitrary zero may be written $-Bq$. The total energy is then

$$Aq^2 - Bq,$$

which has a minimum when $q = q_0$, where

$$q_0 = B/2A.$$

The energy of the electron $(-Bq)$ is lowered by Bq_0; the distortion of the system requires energy equal to

$$Aq_0^2 = \tfrac{1}{2}Bq_0$$

and the energy of the whole system is lowered by $\tfrac{1}{2}Bq_0$. We shall denote this energy resulting from the polarization by W_p.

This conclusion is important in considering absorption spectra. If the Franck–Condon principle is obeyed, the quantum energy $h\nu$ of radiation of frequency ν required to eject an electron from any centre or localized state is always greater (by $\tfrac{1}{2}Bq_0$) than the total energy E released when the electron is freed, which occurs as $\exp(-E/2kT)$ as a factor in, for instance, the conductivity.

For polar lattices the same result can be obtained in the following way. Consider a neutral trap (localized state) in which an electron can

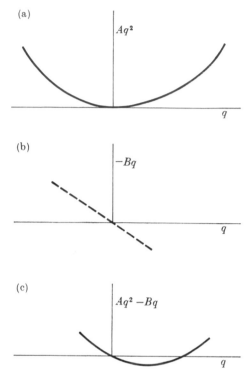

FIG. 4.2. The energy of an electron as a function of a configurational parameter q.

be trapped within a radius r_0 of the order of the lattice constant. Let us introduce an electron into the trap. Then, before the surrounding ions are displaced, the potential energy of (another) electron at distance r is

$$e^2/\kappa_\infty r \qquad (r > r_0),$$

where κ_∞ is the high-frequency dielectric constant. After the ions are displaced, the potential energy becomes

$$e^2/\kappa r.$$

Therefore an electron forms a potential well for itself given by

$$
\left.
\begin{aligned}
V_{\mathrm{p}}(r) &= -e^2/\kappa_{\mathrm{p}} r && (r > r_0)\\
&= -e^2/\kappa_{\mathrm{p}} r_0 && (r < r_0)
\end{aligned}
\right\}, \tag{4.8}
$$

where

$$1/\kappa_{\mathrm{p}} = 1/\kappa_\infty - 1/\kappa. \tag{4.9}$$

The well is illustrated in Fig. 4.3.

The energy of the electron is lowered by $e^2/\kappa_p r_0$. At the same time the polarization energy of the surrounding medium is

$$\tfrac{1}{2}\int_{r_0}^{\infty} EP4\pi r^2 \, \mathrm{d}r = (8\pi)^{-1}\int (e^2/\kappa_p r^4)4\pi r^2 \, \mathrm{d}r$$
$$= \tfrac{1}{2}e^2/\kappa_p r_0.$$

So the energy of the system is lowered by W_p, where

$$W_p = \tfrac{1}{2}e^2/\kappa_p r_0. \qquad (4.10)$$

In practical cases W_p may be of order one-half of an electron volt.

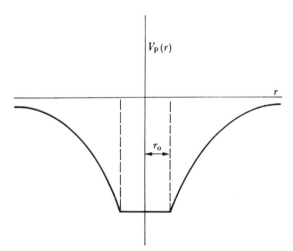

FIG. 4.3. Potential well due to the polarization of an ionic lattice round a trapped electron.

4.5. Transitions from one localized state to another in a polar lattice

We return to the case considered in § 4.3, namely that of two localized states, with energies differing by W_D and with overlapping wave functions, but with the difference that the polarization of the lattice has to be taken into account. W_p may be of the order ~ 0.5 eV, and W_D considerably smaller. The discussion follows that of Austin and Mott (1969 p. 45).

Using the notation of § 4.4, we let q_1, q_2 be the configurational coordinates of two molecules situated on sites with an energy difference W_D. Then we argue that if an electron is to jump from one molecule to the next, the energies of the electron on either site, without the energies of distortion, must be identical; thus

$$B(q_1 - q_2) = W_{\mathrm{D}}.$$

If the electron is initially on molecule 2, the energy required to produce such a state is

$$A(q_2 + W_{\mathrm{D}}/B)^2 + A(q_0 - q_2)^2, \qquad (4.11)$$

which is a minimum when

$$q_2 = \tfrac{1}{2}q_0 - W_{\mathrm{D}}/2B.$$

Substituting in eqn (4.11) we find that the minimum energy required to produce a configuration of the required kind is

$$W = W_{\mathrm{H}} + \tfrac{1}{2}W_{\mathrm{D}} + W_{\mathrm{D}}^2/16W_{\mathrm{H}}, \qquad (4.12)$$

where

$$W_{\mathrm{H}} = \tfrac{1}{2}W_{\mathrm{p}}.$$

It follows that the probability per unit time of jumping from one site to the other will contain an exponential term of the form $\exp(-W/kT)$ with W given by eqn (4.12). In practical cases $W_{\mathrm{H}} \gg W_{\mathrm{D}}$ and the last term in eqn (4.12) can be neglected.

The analysis leads to the important result that the term W_{H} in the hopping activation energy is approximately half the energy of polarization W_{p}. This is true only in a model in which the electron on one molecule does not affect the value of q for the other. It is not true, for instance, in polar materials, in which two polarization wells overlap and can affect each other. For these we picture the process as follows. Initially the electron is trapped in a potential well as in Fig. 4.4(i). If the electron is to be transferred, thermal fluctuations must ensure that the wells have the same depths. If W_{D} is zero or negligible, it is obvious that the smallest activation energy that can produce such a configuration is that when both wells have half the original depth. The energy required to produce this configuration consists of the following terms:

Energy to raise the electron in well a; W_{p}.

Polarization energy released in well a; $W_{\mathrm{p}} - \tfrac{1}{4}W_{\mathrm{p}} = \tfrac{3}{4}W_{\mathrm{p}}$.

Energy to form well b; $\tfrac{1}{4}W_{\mathrm{p}}$.

These give a total activation energy $\tfrac{1}{2}W_{\mathrm{p}}$. If $W_{\mathrm{D}} \neq 0$, formula (4.12) can be used.

For polar lattices, if the distance R through which the electron must be transferred is not large compared with r_0, the formula

$$W_{\mathrm{H}} = \tfrac{1}{2}W_{\mathrm{p}} = e^2/4\kappa_{\mathrm{p}}r_0$$

is no longer valid and must be replaced by (Austin and Mott 1969)

$$W_{\mathrm{H}} = (e^2/4\kappa_{\mathrm{p}})\left(\frac{1}{r_0} - \frac{1}{R}\right). \qquad (4.13)$$

This occurs for the reason already mentioned: the wells overlap and the energy required to produce the intermediate configuration of Fig. 4.4(ii) is diminished.

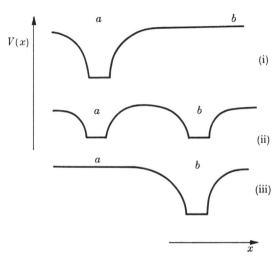

FIG. 4.4. Potential wells on a pair of ions a and b during the hopping process: (i) before hopping; (ii) thermally activated state when electrons can move; (iii) after hopping.

We turn now to the term outside the exponential in the expression for the probability per unit time for a jump from site a to site b. For the case $W_{\mathrm{D}} = 0$ this has been investigated in detail by Holstein (1959) and Emin and Holstein (1969) in their work on the behaviour of polarons; the extension to the case when $W_{\mathrm{D}} \neq 0$ is due to Schnakenberg (1968).† We distinguish two cases:

(a) The 'adiabatic' case in which, during the time of the order of 10^{-12} s in which the activated state of Fig. 4.4 persists, the electron makes several transitions backwards and forwards between the two wells. In this case the analysis shows that the jump rate is of the form

$$p \exp(-W/kT) \qquad (4.14)$$

where p is equal to the frequency ω_0 of an optical phonon (there is no dispersion in the simple model used).

† An extension of Schnakenberg's analysis to a.c. impurity-conduction has been given by Aldea (1971).

(b) The non-adiabatic case when the probability that the electron moves from one well to the other during one lattice vibration is small. In this case for $T > \frac{1}{2}\Theta$ the jump probability is given by eqn (4.14) with

$$p = \pi^{\frac{1}{2}} I^2 / \hbar (W_H k T)^{\frac{1}{2}}.$$

Here I is the energy difference between states of odd and even parity in Fig. 4.1 in the undistorted lattice. In practical cases this is probably not very different from

$$p \sim \omega_0 e^{-2\alpha R}, \tag{4.15}$$

where $e^{-\alpha R}$ is the rate at which the wave function of an electron in one of the localized states falls off with distance, when the effect of the polarization well of Fig. 4.4 is taken into account. To deduce the mobility we multiply by (e/kT) and average over W_H in some way; this problem is treated in Chapter 6.

These results are obtained by a calculation of the probability of the simultaneous emission and absorption of phonons. The phonons are not supposed to interact with each other, so that the anharmonic terms in the force constant, responsible for heat conduction, are neglected. If these terms were strong enough, it would presumably be correct to write $kT/\hbar$ instead of ω_0 in equations (4.14) and (4.15), as in chemical rate theory. The relation between chemical rate theory and the theory described here has not been worked out (Bunker 1964); the absolute magnitude of p does not depend much on which theory is used but its dependence on T does.

4.6. Hopping at low temperatures

As the temperature is lowered below $\frac{1}{2}\Theta_D$, the activation energy drops from $W_H + \frac{1}{2}W_D$ to the much smaller value W_D. The reason can be expressed in various ways. We can say that the zero-point energy produces the activated state of Fig. 4.4(ii). For the factor outside the exponential, Schnakenberg finds that the formulae of § 4.5 can be used, but multiplied by $e^{-2\gamma}$ where

$$\gamma = W_H / \frac{1}{2}\hbar\omega.$$

For α we must take the tunnelling factor between the two wells of Fig. 4.4. At intermediate temperatures W_H should be replaced by

$$\frac{W_H \tanh(\frac{1}{4}\hbar\omega_0/kT)}{\frac{1}{4}\hbar\omega_0/kT} \sim W_H\{1 - \frac{1}{3}(\hbar\omega_0/4kT)^2 \ldots\}$$

(for references see Austin and Mott 1969). At $T \sim \frac{1}{2}\Theta$, the hopping energy has dropped by 8 per cent, at $T \sim \frac{1}{4}\Theta$ by $\sim$30 per cent.

Detailed formulae are given in the original paper by Schnakenberg (1968) and the review by Austin and Mott. Applications to impurity-conduction in polar materials like NiO and to conduction in glasses containing transition-metal ions are given in Chapter 6.

4.7. Polarons in crystalline materials

Up till now we have been discussing strongly localized states in which the radius r_0 of the state is determined primarily by the disorder, as for example round a vacancy, and is not greatly affected by the polarization or some other distortion of the surrounding medium. The opposite case is that of an electron in a crystalline lattice. In a polar lattice, each electron will disturb its surroundings, as it will in a molecular crystal, or indeed in any crystal to some extent. In much theoretical work, for instance calculations of the mean free path or of superconductivity, the effect of the distortion of the lattice is small and is treated as a perturbation. In this section this is not the case.

We shall discuss the problem in terms of an ionic lattice. As for a localized state we introduce a distance r_p from the electron beyond which the medium is fully polarized. Before the displacement of the ions the potential energy of another electron in the field of the electron considered would be

$$V(r) = e^2/\kappa_\infty r,$$

and after displacement of the ions

$$V(r) = e^2/\kappa r,$$

so that as in equation (4.8) the electron 'digs a potential well' for itself, for which

$$\begin{aligned} V_\mathrm{p}(r) &= -e^2/\kappa_\mathrm{p} r && (r > r_\mathrm{p}) \\ &= -e^2/\kappa_\mathrm{p} r_\mathrm{p} && (r < r_\mathrm{p}) \end{aligned} \right\} \qquad (4.17)$$

But—not as in the case of a state localized because of disorder—we must here determine r_p by minimizing the kinetic energy of the electron, which it has by virtue of its localization within a sphere of radius r_p. This to a first approximation is

$$\pi^2\hbar^2/2m^*r_\mathrm{p}^2$$

where m^* is the effective mass in the undisturbed lattice. The energy of the electron is $-e^2/\kappa_\mathrm{p} r_\mathrm{p}$, the polarization energy $\frac{1}{2}e^2/\kappa_\mathrm{p} r_\mathrm{p}$, and the total energy is therefore

$$\frac{\pi^2\hbar^2}{2m^*r_p^2} - \frac{e^2}{2\kappa_p r_p}. \tag{4.18}$$

Minimizing eqn (4.18) we get a value of r_p

$$r_p = 2\pi^2\hbar^2\kappa_p/m^*e^2,$$

and

$$W_p = e^2/4\kappa_p r_p. \tag{4.19}$$

All sorts of corrections can be made to this calculation. There is of course no sharp radius; the work of Fröhlich (1954) and of Allcock (1956) substitutes a self-consistent calculation giving an exponentially decaying wave function; the energy of the polaron is found to be W_p where

$$W_p = 0 \cdot 1\alpha^2\hbar\omega_0 = m^*e^4/20\kappa_p^2\hbar^2, \tag{4.20}$$

where α is the coupling constant given by

$$\alpha = (e^2/\kappa_p)(m^*/2\hbar^3\omega_0)^{\frac{1}{2}}. \tag{4.21}$$

Thus an effective polaron radius is from eqns (4.18) and (4.19),

$$r_p = 5\hbar^2\kappa_p/m^*e^2,$$

which is smaller than the value given above. If $m^* = m$ and $\kappa_p = 10$, r_p is 25 Å.

This calculation is not correct if the value of r_p given by eqn (4.21) is comparable with or smaller than the distance between ions in the solid. If this is so the polaron is called a small polaron. Clearly this can happen only if the effective mass m^* in the undistorted lattice is considerably larger than m. We may therefore think in terms of the tight-binding approximation and a narrow band. We illustrate the situation in Fig. 4.5. We cannot consider the polarization well as extending nearer to the electron than the radius of the ion or atom on which it is placed. The radius of this ion is then a rough approximation to r_p; a treatment by Bogomolov, Kudinov, and Firsov (1968), in which the polarization well is analysed into the normal modes of the lattice vibrations, gives for r_p

$$r_p = \tfrac{1}{2}(\pi/6N)^{\frac{1}{3}}, \tag{4.22}$$

where N is the number of wells per unit volume. The formulae that we have used for localized states are now applicable; the energy of the polaron is $-W_p$ where

$$W_p = \tfrac{1}{2}e^2/\kappa_p r_p. \tag{4.23}$$

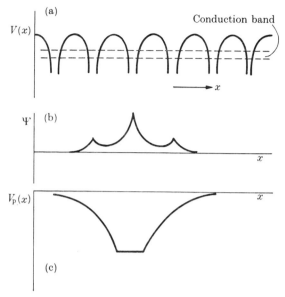

FIG. 4.5. (a) is the potential energy of the electron in the undistorted lattice; (b) is the
wave function of a large or intermediate polaron; (c) is the polarization well.

There is no sharp distinction between a small and large (or extended) polaron. For discussion of the intermediate case see various reviews (Langreth 1967; Appel 1968; Austin and Mott 1969).

4.8. Motion of a polaron in a crystalline lattice

At low temperatures a polaron, whether large or small, will move through a crystal carrying its polarization well with it; it will behave exactly like a heavy particle, being scattered by impurities or lattice vibrations; moreover a high density of polarons can form a degenerate gas (§ 4.13). The important point is to know the effective mass m_p. In the theory of large polarons as developed by Fröhlich (1954) and Allcock (1956),†

$$m_{\mathrm{p}} = 0 \cdot 02 m^* \alpha^4 \tag{4.24}$$

with α given by eqn (4.21). We note that the effective mass contains ω_0^{-2} and is thus proportional to M (ionic mass). This is because outside the radius r_{p} the ions move adiabatically with a velocity proportional to the polaron's velocity. Inside this radius the ions cannot follow the motion of the electron; dynamic terms occur which are obtained by applying perturbation theory to the interaction.

† See also Feynman, Hellwarth, Iddings, and Platzman (1962) and Thornber and Feynman (1970).

9

These are of lower order in α and have been investigated by various authors (for references see Appel 1968); they are not important for the applications in this book.

In practice the large-polaron approximation may begin to break down for a mass enhancement of 2–3. In the small-polaron limit, and in the adiabatic approximation, we may write

$$m_{\mathrm{p}}/m = (\hbar/2\omega_0 mR^2)\exp \gamma', \qquad (4.25)$$

where R is the distance between centres and

$$\gamma' = W_{\mathrm{H}}/\tfrac{1}{2}\hbar\omega_0. \qquad (4.26)$$

W_{H} is the hopping energy defined by eqn (4.13). This may well be a reasonable approximation for polarons of intermediate size, as long as $W_{\mathrm{H}} > \tfrac{1}{2}\hbar\omega_0$; but as r_{p} increases, formula (4.13) shows that W_{H} tends to zero, and, when $W_{\mathrm{H}} \sim \tfrac{1}{2}\hbar\omega$, formulae of type (4.24) are preferable. For materials like TiO_2, however, γ' can be as large as 5. The factor outside the exponential in eqn (4.25), unlike that in eqn (4.24), contains the ionic mass as $M^{\frac{1}{2}}$; this is because we have to think of zero-point vibrations achieving the excited state of Fig. 4.4(ii), which allows the electrons to tunnel; we can no longer think of the polarization well moving adiabatically from one site to the next. For transition-metal oxides, to which polaron theory has been extensively applied, the factor outside the exponential is quite small (2–3) in spite of the term proportional to $M^{\frac{1}{2}}$; this is because of the large value of R ($\sim$4 Å) in eqn (4.25). A value of γ' of order 4 will thus lead to a polaron mass m_{p} of order $100m$.

The investigations of Holstein (1959) and of Emin and Holstein (1969) have shown that a small polaron is strongly scattered by optical phonons, and at a temperature of the order of $\tfrac{1}{2}\Theta_{\mathrm{D}}$ the mean free path for a polaron with thermal energies is of the order of the lattice parameter. For temperatures above $\tfrac{1}{2}\Theta_{\mathrm{D}}$ charge transport is by thermally activated hopping, and the formulae of § 4.3 are valid with $W_{\mathrm{D}} = 0$. Thus the mobility is of the form

$$\mu = (e/kT)pR^2 \exp(-W_{\mathrm{H}}/kT), \qquad (4.27)$$

where p is given by eqn (4.15).

4.9. Energy required to release a charge carrier from a donor centre

An essential point to remember about polarons is that a polaron at a distance R from a charged centre will have a potential energy $e^2/\kappa R$ if

$R > r_p$, where κ is the static dielectric constant. In materials like TiO_2 where $\kappa \sim 100$ the interaction will therefore be weak, and we can thus distinguish two cases for small polarons:

(a) If the radius $\hbar^2\kappa/m_p e^2$ is large compared with R (the distance of the nearest metal ion from the centre), the polaron is described by a hydrogen-like wave function, and the energy required to remove it from the centre is $e^4 m_p/2\hbar^2\kappa_p^2$. This probably occurs only for $\kappa \gg 100$, as for example in $SrTiO_3$ (Chapter 5).

(b) If this is not the case, then the carrier must be thought of as located on the metal lattice site next to the donor, so that the energy required to remove it is $e^2/\kappa R$, where R is the distance between the two sites. This is probably a good approximation for NiO and TiO_2.

If the polaron is not small, so that $r_p \geqslant R$, then a formula of the type

$$E = m^* e^4/2\hbar^2\kappa_{\text{eff}}^2$$

should be used, where κ_{eff} is some mean of κ and κ_∞. In the light of modern polaron theory, the problem may need further investigation; meanwhile the formula of Simpson (1949), which gives

$$\frac{1}{\kappa_{\text{eff}}} = \frac{1}{\kappa} + \frac{5}{16}\left(\frac{1}{\kappa_\infty} - \frac{1}{\kappa}\right), \tag{4.28}$$

is a useful approximation. These formulae are discussed further in Chapter 5 in connection with the metal–non-metal transition.

4.10. Examples of hopping polarons

Polaron theory has been extensively applied to semiconducting oxides of the transition metals. Here, a d electron is thought to move from one metal ion to another via the 2p orbitals of the oxygen ions (Fig. 4.6); effective masses m^* for the undistorted lattice are somewhat greater than m, thus giving band widths ~ 1 eV. A case that has been investigated in detail is slightly reduced TiO_2 (Bogomolov et al. 1968; for a

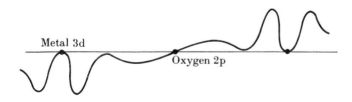

Metal 3d

Oxygen 2p

FIG. 4.6. Wave function ψ of an electron in a transition-metal oxide (schematic). ψ is plotted along a line M–O–M.

review see Austin and Mott 1969). Here the behaviour of the conductivity as a function of the temperature is as shown schematically in Fig. 4.7. The dielectric constant κ is about 100 and, if we take the energy required to free an electron from a centre as $e^2/\kappa R$, nearly all electrons will be free at 100 K. As the temperature is increased further, the resistivity rises, because the carriers are increasingly scattered by phonons. At 300 K, however, the mean free path is comparable with the distance between metal ions, so for higher temperatures hopping sets

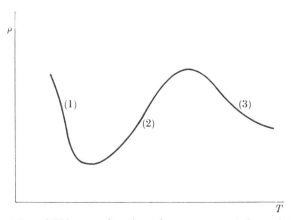

FIG. 4.7. Resistivity of TiO_2 as a function of temperature (schematic). (1) Electrons not yet free from donors. (2) Electrons all free, increasingly scattered. (3) Polaron hopping.

in, and the resistivity drops. Bogomolov *et al.* estimate an activation energy W_H of 0·13 eV and an effective mass $m_p \sim 100m$.

Hopping can also occur in a molecular lattice; owing to the relatively weak coupling between molecules, an injected electron moving from molecule to molecule would have a narrow band of energies in an undistorted lattice. The electron can therefore distort the lattice in which it is, and except at low temperatures a hopping mechanism of conduction is expected. Hopping motion for carriers generated in liquid and solid sulphur has been established by Ghosh and Spear (1968) and interpreted as due to hops from one S_8 ring to another. These authors find a value of 0·24 eV for W_H for electrons. They point out that the overlap between hole orbitals is much greater than for the electron orbitals; the hole mobility is thus higher (see also Chen 1970).

4.11. Thermopower due to polarons

In extrinsic compensated semiconductors the conductivity varies as $\exp(-E/kT)$, and the thermopower S as $(k/e)(E/kT + \text{const.})$; the two values of E, the donor ionization energy, are identical. If however conduction is by small polarons, and the temperature range is such that thermally activated hopping occurs, the conductivity varies as

$$\exp\{-(E+W_\mathrm{H})/kT\}.$$

It is important to realise that W_H does not occur in the expression for the thermopower. Various authors have used this criterion to determine whether or not thermally activated hopping is present in a given material. For instance, Bosman and Crevecoeur (1966) showed that the activation energies in NiO were the same as those deduced from the thermopower and the conductivity, and concluded that conductivity is by a band mechanism, or alternatively that W_H is small. Crevecoeur and de Wit (1968) have made similar measurements for MnO; for this material the activation energy deduced from the conductivity is greater than that deduced from the thermopower. Polaron hopping seems to be present, indeed down to temperatures below $\frac{1}{2}\Theta$.

We may summarize some of the extensive work on lithium-doped nickel oxide as follows (Austin and Mott 1969; Bosman and van Daal 1970). The Ni^{3+} ion adjacent to Li^+ is a small polaron; it does not have cubic symmetry, because the two ions attract each other and are displaced. In hopping round the Li ion it behaves like a heavy particle of mass $\sim 100m$. The energy to remove it from the Li^+ is given by $\sim e^2/\kappa a$. But the free carrier is much lighter ($\sim 6m$); according to formula (4.25) this would correspond to a value of W_H not much greater than $\frac{1}{2}\hbar\omega$. It seems therefore that non-spherical polarons are heavier than spherical ones, as is indeed to be anticipated from formula (4.13). Crevecoeur and de Wit point out that a Jahn–Teller distortion is to be expected round the Mn^{4+} ions in MnO, which could account for the hopping process in this material.

4.12. Anderson localization of polarons

In § 4.4 we have considered the case when disorder in the lattice leads to a strongly localized state with radius r_0, and have calculated the surrounding polarization. In some non-crystalline materials it may be a better approximation to calculate the effective mass of the polaron first, and then to ask if the disorder is sufficient to produce weak Anderson localization with radius of localization r_0 greater than r_p. For instance, if the polaron effective mass is $20m$, a band width of 0·05 eV may be expected, and for a half-full band localization should occur if the spread of energies in the Anderson model (Chapter 2) is greater than

~0·5 eV. Bosman and van Daal (1970) discuss the relation of this kind of localization to a.c. conductivity in transition-metal oxides.

4.13. Degenerate gas of polarons

It is well known that in metals interaction with phonons can increase the effective mass of electrons at the Fermi surface by a considerable factor—as much as two in crystalline mercury (Mott 1966). In calculations of this effect the interaction between the electron gas and the phonons is treated as a perturbation. If the small polaron energy is greater than the Fermi energy, a better approximation may be to consider the metal as a degenerate gas of small polarons; this will of course be possible only if the number of carriers is small compared with the number of atoms. Mott (1969b) and Zinamon (1970) have considered the degenerate gas in doped strontium titanate in this way, and Mott (1969b) has discussed the possibility that VO_2, Ti_2O_3, and V_2O_3 above the transition point are semi-metals with heavy carriers, which should be treated as polarons. The matter is discussed further in Chapter 5.

4.14. Polarons in liquids

An electron in the conduction band of a polar liquid like water or ammonia will form a large polaron round it, the potential energy of the electron in the polarization well being as illustrated in Fig. 4.4(a) and given by formula (4.17). An example is a dilute solution of sodium or lithium in ammonia. The metal dissociates into a solvated cation and a 'solvated electron'. The solution expands by about the volume of three ammonia molecules for each electron; Jortner (1959) first suggested that each electron made a cavity for itself. The generally accepted reason for this (Catterall and Mott 1969) is that any region in the liquid where the polarization changes rapidly with position has high energy; the *Bjerrum defect*, in which two water molecules have their dipoles opposed, has energy 0·34 eV. If there is strong polarization, energy is therefore released by cavity formation.

The solvated electrons in their cavities give rise to an absorption line in the infrared with a tail extending into the red; this accounts for the blue colour of dilute solutions. The conductivity of dilute solutions is due to the electrons moving with their hydration shells, in much the same way as a heavy ion moves in a liquid.

THE METAL–NON-METAL TRANSITION

5.1. Introduction
5.2. Mott–Hubbard insulators
5.3. Band-theory description of Mott–Hubbard insulators
5.4. Behaviour near the transition point
5.5. The Hubbard Hamiltonian
5.6. Effect of long-range forces
5.7. Wigner crystallization
5.8. The excitonic insulator
5.9. Kohn's model for the Mott transition

5.10. Transition-metal oxides
5.11. The MNM transition in disordered systems
5.12. Conductivity near the transition point in a disordered system
5.13. Materials of high dielectric constant; the transition in doped titanates
5.14. Metal–ammonia solutions.

5.1. Introduction

MOST of our discussion so far has neglected the interaction between the electrons in the material under consideration, except in so far as it can be averaged in the sense of the Hartree–Fock approximation. In this approximation, the potential energy $V(x, y, z)$ is that due to the ions and to the averaged field of all the other electrons. If in a crystal V is periodic with the period of the lattice, the solutions of the one-electron Schrödinger equations are of the Bloch type,

$$\psi_k = e^{i(\mathbf{k}.\mathbf{r})} . u_k(x, y, z),$$

and the allowed energies W_k are separated into bands as described in Chapter 2. If any band is partly full at the absolute zero of temperature, the material is a metal, and in a perfect crystal the resistivity falls towards zero as the temperature (T) tends to zero; for an alloy it tends to a finite value. If all the bands are full or empty, the crystal is a non-metal, and the resistivity tends to infinity as T tends to zero. This classification into metals and non-metals was first given by Wilson (1931). For a body-centred or face-centred cubic crystal of an element the number of states in the first band is two electrons per atom, and with this number of electrons a material should be a non-metal unless the first two bands overlap, which is the case for all the divalent metals. If the lattice parameter is increased sufficiently, the width of both bands contracts (§ 2.4), and eventually they will cease to overlap and the material will become a non-metal; expansion of a crystalline lattice by more than a few per cent (by thermal expansion) is not possible, but the appropriate treatment for a non-crystalline material, mercury vapour near the critical point, has been described in Chapter 3. In some divalent metals the overlap disappears also for a contraction of the lattice parameter, so that at high pressures the material becomes a semiconductor. This behaviour has been observed in strontium and ytterbium (McWhan, Rice, and Schmidt 1969; Jullien and Jerome 1971). We shall call a transition of this kind from metallic to non-metallic behaviour a *Wilson transition*.†

In the same class we may put transitions that occur when the crystal structure produces two bands, one fully occupied and one empty, which may or may not overlap. If the crystal parameters change, even without change of volume, a transition from an overlapping to a non-overlapping state may occur. As we shall see in § 5.10, this can occur in some transition-metal oxides such as Ti_2O_3 and VO_2. Other examples are the pressure-induced continuous metal–semiconductor transition observed by Jayaraman, Narayanamurti, Bucher, and Maines (1970) in SmTe, which is caused by contraction of the lattice pushing the 4f levels into the conduction band; and the transition in iodine at 160 kbar (Drickhamer, Lynch, Clendenen, and Perez-Albuerne 1966). In both these materials the resistance at high pressures increases with temperature and there is no discontinuous change in volume or structure.

It has been known for more than thirty years, however, that the one-electron model predicts metallic conductivity in certain crystalline materials that are in fact insulators. De Boer and Verwey at a conference at Bristol University in 1937 pointed out that in nickel oxide, which has the simple cubic rock-salt structure, each nickel ion has eight d electrons, and that the cubic field, though it could split the 3d band into sub-bands with four and six states per nickel ion, could not produce the band structure of an insulator. According to the model of

---

† Just before the transition to the non-metallic state a resistivity varying as T^2 is observed. It was first shown by Baber (1937; see also Ziman 1961; Mott 1964) that electron–hole scattering in a transition metal should give a contribution to the resistivity of the form

$$\rho = \text{const.}\ (\hbar a/e^2)T^2/T_0^2,$$

where T_0 is the degeneracy temperature of the d-band holes. Actually, an effect of this kind should be present for any non-spherical Fermi surface, but will be largest for a pocket of heavy holes or electrons, or for small Fermi energies such as one might expect near the transition, However the occurrence of a large T^2 term in the resistivity cannot be taken as proving that the material is a semi-metal with two weakly overlapping bands because scattering by magnons (compare Mott 1964) or paramagnons (Schriempf, Schindler, and Mills 1969) is expected to produce a similar effect.

non-interacting electrons, pure nickel oxide ought to be a metal, while in fact it is a transparent antiferromagnetic insulator, and non-metallic both above and below the Néel temperature. Peierls at the 1937 conference pointed out that this must be a consequence of the term e^2/r_{12}, giving the energy of repulsion between the electrons, which must be treated in some way that goes beyond the Hartree–Fock approximation. Mott in 1949 gave arguments to show that proper consideration of this term always leads to insulating behaviour for an array of one-electron atoms, or more generally for atoms or ions where the electrons do not fill a band, if the band is narrow enough; if the band is widened, for instance by decreasing the distance between the atoms, a sharp transition from non-metallic to metallic behaviour is to be expected. This will be referred to as the *Mott transition*. Since then, there has been an extensive literature on the subject, some of which will be described in this chapter.

The MNM transition is included in a book on non-crystalline materials because, as Chapter 2 has shown, the electrical behaviour of non-crystalline materials differs most from that in crystals when the allowed energy bands are narrow. Many phenomena, particularly impurity-conduction, cannot be understood even qualitatively without taking into account both the term e^2/r_{12} and the non-periodic nature of the field in which the electrons move.

5.2. Mott–Hubbard insulators

In order to understand why an antiferromagnetic oxide like NiO is non-metallic, we consider first a crystalline array of N one-electron atoms (like hydrogen) with the electron in each atom in the 1s state (Fig. 5.1(a)). The atoms are supposed to be far enough from each other for the overlap of the atomic wave functions to be small, but finite. We denote the ionization energy of each atom by I and the electron affinity by E. Suppose an extra electron is introduced onto the atom j in Fig. 5.1(b). Then we write the Slater determinant for all the electrons in the system containing this extra electron by

$$\Psi_j(q_1, q_2, ..., q_{N+1}).$$

Here q_n denotes the coordinates, including spin, of the nth electron. The extra electron can move through the crystal; its eigenstates have wave functions of the form

$$\sum_j \exp(i\mathbf{k}.\mathbf{a}_j)\Psi_j. \qquad (5.1)$$

The sum is over half the atoms of the lattice, because the electron can only be on those atoms of the antiferromagnetic lattice where the spins are antiparallel to its own. States described by the wave function (5.1) will have energies $W(k)$ lying in a narrow band, of which we denote the width by $2J$. In the one-dimensional tight-binding approximation $W(k)$ has the form

$$W(k) = -2J \cos ka, \tag{5.2}$$

where k is the wave number and J the overlap integral between states $j, j+2$, namely

$$J = \int \Psi_j^* H \Psi_{j+2} \, dq_1 \dots \, dq_{N+1}.$$

The generalization to three dimensions is as in § 2.4.

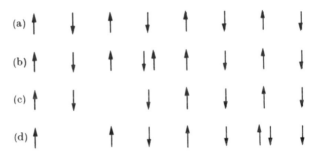

FIG. 5.1. Electron spins on an array of one-electron atoms. (a) An antiferromagnetic array, all atoms neutral. (b) The same, with an extra electron on atom j. (c) With an electron missing (a hole) on atom i. (d) An electron on j and a hole on i.

Similarly we can remove an electron from atom i, leaving a hole as in Fig. 5.1(c). We denote the wave function for the system with an electron missing from atom i by

$$\Psi_i'(q_1, \dots, q_{N-1}).$$

The hole can move, and its eigenstate when it is moving with wave number k' is

$$\sum_i \exp(i\mathbf{k}'.\mathbf{a}_i) \Psi_i'. \tag{5.3}$$

Again the energies of the moving hole will lie in a band and we denote its width by $2J'$.

Consider now the situation in Fig. 5.1(d), in which an electron is removed from atom i and placed on a distant atom j. If the atoms were very far apart, we would expect the energy required to form such a state, which we denote by ε, to be given by

$$\varepsilon = I - E.$$

If the band widths already defined are included, the energy ε will lie between the values

$$I - E \pm J \pm J',$$

depending on the wave numbers k, k'. As long as the minimum value of ε is positive, we should expect the material to be an intrinsic semi-conductor and the number of carriers to depend on temperature as $\exp(-\frac{1}{2}\varepsilon/kT)$. As $T \to 0$ the conductivity will tend to zero. But J, J' increase as the lattice parameter a decreases, and so when the atoms are so close together that ε becomes zero, the material will behave like a metal, no activation energy being necessary to produce carriers of current.

This elementary description of the metal–insulator transition needs amplification in several ways. The first point that needs proof is that the state of Fig. 5.1(a) really is an insulator; in the theory of non-interacting electrons it is a metal. Qualitative arguments were given by Mott (1956, 1961) and a formal proof was given by Kohn (1964). The treatment of Hubbard (1964), and further work that derives from it, predicting an insulating state, will be discussed in § 5.4. Hubbard's was the first work to describe a gap in the energy spectrum of pseudo-particles, and we shall call the minimum energy ε_2 needed to excite the system, given by

$$\varepsilon_2 = I - E - J - J', \qquad (5.4)$$

the *Mott–Hubbard gap*.

The non-conducting nature of the state illustrated in Fig. 5.1(a), when the atoms are sufficiently far apart, needs some further discussion. It occurs only when the number of electrons per atom is integral. Extra electrons or holes, as already stated, can move without thermal activation; in this respect the non-conducting property differs from that produced by disorder (§ 2.4). Secondly, the non-conducting nature of the state is sometimes thought of as being due to the splitting of the band by an antiferromagnetic super-lattice, so that two sub-bands are formed, one of which would be full and the other empty. The next section describes this approach. Further, it is worth emphasizing that the number of states for either spin direction of the type illustrated in Fig. 5.1(b) or defined by equation (5.1) is $\frac{1}{2}N$, since, as already stated, only half the atoms are available to an electron with given spin direction, namely those in which the electron already on the atom has the opposite spin.

We shall now extend these ideas to the situation in antiferromagnetic transition-metal compounds, where each ion contains, instead of a single electron in an s state, several electrons in d states with spins coupled by Hund's rule. Nickel oxide is a case in point. The Mott–Hubbard gap is large,† but the material becomes a p-type extrinsic semiconductor through doping with Li_2O; a Li^+ ion replaces a Ni^{2+} ion, a Ni^{3+} ion is formed to preserve electrical neutrality, and this can move through the lattice (Chapter 4). The wave function of the moving hole will be exactly of type (5.3).‡ There is however one difference between this and an array of atoms in s states; this is illustrated in Fig. 5.2. An electron can jump from C to A without changing the energy of the crystal. If it jumps from C to B, however, the Ni^{3+} ion B will be in a state with four spins down and three up, which by Hund's rule is an excited state; we may denote this energy difference by ΔE. As pointed

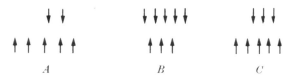

FIG. 5.2. Spin arrangements on Ni^{2+} ions in NiO. A is the carrier (Ni^{3+}).

out by Brinkman and Rice (1970a), the electron can avoid this change in energy by going into an antisymmetrical orbital state with symmetrical spin state. However, the antiferromagnetic lattice should produce some splitting of the band, the states in each sub-band being $\frac{1}{2}N$ in number for each spin direction. In the case of non-degenerate s states, the upper sub-band is absent.

This conclusion is, however, altered if the carrier affects the orientation of the spins on neighbouring atoms. On this important matter, which is discussed further in Chapters 4 and 6, there is an extensive literature (de Gennes 1960; Nagaoka 1966; Brinkman and Rice 1970a). We may distinguish two cases:

(a) The value of the lattice parameter a is far to the insulating side of the transition value a_0. Then the overlap integral J, this time between nearest neighbours, will be small, and coupling terms between the moments, which determine the Néel temperature, an order of magnitude smaller, of order $J^2/(I-E)$. In this case a carrier will orient

† The optical absorption edge observed at 3·8 eV in NiO is thought to be due to the excitation of an electron from the $3d^8$ nickel ion into the 4s band; the true Mott–Hubbard gap, namely the energy needed to form a Ni^{3+} and a Ni^+ ion, is probably much larger (for references see Mott and Zinamon 1970).

‡ Its effective mass is greatly increased by polaron formation (compare Chapter 4).

the moments on neighbouring atoms parallel to it up to a radius r_p. The reason is that the carrier can then move freely through the lattice without having to pass through atoms where the direction of the moment is antiparallel to its own. Estimates of r_p, of order $a(I/J)^{\frac{1}{3}}$, are given in § 6.11.

In the case of non-degenerate states such as s orbitals, the situation as discussed by Nagaoka (1966) is rather different. Here, in the spin polaron formed by an extra electron, the moments are antiparallel to the spin of the carrier.

(b) Near the MNM transition point in, for instance, an array of centres in which each electron is in an s state, we should expect J, $I-E$, and the antiferromagnetic coupling constant all to be of the same order of magnitude. We should not therefore expect any large effect of the carrier on the moments of distant atoms.

5.3. Band-theory description of Mott–Hubbard insulators

Slater (1951) was the first to suggest that insulators of the type treated here could be described in the following way. Consider a crystalline lattice of one-electron atoms in s states. Then he suggested that if a is large an antiferromagnetic lattice can be set up, and this splits the s band. If the splitting is large, the lower sub-band is full and the upper sub-band empty, and the material is a non-metal.

It must be stressed, of course, that a material like NiO remains a non-metal above the Néel temperature, but this is not a cogent objection to the model. Above the Néel temperature an electron sees a different potential on spin-up and spin-down atoms, even though they are arranged in a random way. The situation is then similar to that in a disordered alloy, and the energy gap will persist.† A model must be used in which the moments persist above the Néel point, unlike the model for chromium, where they do not. Or in terms of the Hubbard Hamiltonian to be discussed in § 5.5, if $w/J_0 \gg 1$, moments persist above the transition point. In chromium, where the antiferromagnetism is due to the special form of the Fermi surface, this is not so (Rice, Barker, Halperin, and McWhan 1969).

Recently the model has been extended to transition-metal oxides by Slater (1968a, b) and co-workers, Wilson (1969) for MnO, and Wilson (1970) for NiO, and this work will be discussed next. We refer first, however, to band-theory calculations for solid rare gases. The conduction and valence bands of these materials ought in principle to be

† The case for alloys has been treated by Velicky, Kirkpatrick, and Ehrenreich (1968).

described by wave functions of the types (5.1), (5.3), and the band gap must tend to the value $I - E$ as the interatomic separation a tends to infinity. None the less, the calculations of Mattheiss (1964) for solid argon, which use conventional band theory and the same potential for electrons in the valence and conduction bands, give good values for the band gap. We should therefore expect satisfactory results for the transition-metal oxides.

We turn first to MnO (Wilson 1969) and EuS (Cho 1967, 1970) where a 3d or 4f band is half full. These workers take, in any band of the material, a different potential for an electron on a given metal atom according to whether the spin of the electron is parallel or antiparallel to the moment of the metal atom considered. As appears particularly in Cho's work, the resulting splitting of the band (4f in his case) does not depend on whether the moments are ferromagnetically or antiferromagnetically aligned; it is approximately equal to the difference in the two potentials. For NiO, in the same way, Wilson (1970) considers the four e_g states that are split off from the 3d band, and by taking spin-dependent potentials introduces a splitting of this band into an occupied band with two electrons per atom and an empty band. His splitting is, however, much too small.

This cannot be done with CoO with only one electron in the e_g band. The problem is discussed by Mott and Zinamon (1970). In this material, the orbital motion is not quenched and there is a canted arrangement of spins; thus the *orbital* wave functions are not all the same, and different combinations of d functions would form a super-lattice of lower wave number than the antiferromagnetic lattice. This could split the band again, and lead to a full and an empty sub-band.

5.4. Behaviour near the transition point

As we have seen, as the interatomic distance a in a lattice decreases, the band widths J, J' increase, and at some value a_0 of a the energy ε_2 in equation (5.4) should vanish. An elementary treatment along these lines with applications to impurity conditions was given by Nishimura (1965). In many ways we think this is a satisfactory way to describe the transition. If the intra-atomic term $I - E$ is included in the model, and also the band widths J, J', and the antiferromagnetic coupling, then on the metallic side of the transition there will be a small number of carriers of types (5.1) and (5.3), behaving like electrons and holes. These carriers can be treated as pseudoparticles and can form a degenerate gas just as can the electrons or holes in the theory of non-interacting electrons. The material on the metallic side of the transition will therefore behave like a semi-metal.† The two bands given by formulae (5.1) and (5.3) will overlap, as in Fig. 5.3, and as the distance between the atoms decreases the overlap will increase.

As we shall see later in this chapter, the question of whether the number of carriers increases continuously from zero as $(a_0 - a)$ increases, as this model predicts, is not fully resolved. The original hypothesis of Mott (1949, 1961) predicted a discontinuous transition. More recent

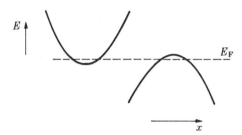

FIG. 5.3. Overlapping conduction and valence bands in a semi-metal. E_F is the Fermi energy.

work, particularly that of Kohn (1967), suggests that this may not be so; his arguments are reviewed later.

As well as considering the carriers, we have to ask what happens to the magnetic moments. The model suggests that magnetic moments, and thus long-range antiferromagnetic order, will persist on the metallic side of the transition. But as a decreases, the system should eventually have the properties of a normal metal like sodium, with no long-range magnetic order. We have to ask at what value of a the moments disappear, and whether the transition is discontinuous or not. No firm answer to this question exists and the following considerations are speculative.

We can hardly doubt that at any rate in some materials the magnetic moments will persist for some range of a on the metallic side of the MNM transition. If the antiferromagnetic coupling is strong, as it should be in the ideal case of an array of hydrogen-like centres, the moments should persist for a considerable range of a and may disappear without any discontinuity. We believe that this may happen in doped

† By a semi-metal is meant a material in which at $T = 0$ there are a *small* number of electrons and an equal number of holes; bismuth is a typical example.

semiconductors. The question, then, whether the disappearance of moments is a first-order or a second-order process (as a is changed) is of major importance. The considerations of Landau (1937) suggest that it should be second order. Landau argues that the energy E must be an even function of the magnitude M of the moment,

$$E = AM^2 + BM^4 + \ldots;$$

moments will disappear when A changes sign, and near the transition M should vary as $(-A/B)^{\frac{1}{2}}$ and thus as $(a-a_0)^{\frac{1}{2}}$. But the later terms in the expansion can in principle lead to a first-order transition, and our tentative conclusion is that both can happen, depending on the form of the density of states (Mott and Zinamon 1970). If so, a first-order metal–insulator transition should be possible.

The treatment so far has neglected the long-range Coulomb forces between electrons and holes. Many papers from Mott (1949) onwards have stressed that when these are taken into account a very small number of free electrons and holes is impossible, because the unscreened potential energy of the form $-e^2/\kappa r_{12}$ always allows for the formation of bound pairs (as in positronium). For this reason, the Nishimura model, in which the number of carriers drops continuously to zero at the transition, may need modification. As we shall see, complicated phenomena may occur near the transition, and these will be described in § 5.8. They may be masked, however, by discontinuous changes in crystal structure and lattice parameter occurring near the transition.

We stress then that, apart from these complications:

(a) On the non-metal side of the transition we expect an antiferromagnetic lattice with strong antiferromagnetic coupling. The orbitals should overlap, so the observed moment may be less than that of the free ion.

(b) On the metallic side there will be a small number of carriers of both signs, so the Hall constant may underestimate the number of carriers. And the density of states $N(E_F)$ at the Fermi energy will be vanishingly small at the transition point.

(c) The moments will persist in the metallic state, and disappear for a value of a smaller than that for the MNM transition.

(d) If a first-order appearance of moments occurs, a first-order MNM transition is possible.

5.5. The Hubbard Hamiltonian

Hubbard (1964) introduced the Hamiltonian

$$\sum_i \{J_0(c_{i\uparrow}c_{j\uparrow}^+ + c_{i\downarrow}^+ c_{j\downarrow}) + w(n_{i\uparrow}n_{i\downarrow})\},$$

where J_0 is the band width for electrons in a narrow band *before* correlation is introduced (i.e. not the same as the J, J' used earlier in this chapter). Here c_i is the creation operator for site i, site j is adjacent to site i, and

$$n_{i\uparrow} = c_{i\uparrow}^+ c_{i\uparrow}.$$

The summation is over all the atomic sites. Correlation is represented by the assumption that, if two electrons are on the same atom,

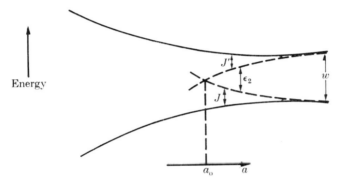

FIG. 5.4. Band limits for pseudoparticles on the Hubbard model. ε_2 is the excitation energy. The sub-bands of width J, J' contain one electron per atom. Overlapping bands have been drawn, and the assumption has been made that moments persist on the metallic side of the transition.

the energy is increased by an amount w. Hubbard was able to describe the behaviour of his model in terms of pseudoparticles with a band form, plotted against the interatomic distance a, as shown in Fig. 5.4. The excitation energy is also shown. For the value (a_0) of a for which the Hubbard gap appears he finds

$$J_0/w = 1 \cdot 15. \tag{5.5}$$

He also finds that the density of states vanishes at the transition point, as shown in Fig. 5.5.

There has been much subsequent work on the Hubbard Hamiltonian; references are given in the volume of the *Review of Modern Physics* devoted to the papers given at the San Francisco conference on the

10

MNM transition,† and more recent reviews are given by Doniach (1969) and Mott and Zinamon (1970). Much of this work is concerned primarily with the conditions for ferromagnetism (Kanamori 1963; Gutzwiller 1963, 1964; Nagaoka 1966). The Hubbard ratio (eqn (5.5)) is obtained to within a few per cent by Kemeny and Caron (1967) and by Caron and Pratt (1968). Herring (1966) has given a review of Hubbard's work and maintains that the low density of states near the transition is incorrect, because the Fermi surface must include one electron per atom. This in our view is because the Hubbard work does not specifically state that

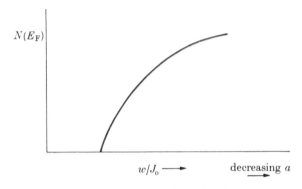

Fig. 5.5. Density of states at the Fermi level as a funcion of a in the Hubbard model.

antiferromagnetic moments are formed, as does that of Nagaoka. In fact, the investigations of this Hamiltonian have not yet made clear the relationship between the appearance of moments and the MNM transition.

Brinkman and Rice (1970b) have investigated the degree of correlation that occurs before moments appear and find that it is high, only 5–10 per cent of atoms carrying two electrons. Since this leads to a small current when an electric field is applied and since the area of the Fermi surface must be unchanged (Luttinger 1960), they conclude that the effective mass is increased by correlation.

5.6. Effect of long-range forces

Neither Nishimura's nor Hubbard's model includes the effect of long-range Coulomb interaction, which was the starting point of the original treatment by Mott (1949, 1956, 1968b). With doped semiconductors in mind, to take this into account we write the potential energy of an electron and hole as $-e^2/\kappa r_{12}$, where κ is the background

† Rev. mod. Phys. (1968) 40, 673–833.

dielectric constant. As we have seen, a free pair of carriers of the kind illustrated in Fig. 5.1(d) cannot exist in the ground state of the system, because a potential energy $V(r)$ that behaves for large r as

$$V(r) \sim -e^2/\kappa r \qquad (5.5)$$

always allows the formation of states in which the electron and hole form a bound pair with energy of order $m*e^4/2\hbar^2\kappa^2$. Therefore a small number of free carriers is impossible; the number n per unit volume in a metal must be large enough to allow eqn (5.5) to be replaced by

$$V(r) \sim (-e^2/\kappa r)\exp(-\gamma r),$$

where γ is so large that there are no bound states. The screening constant γ according to the Thomas–Fermi model is given by

$$\gamma^2 = 4me^2(3n/\pi)^{\frac{1}{3}}/\hbar^2\kappa,$$

and the condition† that the potential shall give no bound states is (Mott 1961)‡

$$\gamma a_{\mathrm H} > 1 \cdot 0...,$$

where $a_{\mathrm H}$ is the hydrogen radius

$$a_{\mathrm H} = \hbar^2\kappa/m*e^2.$$

We obtain therefore for the number of atoms per unit volume at which the MNM transition occurs

$$n^{\frac{1}{3}}a_{\mathrm H} \sim 0 \cdot 25. \qquad (5.6)$$

This formula gives results very similar to those from Hubbard's formula (5.4) (Mott 1969b). It is in good agreement with experiments on the concentration of donors at which the transition occurs in doped semiconductors, as shown in Chapter 6. The method of derivation obviously predicts a discontinuous change in n as a is varied; this is not predicted by the Hubbard and Nishimura models. The conclusion can be avoided only if κ becomes infinite at the transition point. As we shall see below, however, this may be so.

---

† In one dimension all attractive potentials allow of bound states. One might guess therefore that a one-dimensional metal is impossible. This is confirmed by the analysis of Lieb and Wu (1968).

‡ Hulthén and Laurikainen (1951) give 1·19 instead of 1·0.

It may be difficult to determine experimentally the behaviour of a crystal near the transition point. The reason is that crystalline materials at $T = 0$ can change their lattice parameter only under pressure, and it seems that near the MNM transition the energy is high, so that the (free) energy–volume curve may be as in Fig. 5.6. The transition occurs at pressures such that AB is horizontal, and values of the volume v between A and B (the 'invisible region') are not susceptible to observation. Changes of crystal structure may also complicate the issue.

Lifshitz and Kaganov (1963) have discussed a similar problem, namely that in which new 'pockets' of electrons appear in the Fermi

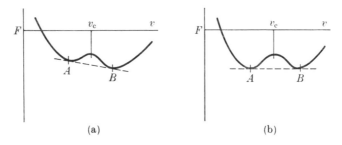

(a)   (b)

FIG. 5.6. Free energy–volume curve for a non-metal: (a) under zero pressure; (b) under the pressure at which the phase change occurs. v_c is the volume at which the MNM transition should occur.

surface as the volume is decreased. They find that the free energy varies as $(v - v_0)^{\frac{5}{2}}$ as the volume v is changed. This behaviour is illustrated in Fig. 5.6; it can produce a two-phase region below the critical point. If so, only at temperatures above the critical point can a continuous transition be observed. On the other hand, as we have seen in § 5.1, there are many cases of the Wilson transition where no discontinuity is observed.

In any case, the problem of a continuous variation of v or a is of theoretical interest and can be investigated in doped semiconductors. We do not at present know whether n should change discontinuously as a is varied. Kohn (1967) put forward a model in which as a is varied there are no discontinuous changes of n, but that leading up to the transition point there is an infinite series of second-order transitions, so that n (and ε_2, eqn (5.4)) go continuously to zero. Mott and Davis (1968) have pointed out that this model may allow κ to tend to infinity on the non-metal side of the transition, so that just on the metallic side n can be zero. These considerations are discussed later.

In view of possible changes in lattice parameter and structure near the transition, the rigid lattice behaviour may be observable only in doped semiconductors of high dielectric constant, like germanium; a can be varied by changing the concentration of donors. Here the forces exerted on the host lattice by the electrons in an impurity band can doubtless be neglected; there is however the additional complication that the position of the atoms is random. This situation will be discussed in § 5.10.

5.7. Wigner crystallization

Before discussing further the behaviour near the transition, we consider an early paper by Wigner (1938), who considered an electron gas in the presence of a background of 'jellium'—i.e. a uniform positive charge. He predicted a crystallization into a non-conducting state when the density is low. Each electron should be described by a localized wave function, of the type $\exp\{(-r/r_0)^2\}$, where r_0 is such that $r_0^3 \sim 1/n$. The lattice is antiferromagnetic. The overlap between these wave functions is small, so that the contribution of the term e^2/r_{12} is smaller than in the metal; on the other hand a kinetic-energy term $\sim \hbar^2\pi^2/mr_0^2$ results from localization. Estimates of the value of n for crystallization are crude; approximately (Mott 1961 p. 303)

$$n^{\frac{1}{3}}a_{\mathrm{H}} = 0 \cdot 08.$$

The properties that one would predict for a Wigner 'crystal' are as follows. In the Hartree–Fock approximation the description is similar to that of the Mott–Hubbard insulator, with wave functions for the two spin directions as in Fig. 5.7. The potential energy that each electron 'sees' in the centre of each well is of the form $\frac{1}{2}\alpha r^2$, where

$$\alpha = (4\pi/3)\rho e,$$

ρ being the charge per unit volume of the jellium. Free carriers would be produced with an activation energy of order $E \sim n^{\frac{1}{3}}e^2/\kappa$ and, at a temperature for which kT is comparable with E, some kind of transition should occur to a non-degenerate gas; details have not been worked out.

Wigner crystallization has not been observed because a material with the properties of jellium would be difficult to produce. In principle germanium, with a high concentration of donors and of acceptors with compensation K such that $1 - K \ll 1$, could have this property. If the distance between centres were small compared to a_{H}, the approximation to jellium would be good.

A phenomenon similar to Wigner crystallization occurs in crystals in which the numbers of carriers are unequal. The best-known case is Fe_3O_4. Here, on octahedral sites there are equal numbers of Fe^{2+} and Fe^{3+} ions; the carrier can be thought of as an extra electron on Fe^{3+}. All spins are parallel (and antiparallel to spins on tetrahedral sites); Fe_3O_4 is a ferrimagnetic. Below 119 K it is a semiconductor, with an activation energy 0·15 eV just below the transition, and the positions of the ions Fe^{2+} and Fe^{3+} are ordered; above this temperature they are disordered and the conductivity is that of a poor metal ($\sim$250 $\Omega^{-1}\,cm^{-1}$).

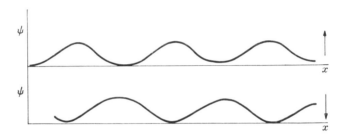

Fig. 5.7. Suggested Hartree–Fock wave functions for the two spin directions in a Wigner crystal.

It should be emphasized that the ordering energy is the Coulomb energy $e^2/\kappa a$ between neighbouring atoms, not the Hubbard intra-atomic term w. The structure of the high-temperature phase is that of a cubic spinel, but below the transition temperature there is a small distortion, of order 0·05 per cent, to orthorhombic symmetry. A distortion will normally occur when the electronic charge density takes up any periodicity different from that of the lattice.

Few theoretical developments exist about the Wigner transition, but we can envisage a crystallization that sets up energy gaps along planes in k-space producing zones such that the Fermi surface overlaps from one zone to the next. Wigner crystallization then becomes indistinguishable from the spin-density waves envisaged by Overhauser (1962), or the antiferromagnetism with period incoherent with the lattice parameter observed in chromium. What is uncertain is whether the setting up of a spin-density wave (or charge-density wave) as a increases is a first-order or second-order transition. Penn and Cohen (1967) maintain that the first instability should be ferromagnetic, but antiferromagnetism is more likely in a real lattice. Some examples will be given in § 5.10. We conjecture that what happens when the density of an electron gas is decreased is the following. First of all, spin-density waves are set up of the Overhauser type. Their amplitude will increase as a increases. Their wave number will assume values such that the energy gaps formed divide k-space into two zones, with the Fermi surface partly in one and partly in the other. Eventually as a increases, the number of electrons and holes will become very small, just as in the Mott transition. What happens next is described in the following section.

5.8. The excitonic insulator

In § 5.1 it was pointed out that in a cubic divalent metal a MNM transition would occur if some parameter such as the lattice parameter, which affects the band gap, were changed continuously. We called the transition a Wilson transition because it is a consequence of Wilson's (1931) classification into conductors and insulators on the basis of a model of non-interacting electrons.

On the metal side of the Wilson transition, the material should have a very small number of free electrons and holes. Mott (1961) pointed out that this was impossible; the electrons and holes, attracting each other as before with an attractive potential energy $-e^2/\kappa r$, would form pairs bound together with energy E such that

$$E \sim m^* e^4 / 2\hbar^2 \kappa^2. \qquad (5.7)$$

He proposed that, just as for the positive and negative holes in a one-electron insulator, there would be a discontinuous change in the number of carriers. The state in which there is some overlap between two zones—that is, in materials that are just semi-metals, but in which the electrons and holes form pairs—has been described as an *excitonic insulator*, and has been the subject of extensive theoretical investigation. As Knox (1963) first pointed out, the same situation can occur in a semiconductor in which a band gap ΔE exists, if ΔE is less than the exciton energy (5.7); excitons will be formed spontaneously.

These concepts have been developed in detail by Keldysh and Kopaev (1965), des Cloizeaux (1965), Kohn (1967), Halperin and Rice (1968), and others. They envisage a 'Bose condensation' of excitons—i.e. electron–hole pairs, which may or may not be non-metallic. In the latter case we use the term *excitonic insulator*. We shall not give a detailed account of these developments, but will emphasize two points:

(a) There is little difference in principle between the excitonic insulator and the phenomena occurring in the Mott transition if there is no discontinuous disappearance of moments. In the former, a band gap is produced by the crystal structure, in the latter a Hubbard gap. In either case there will be a small number of electrons and holes near the transition, and the kinds of condensation to be expected are similar.

(b) The original prediction of a discontinuous change in n may be wrong, if an alternative description can be given that allows κ to tend to infinity at the transition. As we shall see in the next section, this is possible.

Observations of the excitonic insulator are likely to be difficult. As stated in § 5.1, McWhan, Rice, and Schmidt (1969) and Jullien and Jerome (1971) have investigated some divalent metals (Sr, Ba, Yb) for which the band gap is likely to form under pressure, giving at any rate a small separation of the valence and conduction bands (see § 5.1). For these materials McWhan et al. find that the resistivity at 4·2K rises from $\sim 10^{-6}$ to $10^{-1} \, \Omega$ cm. (Fig. 5.8). It then flattens out, and the conductivity then is probably caused by a degenerate gas of electrons due to impurities. Unless these can be eliminated it is unlikely that the properties associated with an excitonic insulator can be observed. The background dielectric constant is likely to be high, so very great purity and very low temperatures are essential.

Rogachev (1968) has presented evidence that metallic conduction can be observed in germanium when a high concentration of electrons and holes is excited optically. His results are shown in Fig. 5.9. The transition, apparently at $n \simeq 3 \times 10^{15}$ cm^{-3}, is at somewhat lower value of n than might be expected. Rogachev points out that the optical recombination line associated with excitons retains its shape up to $n \sim 10^{17}$ cm^{-3}; an analogy with the merging of an impurity band into the conduction band (§ 6.5) seems possible, the 'electrons' moving in an impurity band due to the holes. It is conjectured that in the flat part of Fig. 5.9 the gas is non-degenerate even at 4 K so that electron–hole collisions are proportional to the number (n) of either, and the resistivity independent of n. For higher concentrations and a degenerate gas the Baber T^2 term should determine the dependence of ρ on T and on the concentration, and σ should vary as

$$\sigma = (ne^2/mv_F A_0 n)(E_F/kT)^2.$$

A_0 is here the collision cross-section, and if this is independent of n, σ should vary as E_F^2/v_F and thus as n. As Fig. 5.9 shows, it does in fact increase more rapidly, and this may be due to a decrease in A_0.

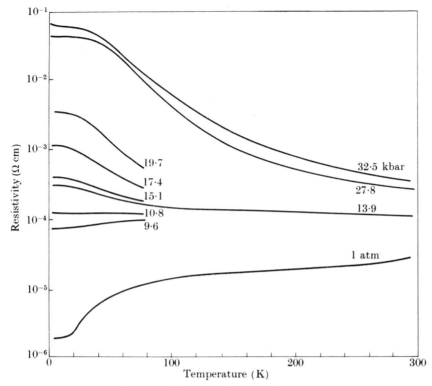

FIG. 5.8. Resistivity of f.c.c. ytterbium as a function of temperature at various pressures
(McWhan, Rice, and Schmidt 1969).

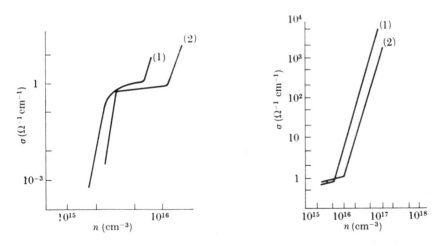

FIG. 5.9. Dependence of conductivity of illuminated germanium on concentration of
electron–hole pairs: (1) 1·7 K; (2) 4·2 K (Rogachev 1968). The two drawings are on
different scales.

5.9. Kohn's model for the Mott transition

We have already seen that a simple model of the transition, which neglects the long-range Coulomb force between the atoms, predicts that when the Hubbard gap disappears there will be a *small* number of electrons described by equation (5.1), and holes described by equation (5.3). Any arguments, therefore, about condensation of electrons and holes that apply to divalent metals or semi-metals with electrical behaviour depending on the crystal structure will apply equally to the MNM transition for an array of monovalent atoms (Mott transition).

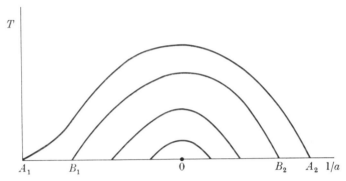

FIG. 5.10. Phase diagram near MNM transition according to Kohn.

Kohn (1967) first suggested that, for the Mott transition, and for MNM transitions of any other kind, there would be an infinite series of second-order transitions leading up to the transition point, as illustrated in Fig. 5.10. At the zero of temperature, at each of the points A_2, B_2, ... there is no discontinuity in n, but a new charge-density or spin-density wave is set up, with amplitude at first zero but increasing as a increases. The wave number q also will change with a. On the insulator side as well, these transitions will exist, showing up as weak band-type spin fluctuations. The values are determined in such a way as to minimize the energy, and therefore so as to produce a band gap near the Fermi surface depressing the energy of the electrons there.

The reason for the occurrence of an infinite series is that, as a approaches O from the metal side, the number of carriers decreases and some kind of condensation must occur. The condensation is equivalent to the setting up of a charge-density or spin-density wave. This does two things:

(a) It increases the background dielectric constant κ, because transitions across the very small energy gap ΔE in k-space make a large contribution to κ. Thus the critical parameter $\hbar^2\kappa/m^*e^2$ for condensation is increased, and a smaller number of free carriers is allowed.

(b) It should also decrease m^*.

As a is increased further, the new band gap widens, and the number of carriers is decreased until a further condensation occurs described by a charge-density wave with a new wave number q_2. The process is repeated *ad infinitum*. Near the transition point the Fermi surface will be 'fenced in' by a very large number of gaps along planes in k-space, as illustrated in Fig. 5.11. Mott and Davis (1968) pointed out that

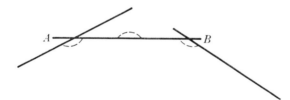

FIG. 5.11. Fermi surface near the transition. The line AB represents an energy gap due to charge-density waves, and the dotted line is the Fermi surface.

optical transitions across these gaps can occur for very small values of the energy, with the consequence that κ may become large. Reasons are given by Mott and Davis for thinking that $\kappa \to \infty$ as a tends to the value marked O in Fig. 5.10 for the transition, though this has not been proved. If so, the argument originally due to Mott (1949) and outlined in § 5.3 that n must change discontinuously at the transition falls to the ground.

If this is so, the success of formula (5.6) in describing the concentrations at which the transition occurs must be regarded as fortuitous (Mott 1969b). The metal near the transition is *not* a normal metal. It has magnetic moments and a low density of states. Like so many other properties near the transition point, it may be very difficult to see whether this is so experimentally. As shown in Fig. 5.6, the free energy near the transition point may lie in a two-phase region. Moreover, if charge-density waves are set up with wave number unequal to the lattice parameter, a distortion of the lattice must occur. For both reasons, first-order transitions are expected; one such transition is described in the next section.

Kohn's model depends essentially on the assumption that all MNM transitions are second order. If this is not so, then the original Mott model of a first-order transition from antiferromagnetic insulator to normal (if highly correlated) metal is valid, as maintained by Brinkman and Rice (1970*b*).

5.10. Transition-metal oxides

A number of transition-metal oxides and sulphides show a metal–non-metal transition as the temperature is raised. These include V_2O_3 and VO_2, Ti_2O_3, and NiS; references are given in Adler (1968) and in

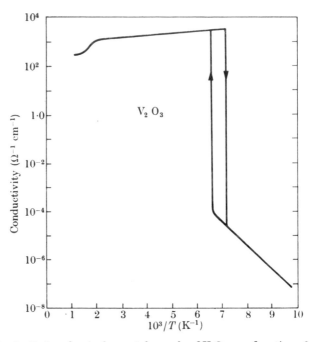

FIG. 5.12. Conductivity of a single crystal sample of V_2O_3 as a function of temperature.

the report of the San Francisco conference.† Figure 5.12 shows the behaviour of V_2O_3. For this material there is a drop (∼1 per cent) in volume as the temperature increases through the transition point; Austin (1962) was the first to show that the transition temperature drops with pressure, and McWhan and Rice (1969) found that for pressures of about 23 kbar V_2O_3 remains metallic down to the lowest temperatures. Figure 5.13 shows the results of these authors on the metallic resistance as a function of temperature.

All these materials have crystal structures (rutile, corundum) with two or more metal atoms per unit cell, so that the basic Brillouin zone

† *Rev. mod. Phys.* (1968) **41**.

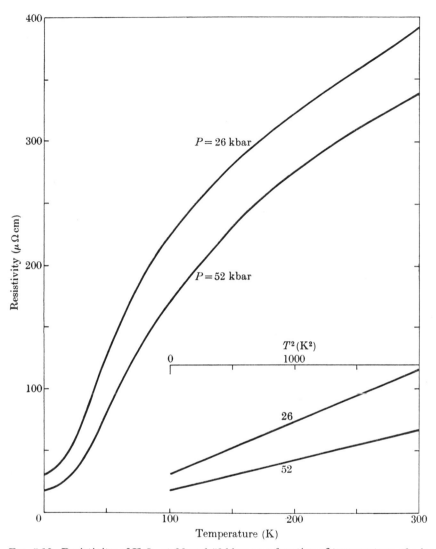

FIG. 5.13. Resistivity of V_2O_3 at 26 and 52 kbar as a function of temperature; the inset shows a plot against T^2 (McWhan and Rice 1969.)

will contain not more than one electron per atom. There is thus the possibility mentioned in § 5.1; if correlation (the term e^2/r_{12}) and magnetic moments are not taken into account, the material, whatever the number of d electrons, could be either a non-metal with all bands full or empty, or a metal with overlapping bands.

Now Ti_2O_3 and VO_2 have no moments in the non-metallic state, and it is known that the crystal parameters change on going through the transition. The transition, therefore, can be thought of as a Wilson transition; it is due to a change in the lattice parameters, and occurs because the metallic phase has higher entropy than the non-metallic. Van Zandt, Honig, and Goodenough (1968) have given a description of Ti_2O_3 along these lines. In order that the metallic phase should have sufficient entropy to cause the transition, the effective mass of the carriers must be high, so that the electron gas is non-degenerate or nearly so; Mott (1969b) has suggested that mass enhancement by polaron formation is responsible for this, and that the effective mass (m_p) is of order $10m$, in contrast with a probable value of $\sim m$ for the undistorted lattice. For VO_2, Paul (1970) maintains that the entropy is due to a soft-phonon mode in the metallic phase, though this has been queried (Mott and Zinamon 1970).

In V_2O_3, as we have already stated, the transition can be caused by pressure, and Fig. 5.13 shows the dependence of the resistance on temperature at pressures where the metallic phase is stable at low temperatures. At low temperatures the resistance varies as T^2, saturating at higher temperatures. The similarity with the behaviour of ytterbium under pressure is striking, and we believe that the same mechanism operates in both cases; the resistance is due to electron–hole collisions, giving Baber T^2 scattering at low temperatures, and a constant resistance when the gas becomes non-degenerate at higher temperatures. These results, then, give further evidence for a high effective mass, whether or not it is due to polaron formation.

V_2O_3 differs from VO_2 and Ti_2O_3 in that the semiconducting phase does show antiferromagnetism with a moment of $1\cdot2$ μ_B (Moon 1970); in the metallic phase, however, there is no long-range magnetic order. This has led McWhan, Rice, and Remeika (1969) to classify the transition as a Mott transition. These authors also find that alloying with chromium or titanium is equivalent to a positive or a negative pressure change; the phase diagram of an alloy $(V_{1-x}Cr_x)_2O_3$ is shown in Fig. 5.14. It is thus possible in alloys containing a few per cent of chromium to measure the Néel temperature at which the material transforms from an antiferromagnetic insulator to an insulator with no long-range magnetic order. The Néel temperature lies below 200 K; this shows in our view that the phenomenon is not a straightforward Mott transition, for which the Néel temperature should be much higher. Zinamon and Mott (1970) account for this by the following assumptions:

(a) Hund's rule is broken down and one electron per V atom lies in a full band.

(b) For the second electron, without taking correlation into account, two bands are available; if ΔW is the separation between the bands, and w the (Hubbard) energy gained by forming moments, w is only just greater than ΔW. If the bands overlap, an electron will gain the energy ΔW while losing the energy w. Thus overlap can occur, even though the term J_0 in eqn (5.5) is much less than w.

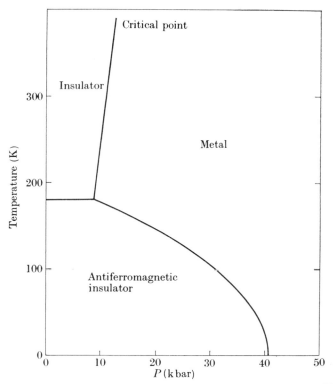

Fig. 5.14. Phase diagram of $(V_{1-x}Cr_x)_2O_3$ for $x = 0.0375$ (Jayaraman, McWhan, Remeika, and Dernier 1970).

Zinamon and Mott (1970) have put forward another suggestion. In materials like V_2O_3 and Ti_2O_3 in the non-metallic phase, where at $T = 0$ the energy difference between a non-magnetic and a magnetic phase is small, a transition from one to the other may occur when the lattice parameters change. Also, this could be a first-order change, the moments jumping suddenly from a finite value to a zero value as crystal parameters are varied (Mott and Zinamon 1970). The evidence on V_2O_3 certainly suggests that this is so, the change in volume and crystal parameters being a consequence of the electronic change. Thus we picture metallic V_2O_3 as a semi-metal with slightly overlapping bands and polaron enhancement of the effective mass of the carriers; the formation of moments produces a gap.

5.11. The MNM transition in disordered systems

A transition due to a continuously varying value of the distance between atoms, unaffected by lattice distortions, is, as we have seen, probably impossible to observe in crystals under pressure. It can, however, be studied in doped semiconductors, where the mean distance between (say) donors can be changed by varying the composition. If the radius $\hbar^2\kappa/me^2$ is large compared with the lattice parameter, as it is in germanium, any distortion of the lattice caused by the electrons is likely to be small. However, the centres are now distributed at random, and the effect of this needs to be discussed.

We consider then a high concentration of donors, distributed at random, and with one electron per atom. This situation is considered in detail in the next chapter; near the MNM transition an impurity band exists separate from the conduction band, and the concentration at which the transition occurs is given satisfactorily by equation (5.6). Suppose now that a, the mean distance between centres, is increased. For a regular (crystalline) array of centres, the first effect of the term e^2/r_{12} would be to produce an antiferromagnetic lattice, introducing a band gap and making the material behave like a semi-metal. Mott and Davis (1968) have suggested that, when the distribution of centres is random, the term e^2/r_{12} will produce *random* fluctuations of spin or charge density and that these will increase as a increases. In the sense of Hartree–Fock, they will produce a random potential $V(x, y, z)$ in the field in which each electron moves. In other words we can say that, for values of a much below that for which the transition to the non-metallic state occurs, moments on the atoms have appeared, so that electrons with opposite spins 'see' a different potential energy. At a certain value of a, this random potential becomes great enough to cause Anderson localization at the Fermi level. An activation energy ε will appear at a definite value of a, but there will be no discontinuity in ε as a function of a.

In this model we can envisage the Hubbard gap turning into a pseudogap; at the value of a where conduction at $T = 0$ begins, $N(E_F)$ will be small ($\sim 0.3N(E_F)_{free}$). The formulae of § 3.14 should be applicable to this case. Moreover, if the behaviour of σ near the transition is regarded as an Anderson transition, then from eqn (2.39) we expect, if ε_2 is plotted against $a-a_0$ where a_0 is the value of a at the transition, a proportionality of the form

$$\varepsilon_2 = \text{const.}(a-a_0)^{\frac{3}{2}}. \tag{5.8}$$

The prediction that the activation energy for conduction approaches zero at the transition point, without a discontinuity, in accordance with equation (5.8), is in agreement with observation for doped germanium. Figure 5.15 shows the observations of Davis and Compton (1965) for

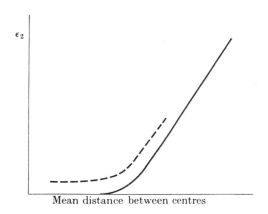

Fɪɢ. 5.15. Activation energy ε_2 for n-type germanium as a function of mean distance between the centres for low compensation (using results of Davis and Compton 1965; for scale see Fig. 6.6). The dotted line shows the behaviour for high compensation.

n-type crystals. The activation energy ε_2 goes to zero, as we expect. These results are discussed further in Chapter 6.

The fact that, for large values of the compensation K, the activation energy does not disappear on the metallic side of the transition will be discussed in detail in Chapter 6. We think this behaviour is due to Anderson localization at the Fermi energy in the tail of the band, because of the random field of the donors and acceptors. The impurity band for $K = 0\cdot8$ is only 20 per cent full, which may lead to localiz- ation at the Fermi level even if there is no localization in the middle of the band.

It is important to obtain evidence on whether moments persist in the metallic phase. The negative magnetoresistance of heavily doped semiconductors is discussed in the next chapter, and n.m.r. results in metal–ammonia solutions in § 5.14.

11

5.12. Conductivity near the transition point in a disordered system

For a material near the MNM transition we expect the Hubbard gap to turn into a pseudogap just as in § 3.14. Anderson localization should occur when $g \sim 0.3$ and the minimum metallic conductivity will be

$$\sigma = Se^2ag^2/12\pi^3\hbar,$$

where a is the distance between centres. For doped semiconductors we must replace e^2 by e^2/κ. Since at the MNM transition eqn (5.6) is satisfied, putting $n \sim a^{-3}$, we find for the minimum metallic conductivity in a doped semiconductor

$$2m^*e^4g^2/6\hbar^3\kappa.$$

Another way to get a similar result is to use formula (2.31) for the minimum electrical conductivity near the Anderson transition, in the form

$$\sigma = 0.06e^2/\hbar a = 0.06m^*e^4/\hbar^3\kappa. \tag{5.9}$$

This rather larger value may be more reliable. It is however calculated using a coordination number 6. The ratio $(J/U_0)^2$ at which the Anderson transition occurs is sensitive to the coordination number, and for a random array of centres there is at present no calculation available to determine the value of z that we ought to take. Evidence presented in Chapter 6, however, suggests that these formulae are not far wrong.

5.13. Materials of high dielectric constant; the transition in doped titanates

A MNM transition occurs in doped or reduced $SrTiO_3$ and in similar materials, and in tungsten bronzes (Na_xWO_3) as the concentration x is changed, and in metal–ammonia solutions. We have to ask whether formula (5.6) is applicable, and if so what value of the dielectric constant, the static value (κ) or the high frequency value (κ_∞), should be used. This will depend on the considerations of § 4.9; unless a small polaron is formed, some mean of κ and κ_∞ such as that of formula (4.28) will be appropriate. For materials of high dielectric constant, this will be about $2.5\kappa_\infty$. This seems to be roughly in agreement with experiment for metal–ammonia (discussed in the next section) and for tungsten bronzes; for the latter the results of Shanks, Sidles and Danielson (1963) are reproduced in Fig. 5.16, showing a transition at $x \simeq 0.2$. For this material $\kappa_\infty \simeq 6.2$. The analysis of Mackintosh (1963) suggests that a transition at $x = 0.2$ can be explained using this value of κ rather than any higher value. This is in spite of the very large value of the static dielectric constant. Measurements of nuclear magnetic resonance suggest that the electron resides on the surrounding metal ions and not primarily on the sodium ions; but the overlap with the Na^+ ion must be large enough for the attraction to be determined by κ_∞.

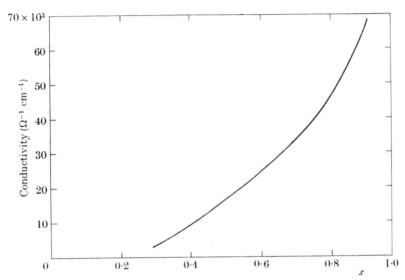

FIG. 5.16. Electrical conductivity of $M_x WO_3$ at 300 K as a function of x (Shanks *et al.* 1963). M is an alkali metal.

If small polarons are formed, so that the interaction energy of the electrons with the donor is essentially determined by the potential energy $-e^2/\kappa r$, then no MNM transition is to be expected in the first case considered in § 4.9, namely that in which the binding energy is $e^2/\kappa R$. This case probably applies to NiO doped with lithium and to reduced TiO_2. But if the radius $\hbar^2\kappa/me^2$ is greater than R, then we may envisage a hydrogen-like orbital for the small polaron, and a transition to a degenerate gas of polarons when

$$n^{\frac{1}{3}}(\hbar^2\kappa/m_p e^2) \sim 0.25.$$

This case doubtless applies to $KTaO_2$, $SrTiO_3$, and other materials that appear to be metallic for concentrations of electrons above $\sim 10^{17}$ cm^{-3}. For experimental observations see Wemple (1965), and for a theoretical discussion Mott (1969b); a description of superconductivity using this model has been given by Zinamon (1970). The condition for this behaviour is then that κ must be very high, and m_{p} must be large enough for the interaction of the electron with the donor to be given by $e^2/\kappa r$, but not too large for $\hbar^2\kappa/m_{\mathrm{p}}e^2$ to be greater than the lattice parameter.

5.14. Metal–ammonia solutions

The properties of dilute solutions have been discussed in Chapter 4; the electrons and metal ions separate and each electron forms a cavity and polarizes its surroundings. For high concentrations of metal, on the

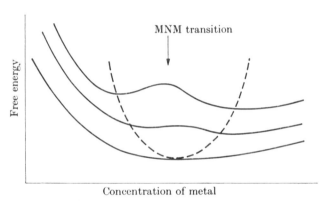

FIG. 5.17. Free energy of metal–ammonia solutions, showing (dotted line) the solubility gap (Catterall and Mott 1969).

other hand, the material is metallic and the conductivity approaches that of liquid sodium. It has long been conjectured that we have to do here with a Mott transition of the kind described in this chapter (Mott 1961; Thompson 1965). Sienko (1964) concludes that equation (5.6) gives the concentration for the transition if equation (4.28) is used for the dielectric constant. The transition can only be observed at comparatively high temperatures, because of the solubility gap shown in Fig. 5.17. This doubtless implies a free-energy curve of the type shown.

The nature of the transition has been discussed by Cohen and Thompson (1968) and by Catterall and Mott (1969). If the problem is examined from the point of view of this chapter, we see that on the metal side of the transition there is a small number of cavities each containing two electrons, and metallic conduction will occur by the extra electrons moving to singly charged cavities. The empty cavities will collapse. The transition has been discussed by Catterall and Mott from this point of view. One of the main points both in their treatment and that of Cohen and Thompson is that the cavities persist on the metallic side of the transition, and that the electrons consequently move in a comparatively narrow impurity band similar to that in doped semiconductors.

Acrivos and Mott (1971) have discussed n.m.r. evidence in metal–ammonia solutions near the transition point. In a solid, random moments should greatly broaden any n.m.r. line,† but in a liquid, the constant change of configuration of the atoms should give a vanishing mean magnetic field over the time scale of this resonance. The Knight shift can then give a measure of the density of states at the Fermi level, as in § 3.17. The experimental evidence then shows clearly that $N(E_F)$ drops as we approach the transition, as would be expected from the pseudogap model of § 5.11. Supporting evidence from electron spin resonance has been discussed by Catterall (1970).

† At the time of writing it is not known whether a non-crystalline array of moments with antiferromagnetic coupling should show a Néel temperature. Calculations suggesting that this is the case have been given by Simpson (1970) and by Kobe and Handrich (1970). On the other hand Sundfors and Holcomb (1964) find that in silicon doped with phosphorus on the insulator side of the MNM transition there is no broadening due to moments down to 1·3 K. This suggests that the Néel temperature, if one exists, is lower than this.

6

IMPURITY BANDS AND
IMPURITY-CONDUCTION

6.1. Introduction
6.2. Models of Twose and of Miller and Abrahams
6.3. Impurity-conduction in silicon and germanium
6.4. Thermopower
6.5. Anderson localization on the metallic side of the MNM transition
6.6. Anderson localization in cerium sulphide and vanadium monoxide

6.7. Impurity-conduction in ionic materials
6.8. Conduction in glasses containing transition-metal ions
6.9. Magnetic susceptibility
6.10. Hall effect
6.11. Magnetic polarons
6.12. Magnetic semiconductors
6.13. Magnetoresistance
6.14. Optical absorption and a.c. conduction

6.1. Introduction

THE phenomenon now known as impurity-conduction was first observed by Hung and Gleissman (1950) as a new conduction mechanism predominant at low temperature in doped germanium and silicon. Fig. 6.1 shows some experimental results of Fritzsche and Cuevas (1960) on the resistivity of doped p-type germanium. As we shall see, the conductivity at low temperatures has the following characteristics:

(a) It is of the form

$$\sigma = \sigma_3 \exp(-\varepsilon_3/kT),$$

where the activation energy ε_3 is usually an order of magnitude less than that required to free an electron from a donor or a hole from an acceptor (ε_1).

(b) σ_3 depends strongly on the concentration of donors or acceptors.

Transport of current with these characteristics is known as impurity-conduction. The now accepted mechanism is that illustrated in Figs. 6.2 and 6.3; the electrons are thought to tunnel from one centre to the next. Since in the case considered in this section the concentration N_D of donors is well on the insulator side of the metal–non-metal transition, this process is only possible if the material is *compensated*, or in other words if it contains acceptors.† This was first stressed by Conwell

† If N_D is the concentration of donors and N_A of acceptors, for an n-type conductor $N_A < N_D$. The compensation K is N_A/N_D.

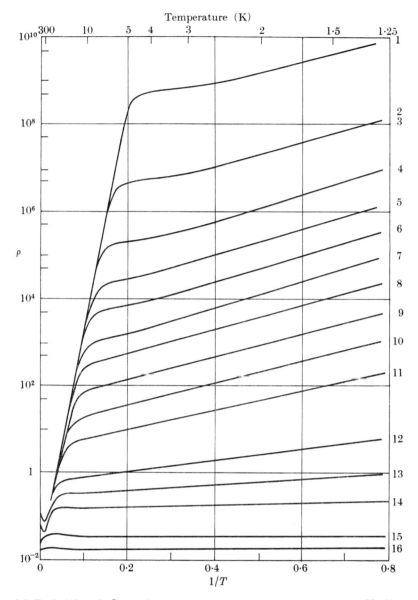

FIG. 6.1. Resistivity ρ in Ω cm of p-type germanium with compensation $K\,(=N_D/N_A)=0{\cdot}4$ (Fritzsche and Cuevas 1960). The concentrations of acceptors are as follows (in cm^{-3}): (1) $7{\cdot}5\times10^{14}$; (2) $1{\cdot}4\times10^{15}$; (3) $1{\cdot}5\times10^{15}$; (4) $2{\cdot}7\times10^{15}$; (5) $3{\cdot}6\times10^{15}$; (6) $4{\cdot}9\times10^{15}$; (7) $7{\cdot}2\times10^{15}$; (8) $9{\cdot}0\times10^{15}$; (9) $1{\cdot}4\times10^{16}$; (10) $2{\cdot}4\times10^{16}$; (11) $3{\cdot}5\times10^{16}$; (12) $7{\cdot}3\times10^{16}$; (13) $1{\cdot}0\times10^{17}$; (14) $1{\cdot}5\times10^{17}$; (15) $5{\cdot}3\times10^{17}$; (16) $1{\cdot}35\times10^{18}$.

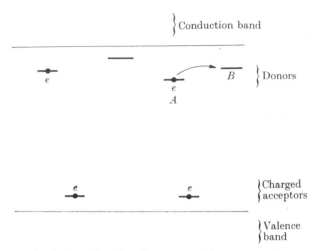

FIG. 6.2. Energy levels for a doped and compensated n-type semiconductor; the rate-determining process is the hopping (i.e. thermally assisted tunnelling) of an electron from an occupied centre such as A to an empty centre B.

(1956) and Mott (1956) as the theoretical condition for this form of conduction, and was confirmed by the experimental work of Fritzsche (1958, 1959, 1960). The acceptors all carry a negative charge, but some of the donors are neutral and others positively charged. Current is carried by electrons tunnelling from neutral (occupied) to charged (empty) donors (Fig. 6.3). The random field of the charged acceptors is usually taken as producing the spread of energy levels shown in Fig. 6.2, of order $e^2/\kappa R_A$, where R_A is the average separation between acceptors, though, as we shall see, the charged donors must play a part too. Therefore an electron can move from one centre to another only by exchanging energy with phonons. At low temperatures, processes in which an electron receives energy from phonons will be rate-determining, and these processes are responsible for the activation energy ε_3, which is thus of the order of the spread of energy levels. All this is true also for compensated p-type conductors ($N_A > N_D$).

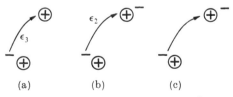

FIG. 6.3. Positions in the lattice of donor centres marked $\oplus$; the processes shown are (a) hopping, with activation energy ε_3; (b) the excitation of an electron into the ε_2 band; (c) the motion in the ε_2 band, the arrow representing an additional electron.

We have stated that impurity-conduction normally takes place for concentrations on the insulator side of the MNM transition (Chapter 5), and thus when the centres are reasonably far apart. On the other hand their orbitals must overlap to some extent, so that tunnelling is possible. A band of energy states will be formed, of breadth determined both by the overlap and by the random displacement of energy levels shown in Fig. 6.2. But well on the insulator side of the MNM transition, the Hubbard gap due to the intra-atomic repulsion e^2/r_{12} between a pair of electrons will be bigger than the band width. In other words the energy,

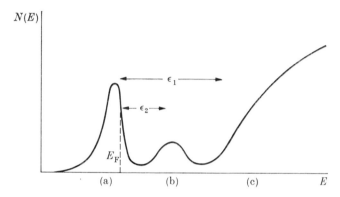

F𝚒ɢ. 6.4. Density of states for an electron in an n-type semiconductor showing the splitting of the impurity band into the ε_3 band (a), and the ε_2 band (b). (c) is the conduction band. The position of the Fermi level is shown for compensation $K < \frac{1}{2}$.

which we denote by ε_2, required to remove an electron from one donor and put it on another donor *that already has an electron* is bigger than the band width. This electron can move and has a band of levels (compare eqn (5.2)), which we call the ε_2 band. The density of states will therefore be as illustrated in Fig. 6.4, with *two* impurity bands, each containing *one* state per donor centre. If the semiconductor is compensated, the Fermi energy will be in the lower band; conduction in this band is by hopping, with activation energy ε_3, and we call this band the ε_3 band. The energy required to excite an electron into the conduction band will be denoted by ε_1; in certain ranges of composition ε_2 and ε_3 differ sufficiently for both to be determined experimentally (Fritzsche 1960; Davis and Compton 1965).

In principle, conduction in the ε_2 band might be by hopping, if the Anderson condition were fulfilled, or the wave functions might be extended (non-localized), giving the usual band mechanism. The experiments of D'Altroy and Fan (1956) on the a.c. conductivity have been interpreted by Pollak (1964) as showing that the latter is the case.

We must now discuss further the origin of the hopping activation energy ε_3 for impurity-conduction. If the centres were arranged on a lattice, the energies of a carrier moving in the ε_3 band would have a certain width J, which could be calculated by the tight-binding approximation, as in Chapter 5. The fact that the centres are distributed at random in space must lead to a certain additional broadening (Chapter 2). But probably much more important for broadening the band is, as already mentioned, the random potential energy U_0 (compare § 2.4) due to the charged acceptors. The resultant spread of the energy levels is illustrated in Fig. 6.2. Impurity-conduction, therefore, provides a particularly simple case of Anderson localization, differing from his model (Chapter 2) only in that the centres are distributed at random. This seems to have been pointed out first by Twose (1959; Mott and Twose 1961). If $U_0 > 5J$, all states in the impurity band are localized. We have to ask whether this condition always leads to Anderson localization on the non-metal side of the MNM transition. We think that it normally does, for reasons discussed in § 6.3, and this will be assumed in the remainder of this section.

We note however that there is one case in which, even if J is small, conduction may *not* be by hopping; this is if the compensation K is very small. Then we should consider the carriers (holes in the lower sub-band of Fig. 6.4) as trapped by the charged acceptors, with an energy $\sim e^2/\kappa R_\mathrm{D}$ required to release them. The material should behave like a narrow-band extrinsic semiconductor, and conduction will not be by hopping, unless of course the random arrangement of the donors is sufficient to produce localization of the mobile hole (§ 2.7.1). Mott (1956), at a time before Anderson localization was understood, proposed this as an explanation of the activation energy ε_3. As far as we know, there are no experimental investigations that relate to this case. An obvious test would be the thermopower, which would contain a term $(k/e)\varepsilon_3/2kT$ on this model, but which would tend to a constant value as $T \to 0$ on the model of thermally activated hopping (§ 2.9.3). Another test would be the a.c. conductivity (Pollak 1964).

The model of thermally activated hopping was first described in detail by Twose (1959) and by Miller and Abrahams (1960, 1961) and is undoubtedly applicable to most observations of impurity-conduction; it will now be described here.

6.2. Models of Twose and of Miller and Abrahams

Miller and Abrahams assume strong localization, so that the wave functions of the localized states are almost identical with those on the individual centres, overlap between orbitals being small. The calculation consists of three parts:

(a) The calculation of the probability p of a transition (because of interaction with phonons) from one centre to another between which the energy difference is W_D. This is the problem considered in §§ 2.9.1 and 4.3. The result is, if $W_D \gg kT$ and $W_D \ll k\Theta$, for transitions upwards, putting $I_0 = \frac{1}{2}e^2\alpha/\kappa$ in eqn (4.7),

$$p = \frac{E_1^2 W_D}{2\pi\rho_0 s^5\hbar^4}\left(\frac{e^2\alpha}{2\kappa}\right)^2 \exp\left(-2\alpha R - \frac{W_D}{kT}\right). \qquad (6.1)$$

Here s is the velocity of sound, E_1 the deformation potential, ρ_0 the density, and R the distance between the centres. The wave functions on the centres are taken to have spherical symmetry, falling off as $\exp(-\alpha r)$. The radius $1/\alpha$ of a centre is of course large ($\sim$50 Å). The term outside the exponential is about 10^{12} s^{-1} for germanium, but as pointed out in Chapter 4 a wide variation of values is possible, and the approximation on which this formula is based may not be valid.

(b) An averaging over all energies W_D to give the observed hopping energy ε_3.

In the work of Miller and Abrahams it is assumed that, since the factor $\exp(-2\alpha R)$ is very sensitive to R, electrons always jump to a nearest neighbour. In this case $W_D \sim 1/N(E_F)R_D^3$ (eqn 2.37). In § 2.9.1 it was emphasized that this cannot be the case at very low temperatures; transitions are most probable to a more distant centre where on the average the smallest available value of W_D is less. At these temperatures a proportionality between $\ln \rho$ and $1/T^{\frac{1}{4}}$ is deduced. This effect has not been observed with certainty in doped crystalline silicon and germanium, but an example (EuO) is illustrated in § 6.12, and the effect for amorphous materials is discussed in Chapters 7 and 8.

For hopping to nearest neighbours Miller and Abrahams found for n-type material and for small values of the compensation K

$$\varepsilon_3 = \frac{e^2}{\kappa}\left(\frac{1}{R_D} - \frac{1\cdot 35}{R_A}\right), \qquad (6.2)$$

where R_D, R_A are the average distances between donor and acceptor sites respectively. Since R_D is also the average donor–acceptor separation, the first term is simply the energy required to separate the carrier from the nearest charged acceptor. Calculations for all values of K were carried out and the plot of ε_3 against K is as in Fig. 6.5. As shown in the next section, for small overlap ε_3 increases as

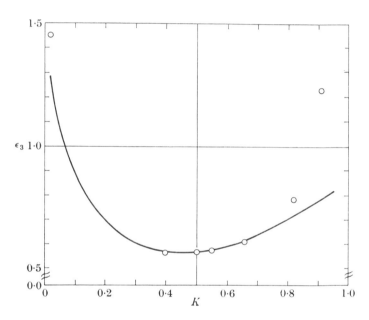

FIG. 6.5. Activation energy ε_3 in meV as a function of compensation calculated from equation (6.2) with $N_D = 2 \cdot 66 \times 10^{15} \ \text{cm}^{-3}$. The circles are experimental points (Mott and Twose 1961).

predicted with decreasing distance between sites (R_D in Fig. 6.6, R_A in Fig. 6.7).

(c) The next step in the calculation is to obtain the conductivity from the jump probability p given by equation (6.1). As in § 2.9.1 we assert that only a fraction $R_D\, N(E_F)kT$ of all electrons takes part in the conduction. $N(E_F)$ may be written for moderate values of K as equal to $\sim 1/W_D R_D^3$ where W_D is the spread of energy levels illustrated in Fig. 6.2. Thus the diffusion coefficient is

$$\tfrac{1}{6}p\ R_D kT/W_D, \tag{6.3}$$

the factor kT/W_D representing the fraction of electrons that can hop.

The conductivity σ, from Einstein's relation, is given by

$$\sigma = \tfrac{1}{6}e^2 p / W_D R_D$$

$$= \frac{e^2 E_1^2}{12\pi\rho_0 s^5 \hbar^4 R_D}\left(\frac{e^2\alpha}{2\kappa}\right)^2 \exp\left(-2\alpha R_D - \frac{\varepsilon_3}{kT}\right). \tag{6.4}$$

There is one further step in the calculation. The factor $\exp(-\alpha R)$ varies enormously with R, and the final evaluation involves computing the conductivity due to a network of widely varying impedance elements. Twose and Miller and Abrahams have done this in different ways; the main result of the latter authors is that the factor $\exp(-2\alpha R)$ is replaced by $\exp\{-1\cdot 09(\alpha R)^{\frac{3}{2}}\}$. This does not appear from Twose's calculations.

6.3. Impurity-conduction in silicon and germanium

Many observations have been made on these two materials. For comparison with theory they have two advantages: the band structure is well known, and they do not present the complication of two dielectric constants (κ_∞ and κ).

Prior to 1960, measurements in silicon and germanium were made with samples doped with suitable impurities. For quantitative comparison with experiment, however, it is desirable to keep the concentration of majority carriers constant and vary the compensation (K), or alternatively to keep K constant and vary the concentration. This was first achieved by Fritzsche and Cuevas (1960) by introducing impurities by slow-neutron bombardment, producing transmutation of the germanium atoms. The proportion of different impurities produced is determined by the cross-sections for neutrons captured and the decay schemes of the various germanium isotopes; thus K is kept constant. The results of Fig. 6.1 were obtained in this way.

In discussing these results we express the conductivity in the form

$$\sigma = \sigma_1 e^{-\varepsilon_1/kT} + \sigma_2 e^{-\varepsilon_2/kT} + \sigma_3 e^{-\varepsilon_3/kT}, \tag{6.5}$$

where $\sigma_1 \gg \sigma_2 \gg \sigma_3$, and $\varepsilon_1 > \varepsilon_2 > \varepsilon_3$. Here as before ε_1 is the energy required to eject an electron into the conduction band, ε_2 into the ε_2 band of Fig. 6.4, and ε_3 the activation energy for hopping conduction in the ε_3 (impurity) band. There are various questions we could ask about the comparison between theory and experiment. Figure 6.6, taken from the work of Davis and Compton (1965), shows the dependence on concentration of all three activation energies, ε_1, ε_2, and ε_3.

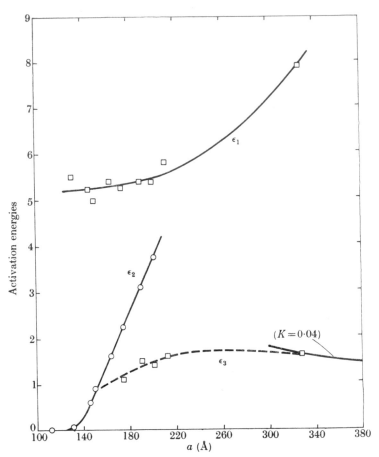

Fig. 6.6. Variation of the activation energies ε_1, ε_2, and ε_3 in meV with distance a in Å between donors for n-type germanium (Davis and Compton 1965). For ε_3 the calculations of Miller and Abrahams for $K = 0.04$ are shown.

(a) We can ask whether ε_3 is proportional to $1/R_D$ (i.e. $N_D^{\frac{1}{3}}$) for constant and small K as predicted by formula (6.2). According to Fig. 6.7 (from Mott and Twose 1961) it is for low concentrations, but drops for high concentrations. The same behaviour is shown in Fig 6.6. The drop may in our view be due either to the approach to the Anderson transition (at which ε_3 must vanish) or to the increasing dielectric constant caused by a high concentration of centres.† We shall see below that the Mott and Anderson transitions are predicted to occur for about the same value of R.

† This is probably also the reason for the drop in ε_1 (Castellan and Seitz 1951; Mott and Davis 1968).

(b) Does ln σ_3 vary as $-2\alpha R$ or as $-\text{const.}\ R^{\frac{3}{2}}$? Here the evidence is not decisive; Twose's expression agrees with experiment at least as well as that of Miller and Abrahams (Fritzsche and Cueavas 1960).

(c) Does ε_3 vary with K as predicted by Miller and Abrahams? Figure 6.5 shows the extent of the agreement.

Of particular importance is the behaviour near the MNM transition, defined as the value of R where ε_2 disappears, shown in Fig. 6.6. Figure 6.8 shows also the resistivity of Si+P plotted by Alexander and

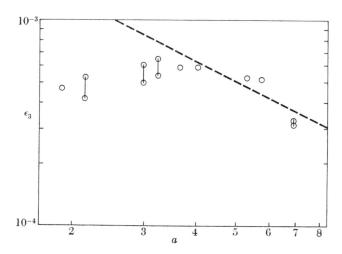

FIG. 6.7. The activation energy ε_3 in eV for impurity conduction for the samples shown in Fig. 6.1, plotted against average impurity separation R_A in cm $\times 10^6$. The dashed curve represents the results of formula (6.2) (Mott and Twose 1961).

Holcomb (1968) from the results of Yamanouchi, Mizuguchi, and Sasaki (1967).

The points to note are:

(a) ε_2 goes continuously to zero. A discussion of this point is given in § 5.11.

(b) The value of n for the transition depends little on K. Some speculations about the reason for this are given by Mott and Davis (1968). It is conjectured that the charged minority carriers produce spherical regions that are opaque to the electrons, so that for a given donor density n is roughly independent of K.

(c) ε_3 diminishes for concentrations approaching the MNM (Mott) transition. We expect ε_3 to vanish when the condition for Anderson localization is no longer satisfied, and this may be estimated very roughly as follows. If we take for the band width in the absence of disorder

$$J = 2z(e^2\alpha/\kappa)e^{-\alpha R},$$

and for the spread of energy levels $U_0 = 0{\cdot}3e^2/\kappa R$, then the condition for localization is $U_0 \sim 5J$. This gives for $z = 6$

$$1/\alpha R \sim 200e^{-\alpha R},$$

i.e.

$$\alpha R \sim 9, \qquad n^{\frac{1}{3}}a_{\mathrm{H}} \sim 0{\cdot}1.$$

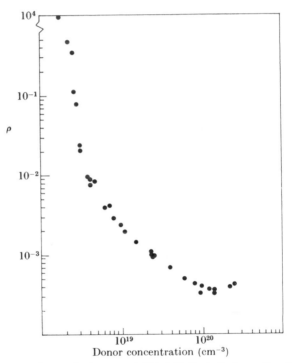

FIG. 6.8. The resistivity ρ in Ω cm at $4{\cdot}2$K of Si:P plotted as a function of donor concentration (Alexander and Holcomb 1968).

This is less than the value of n for the Mott transition, so an Anderson transition for a degenerate gas can be observed only when K is large (§ 6.4).

(d) Formula (5.6) gives quite satisfactory values for the concentration at which the MNM transition occurs. According to a table given by Alexander and Holcomb (1968, p. 823), $n^{\frac{1}{3}}a_{\mathrm{H}}$ varies between $0{\cdot}20$ and $0{\cdot}25$ for Si:P, Ge:Sb, Ge:As, and Ge:P. The agreement is slightly less good for p-type material, where the nature of the acceptor affects the transition more. Similar results are obtained by Antonov, Kopaev,

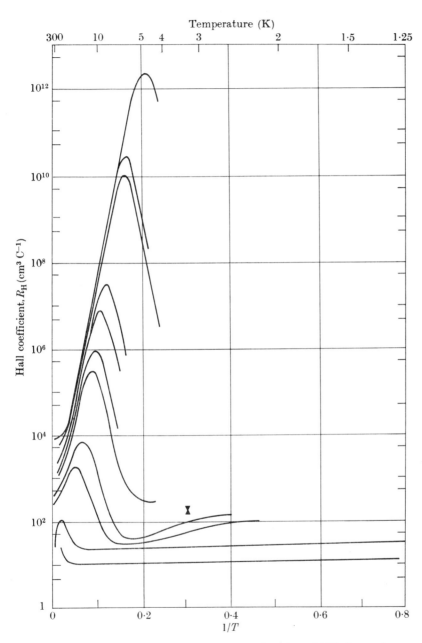

FIG. 6.9. Hall coefficient of p-type germanium as function of $1/T$; the specimens are the same as those shown in Fig. 6.1 (Fritzsche and Cuevas 1960).

Pashintsev, and Rakov (1969) for silicon, for which the MNM transition occurs at about 3×10^{18} cm^{-3} electrons (and the same number of holes). These values are very close to those given by Alexander and Holcomb for doped silicon (3 $\times$ 10^{18} in Si:P, $\sim$5 $\times$ 10^{18} in Si:As).

(e) There is much evidence that at the MNM transition the impurity band is separate from the conduction (or valence) band, and merges with it when n is about ten times higher. Mott and Twose pointed out

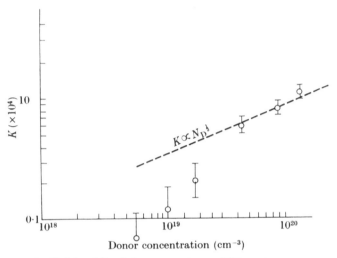

FIG. 6.10. The Knight shift of the n.m.r. signal of ^{29}Si in Si:P at 1·6 K (Alexander and Holcomb 1968).

that, for samples with n just above the transition, the bump at $T = 5$–10 K in the graph of the Hall coefficient against $1/T$ shown in Fig. 6.9 suggests the existence of a separate impurity band. The evidence has been reviewed by Alexander and Holcomb (1968). Perhaps the strongest evidence is the Knight shift of the silicon n.m.r. signal plotted in Fig. 6.10. The Knight shift is proportional to $N(E_{\mathrm{F}}) |\psi(0)|^2$, where $\psi(0)$ is the amplitude of the wave function at the silicon nucleus. Since $N(E)$ will vary as $\exp(\alpha R)$ and $\psi(0) \sim \exp(-\alpha R)$, the *drop* in the Knight shift when a separate narrow band forms is understandable.

Rogachev and Sablina (1969) came to a similar conclusion from their investigations of recombination radiation in arsenic-doped silicon.

6.4. Thermopower

We emphasize that, whether conduction is by hopping or not, the thermopower should be given by the formula (§ 2.9.3)

$$S\sigma = -\frac{k}{e} \int (E - E_{\mathrm{F}}) \sigma_{\mathrm{E}} \frac{\partial f}{\partial E} \, \mathrm{d}E, \qquad (6.6)$$

and that for a degenerate gas this goes over to the metallic formula

$$S = \frac{\pi^2}{3} \frac{k^2 T}{e} \left\{ \frac{d(\ln \sigma)}{dE} \right\}_{E=E_F}. \qquad (6.7)$$

In the metallic range of concentration, S should be proportional to T, in the hopping range it should be of the form $A + BT$. In either case, the density of states is likely to be the predominating term in S (§ 3.16),

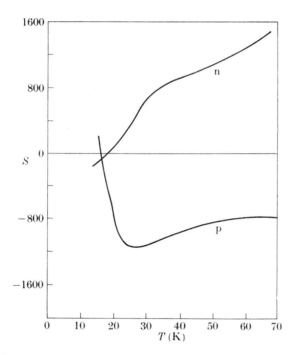

FIG. 6.11. Low-temperature values of the thermoelectric power S (in $\mu V\ K^{-1}$) for samples of silicon containing 10^{18} cm^{-3} donors or acceptors, showing the reversal in the sign at low T (Geballe and Hull 1955).

so in the hopping case S will be p-type for an impurity band of donors if the compensation K is less than $\sim\frac{1}{2}$. Thus, unless $K > \frac{1}{2}$, we expect a change of sign of the thermopower as the temperature drops into the range where impurity-conduction is predominant. This effect was observed by Geballe and Hull (1955), whose results are shown in Fig. 6.11. It is also observed for impurity-conduction in NiO (§ 6.7), and, as shown in Chapter 8, for amorphous germanium.

If there is a metallic impurity band separate from the conduction band, then if K is small the thermopower should be small, because the band is half full, and $d\sigma/dE$ would be expected to vanish. For moderate values of K, S should be n-type for n-type conductors. S is expected to be proportional to T at low temperatures, and then to go through a range where the conductivity is mainly due to electrons excited into the conduction band, so that $S \propto 1/T$, before flattening on to the curve ($S \propto \ln T + \text{const.}$) characteristic of a non-degenerate gas. Results by Fistul (1969) and by Brinson and Dunstan (1970) are relevant, but have not been analysed in terms of these formulae.

6.5. Anderson localization on the metallic side of the MNM transition

It will be seen from Fig. 5.15 that, quite far on the metallic side of the MNM transition, the activation energy does not disappear if the

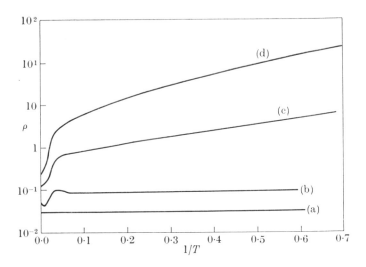

FIG. 6.12. Resistivity in Ω cm of heavily doped p-type germanium for $N_A = 2 \cdot 5 \times 10^{17}$ cm^{-3} and varying values of K, namely (a) 0·0, (b) 0·33, (c) 0·7, (d) 0·8 (Fritzsche and Lark-Horovitz 1959).

compensation K is large. Mott and Davis (1968) suggested that this is because the states in the tail of the impurity band, or even of the conduction band, remain localized, and that for large values of K the Fermi energy lies in this region. An increase in K should also increase the random field and therefore the range of energies in which states are localized. Fig. 6.12 shows the same effect for degenerate p-type germanium, studied by Fritzsche and Lark-Horovitz (1959); the concentration was $2 \cdot 5 \times 10^{17}$ cm^{-3}, quite near the MNM transition. Fig. 6.13 shows similar results due to Davis and Compton (1965). It is

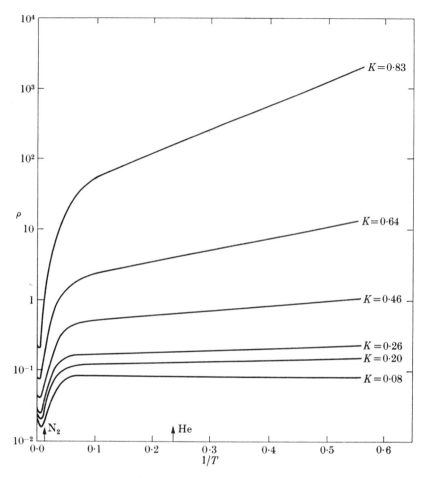

FIG. 6.13. Resistivity in Ω cm of germanium as a function of $1/T$ for varying compensation and $N_D = 1.7 \times 10^{17}$ cm^{-3} (Davis and Compton 1965).

instructive to compare these results with the minimum metallic conductivity predicted in Chapter 2 and given by $\sim 0.06e^2/\hbar a_E$. In such a situation, when K is not very large, a_E ought not to differ greatly from a, the mean distance between the centres, which is about 1.6×10^{-6} cm. Thus σ would be about $10 \; \Omega^{-1}$ cm^{-1}, which agrees well with the observations.

6.6. Anderson localization in cerium sulphide and vanadium monoxide

The observations of Cutler and Leavy (1964) on conduction in cerium sulphide provide, according to the interpretation of Cutler and Mott

(1969), a particularly simple example of Anderson localization. With the composition Ce_2S_3 the material is an insulator, but with excess cerium the conductivity rapidly rises, presumably because of excess electrons in the cerium d band. Ce_2S_3 has the crystal structure of Ce_3S_4, the excess sulphur being introduced as randomly situated cerium vacancies. Electrons introduced by changing the composition to $Ce_{2+2x}S_{3-3x}$ are therefore not associated with donors, but are due to a small change in the concentration of these negatively charged point defects. The electrons are thus thought to move in a random field of the kind illustrated in Fig. 6.14. For such a field acting on a comparatively

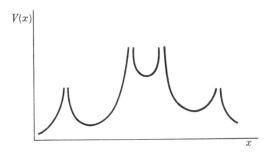

FIG. 6.14. Suggested potential energy in conduction band of cerium sulphide (Cutler and Mott 1969).

narrow d band, localization would be expected for the lower levels, but not for the upper levels. Plots of conductivity against temperature are thus expected to be of the form of Fig. 2.9. Some observed curves are shown in Fig. 6.15. The Anderson transition from metallic to hopping conduction is clearly seen. The minimum metallic conductivity is seen to be about $10^2 \, \Omega^{-1} \, cm^{-1}$.[†]

Figure 6.16 shows the observations of the same authors on the thermopower. In the hopping region, the behaviour predicted in § 2.9.3, namely a dependence on T as $A + BT$, is observed. The Hall mobility in the hopping region shows an activation energy of $\sim \frac{1}{3} W_D$, in agreement with Holstein and Friedman's predictions as described in Chapter 2.

Another material in which the conductivity has been interpreted in terms of Anderson localization is VO, which has the simple cubic structure and a high concentration (~ 15 per cent) of vacancies of both

[†] In comparing this value with the formulae of § 2.9.1, one would have to estimate a_E, and we do not have enough evidence to enable this to be done. Mott (1970) takes a_E to be the mean distance between electrons, which leads to fair agreement.

signs. In such a material, the three electrons per atom half fill a t_{2g} band. The work of Banus and Reed (1970) shows that the material is not antiferromagnetic, so no Hubbard gap can occur; on the other hand, the conductivity shows an activation energy of order 10^{-2} eV, which varies with the relative concentration of V and O vacancies.

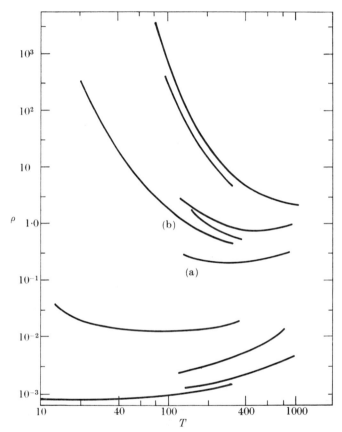

FIG. 6.15. Resistivity ρ in Ω cm of cerium sulphide of various compositions as a function of temperature. The electron concentration of the top curve is the lowest (Cutler and Mott 1969).

Calculations by Norwood and Fry (1970) give a very *high* density of states at the centre of the band, because of a high effective mass there, and Mott and Zinamon (1970) suggest that the random field due to the vacancies is sufficient to produce Anderson localization at the Fermi energy there, so that conduction is by hopping. The thermopower changes sign at the Fermi limit and is of the order expected, according to formula (6.7), for a Fermi energy of a few tenths of an electron volt.

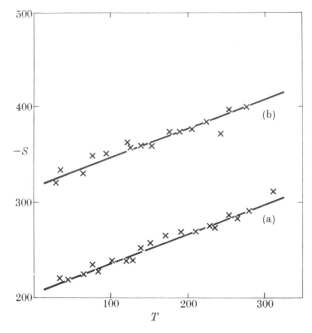

FIG. 6.16. Typical plots of thermopower S in μV K^{-1} of two specimens of cerium sulphide as a function of temperature (Cutler and Mott 1969).

Also, $\ln \sigma$ varies with $1/T^{\frac{1}{4}}$ at sufficiently low values of T. Mott (1971c) has discussed these phenomena in detail, and also the observation that about one atom in ten carries a free magnetic moment. The material behaves as if it had two overlapping Hubbard bands, although there is no long-range antiferromagnetic order.

6.7. Impurity-conduction in ionic materials

The theory of impurity-conduction developed so far neglects the distortion of the crystal round the impurity centres. It must be emphasized that this is likely to be a good approximation only if the radii of the centres are large compared with the lattice parameter; otherwise the distortion of the lattice must be taken into account, and the polaron hopping energy W_{H} of Chapter 4 becomes important, whether the material is ionic or not.

One of the clearest examples of the importance of W_{H} is that of impurity-conduction in nickel oxide, observed by Bosman and Crevecoeur (1966) and by Springthorpe, Austin, and Smith (1965). Some results are shown in Fig. 6.17. Conductivity is due to lithium doping, the acceptor centres being lithium (Li⁺), replacing Ni^{2+} in the lattice. To preserve electrical neutrality a neighbouring Ni ion has the charge of Ni^{3+}. Donors of unknown nature are present, so some of these centres acquire an electron that can hop from one to another. The activation energy drops from a value of 0·2–0·4 eV at high temperatures to ∼0·004

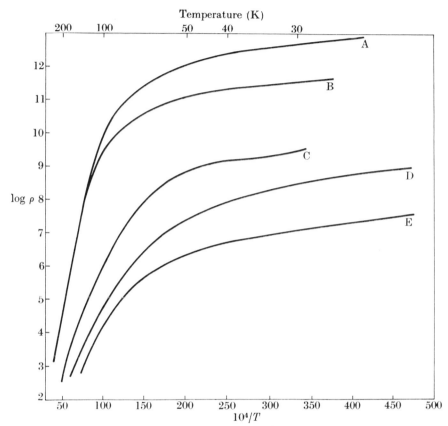

Fig. 6.17. Impurity-conduction in crystalline NiO; log (resistivity) in Ω cm as a function of $1/T$. The values of x in the formula $Li_xNi_{1-x}O$ were: A, 0·002, B, 0·003, C, 0·018, D, 0·026, E, 0·032.

eV or less at 10 K. The larger value is undoubtedly the polaron term (W_H) of Chapter 4, which as we have seen should drop away to zero as $T/\Theta \to 0$. At low temperatures we should expect to find Miller and Abrahams' term ε_3, which can be estimated to be about 0·03 eV. The measured activation energies are much lower. A discussion of the reason for this is given by Austin and Mott (1969); it is possible that the $T^{-\frac{1}{4}}$ law is playing a part, but there are other possibilities.

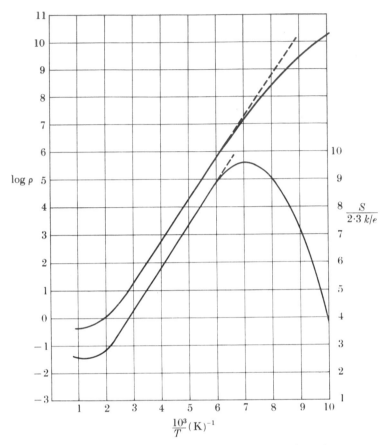

FIG. 6.18. Logarithm of resistivity (Ω cm) and thermopower ($S/2\cdot3(k/e)$) of NiO doped with 0·088 % Li_2O (Bosman and Crevecoeur 1966).

Figure 6.18 shows the thermoelectric power, which changes sign when impurity-conduction carries most of the current. The reason for this is the same as for non-polar materials, as set out in § 6.4.

6.8. Conduction in glasses containing transition-metal ions

Many glasses containing transition-metal ions, for instance vanadium or iron, are semiconductors. It is generally recognized that the conductivity in such glasses is due to the presence in the glass of ions of more than one valency, for instance V^{4+} and V^{5+} and Fe^{2+} and Fe^{3+}; an electron can pass from one ion to another, and the process is similar to impurity-conduction in nickel oxide, as described in the last section.

There is, however, one important difference: in a crystal the different sites (Li$^+$, Ni^{3+}) on which an electron may be are crystallographically identical, differing only in their proximity to a charged minority centre that introduces the Miller–Abrahams spread of energies W_D; but in a glass, the environments of the ions with the two valencies may or may not be different; there might be in principle a situation similar to that of Fig. 2.15, in which the configuration of atoms ensures during cooling of the glass that the electron on V^{4+} can form a bond. This does not appear to happen in vanadium phosphate glasses; it does in glasses containing Cu$^+$ and Cu^{2+} investigated by Drake and Scanlan (1970), for which a conducting and a non-conducting state can be formed depending on the rate of cooling.

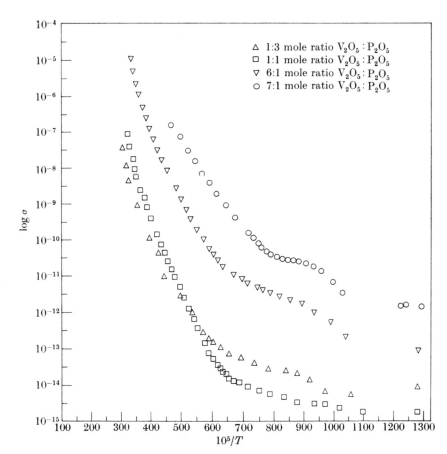

Fig. 6.19. Log conductivity (in Ω^{-1} cm^{-1}) as a function of $1/T$(K) of some vanadium phosphate glasses (Schmid 1968).

For vanadium glasses a suitable formula for the conductivity is

$$\sigma = c(1-c)(e^2/RkT)\exp(-2\alpha R - W/kT). \tag{6.8}$$

Here R is the mean distance between the ions, c and $(1-c)$ are the proportions of V^{4+} and V^{5+} respectively, α as in other sections is the rate of decay of the wave function $(\psi \sim \exp(-\alpha r))$ of an electron on V^{4+}, and

$$W = W_H + \tfrac{1}{2}W_D.$$

W_H is the polaron term and W_D the Miller–Abrahams term. A detailed discussion of this formula is given by Austin and Mott (1969). Two points stand out. The quantity W_H, quite large ($\sim 0\cdot 4$ eV) at room temperatures, drops towards zero at low temperatures, as it does for impurity-conduction in NiO. This is shown in Fig. 6.19. The reason for the drop is the same as in impurity-conduction (§ 6.7). The other point is the very small values of W_D found at low temperatures; the $\ln \rho$–$1/T$ curve seems to be almost flat. There is other evidence for this. Vanadium glasses satisfy quite well the Heikes formula for the thermo-power,

$$S = (k/e)\ln\{c/(1-c)\}. \tag{6.9}$$

As we have seen in § 2.9.3, this must imply a value of W_D less than kT. The reason for this small value is not understood.

6.9. Magnetic susceptibility

Electrons in donors, acceptors, and the impurity and conduction bands make a considerable contribution to the Landau diamagnetism, and this in most cases is larger than the paramagnetic contribution of the spins. A detailed discussion of this for concentrations well on the metallic side of the MNM transition has been given by Saitoh, Fukuyama, Uemura, and Shiba (1969). This will not be reviewed here. The Pauli spin paramagnetism is small compared with the Landau term.

For non-metallic concentrations, the magnetic contribution of donors in n-type silicon has been measured by Sonder and Stevens (1958). The paramagnetic contribution is shown in Fig. 6.20. It will be seen that for $n > 5 \times 10^{17}$ cm^{-3} there are departures from the linear behaviour $(1/\chi = kT/n\mu^2)$, probably due to overlap between the centres. The MNM transition is at a concentration of $\sim 4 \times 10^{18}$ cm^{-3}. It should be emphasized that near the transition a large interaction would be expected, and large deviations from the Curie law.

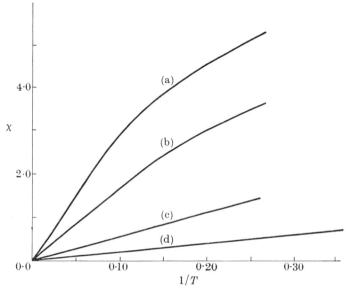

FIG. 6.20. The paramagnetic contribution to the magnetic susceptibility $\chi(\times 10^{-8})$ of a doped semiconductor in the non-metallic region near the MNM transition (Sonder and Stevens 1958). The concentration of centres (cm^{-3}) is (a) $3{\cdot}5 \times 10^{16}$, (b) $2{\cdot}5 \times 10^{17}$, (c) $5{\cdot}7 \times 10^{17}$, (d) 5×10^{18}.

6.10. Hall effect

In the hopping region, as stated in § 2.13, we expect the Hall coefficient R_H to be *greater* than $1/nec$. In this region the Hall coefficient has not been observed (Amitay and Pollak 1966). On the metallic side, the effect is as shown in Fig. 6.9. R_H^{obs} does not differ much from $1/nec$. In this it is consistent with the other evidence reviewed in § 2.12. The sign, however, is p-type for p-type materials.

Sasaki (1970) reports measurements of Hall mobilities for the case considered in § 6.5.

6.11. Magnetic polarons

A carrier moving in the conduction or valence band of a semiconductor in which the atoms have magnetic moments will interact with these moments, the interaction being in general ferromagnetic, giving the lowest energy when the spin of the carrier is parallel to that of the moments. Coupling of this kind was first introduced into the literature by Zener (1951), who suggested that the moments in d shells in ferromagnetic metals could be coupled through the conduction electrons, which would themselves be slightly polarized. We may distinguish two rather different situations:

(a) The carrier is in a normal conduction or valence band, interacting with localized magnetic moments due to electrons in states with a different quantum number. EuS and similar materials are examples, where the conduction band is believed to have 6s symmetry at the lowest point, and the moments concerned are 4f. These will be discussed below.

(b) When the carriers are in the same band as the electrons that give the moments. Examples are a hole (i.e. a Ni^{3+} ion) in antiferromagnetic NiO, or a V^{4+} or V^{2+} ion in V_2O_3, with motion as described in § 5.2.

De Gennes (1960) was the first to discuss in detail the effect of a gas of electrons on the moments in a material like EuS doped with GdS; canted and spiral arrangements are possible. White and Woolsey (1968), Brinkman and Rice (1970a), and Mott and Zinamon (1970) have discussed the effect of the moments on the effective mass of an electron and found it to be small, except for an electron in the tail of the band as the following considerations show. The discussion relates to a carrier at zero temperature in an antiferromagnetic material, such as NiO. We introduce the interactions J_1 between carrier and moments, and J_2 between the moments themselves, and suppose that $J_1 \gg J_2$. Then let us assume that the carrier orients all moments within a radius R parallel to its own; it is then located in a 'box' of radius R, and, as in our discussions of polarons in Chapter 4, its kinetic energy is $\hbar^2\pi^2/2mR^2$. The carrier with its oriented cluster of spins is called a *spin polaron* and its total energy is

$$\frac{\hbar^2\pi^2}{2mR^2} + \frac{4\pi}{3}\frac{R^3}{a^3}J_2 - J_1. \tag{6.10}$$

Minimizing with respect to R we get

$$R^5 = \hbar^2\pi a^3/4mJ_2, \tag{6.11}$$

and the total energy is thus

$$\frac{5\hbar^2\pi^2}{6m}\left(\frac{4mJ_2}{\hbar^2\pi a^3}\right)^{\frac{2}{5}} - J_1. \tag{6.12}$$

Only if this quantity is negative will a spin polaron be formed in which the moments are fully oriented parallel to that of the carrier; otherwise there will be some smaller effect.

Following de Gennes, we do not suppose that the moments in the spin polaron are all parallel up to a radius R, but rather that θ, the inclination to the spin direction in the absence of the carrier, tends gradually to zero as r/R exceeds unity. We can estimate the effective mass by computing the transfer integral when the polaron moves through one atomic distance. The spins will contribute a term

$$\prod_r \cos \theta_{r,r+1} \qquad (6.13)$$

where $\theta_{r,r+1}$ is the change in the orientation of the spin when the carrier moves through one atomic distance. We may expect that $\theta_{r,r+1} \sim a/R$, so eqn (6.13) becomes

$$\prod (1-a^2/2R^2)^{(R/a)^3},$$

and will thus vary for large R as

$$\text{const. } e^{-\gamma R/a},$$

where γ is some constant of order unity that we have not attempted to calculate. The effect of the moments on the effective mass m_p of a large spin polaron may be considerable, as we see by equating this with $\hbar^2/m_p a^2$. A large spin polaron will thus have effective mass considerably above that of the free carrier, but we do not think that spin-polaron formation can give rise to hopping motion in a perfect lattice.

Above the Curie or Néel temperature, a spin polaron will move by a diffusive mechanism. A tentative description is as follows. A moment on the periphery of the polaron will reverse in a time τ (the relaxation time for a spin wave). Each time it does so, the polaron can be thought to diffuse a distance $(a/R)^3R$, and the diffusion coefficient is thus

$$D \simeq \tfrac{1}{6}a^6/R^4\tau.$$

By Einstein's relation, we may write

$$\mu \simeq \tfrac{1}{6}ea^6/R^4\tau kT.$$

The mobility thus decreases rapidly with the polaron radius.

Another treatment, in which the motion is assumed similar to that of domain-wall movement, has been given by Kasuya, Yanase, and Takeda (1970).

6.12. Magnetic semiconductors

The semiconductors EuS and EuSe are ferromagnetic with weak coupling between the 4f moments on the Eu ions, the Curie temperature T_c being in the helium range. Doping with GdS or LaS by substituting a trivalent for a divalent atom produces an extrinsic semiconductor. The conduction band is of 6s type, and the mobility in this band is high,

$\sim 10^3$ cm^2 V^{-1} s^{-1} (Methfessel and Mattis 1968 p. 561). Doping greatly increases T_c. This is an example of the effect mentioned in § 5.2, namely that the 6s–4f coupling is much stronger than the direct f–f coupling. One would expect therefore to find strong scattering by the random spins near the Curie temperature; for maximum scattering, fluctuations in the moments should occur over distances comparable

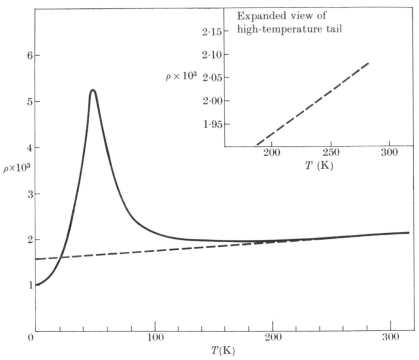

FIG. 6.21. Dependence on temperature of resistivity $\rho(\Omega$ cm$)$ of Eu$_{0.95}$Gd$_{0.05}$S (von Molnar and Kasuya 1968).

with the electron wavelength, and these will occur near the Curie temperature (de Gennes and Friedel 1958). Figure 6.21 shows the behaviour observed for Eu$_{0.95}$Gd$_{0.05}$S (von Molnar and Kasuya 1968). The resistivity is clearly metallic, and the strong scattering near the Curie point cuts down the mean free path by about five.

For certain lower concentrations (0·01 % Gd or 0·05 % La), however, the interesting phenomenon shown in Fig. 6.22 occurs. At low temperatures conduction is metallic: the concentration of carriers is on the metallic side of the Mott transition; but near the Curie temperature the resistivity increases by seven orders of magnitude. This cannot possibly be due to spin scattering. According to the interpretation of Kasuya and Yanase (1968), the approach to the Curie temperature relocalizes the electrons on the impurity centres; they there orient the 4f spins on their nearest neighbours, but it would cost them a lot of free energy to move into the conduction band, since above the Curie point the entropy of disorder would prevent their forming a spin polaron. Current is thus carried by impurity-conduction, the electrons hopping from one centre to another. The large activation energy

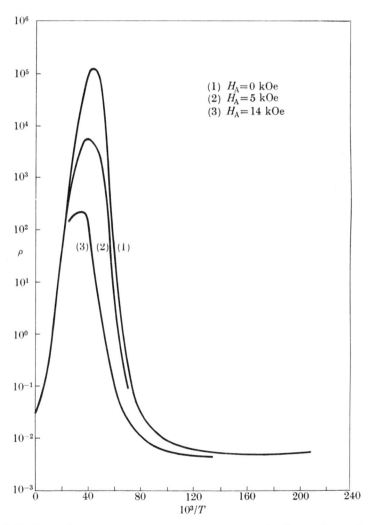

FIG. 6.22. Dependence on temperature of resistivity ρ in Ω cm of $Eu_{0.95}La_{0.05}S$ for various magnetic fields H_A (Methfessel and Mattis 1968).

13

arises because the electron has to jump from a site where it has had time to polarize its surroundings to an empty site where the spins are randomly oriented. This activation energy is destroyed if the moments are lined up by a magnetic field, and these materials therefore show an extremely large negative magnetoresistance (Fig. 6.22).

Penney (1969; see also Wachter and Weber 1970) has found that the photoconductance in undoped EuSe shows the same temperature

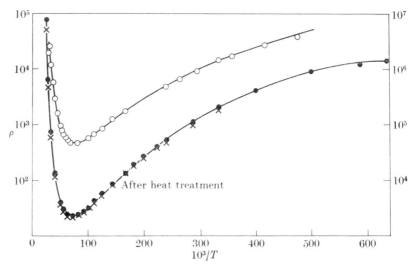

FIG. 6.23. Resistivity ρ in Ω cm of EuO doped with excess Eu, showing the $T^{-\frac{1}{4}}$ behaviour at low temperatures (von Molnar 1970). The scale on the right is for the upper curve.

dependence as the dark conductivity in EuSe doped with Gd. The dark conductivity at high concentrations of Gd suggests strongly that the mobility of a spin polaron in a crystalline conduction band does not have an activation energy, and this is in agreement with our theoretical considerations and the properties of NiO (Chapter 4). It seems highly probable therefore that the photoelectrons in EuSe move in an impurity band formed by anion vacancies. A spin polaron that would count as 'large' relative to the lattice parameter would be 'small' relative to the distance between centres, so the Kasuya–Yanase theory is applicable.

Figure 6.23 shows similar behaviour for the dark conductivity in EuO doped with Eu. In the ferromagnetic region ($10^3/T > 100$), conduction is clearly by hopping; the logarithm of the resistivity is found to be proportional to $1/T^{\frac{1}{4}}$, as is expected for impurity conduction.

An effect that does not depend on impurities is the production of an exciton by the 4f–5d absorption line. The energy of this line drops by 0·05 eV below the Curie point, because the excited electron then finds itself with spin parallel to the 4f moments. The effect is shown in Fig. 6.24.

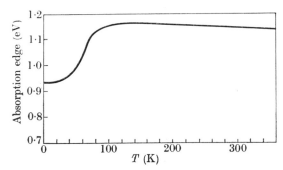

FIG. 6.24. Absorption edge in eV in a crystal of EuS, showing a magnetic red shift (Freiser, Holtzberg, Methfessel, Pettit, Shafer, and Suits 1968). The edge is defined as a value of the absorption coefficient such that $\alpha \sim 800$ cm^{-1}. The field is 2 kOe.

6.13. Magnetoresistance

In normal metals and semiconductors, the quantity $(\rho - \rho_0)/\rho$ increases in a weak magnetic field H as H^2. In metallic alloys, Kohler's rule is valid; this states that for alloys of differing residual resistance ρ_0, if $\Delta\rho$ is the change of resistance in a field H, then $\Delta\rho/\rho_0$ is a function of H/ρ_0. This may be explained in terms of the orbits of an electron in a magnetic field (Pippard 1965), it being assumed that the electron traverses only a small part of its orbit between collisions; the dimensions of the effect are then

$$\Delta\rho/\rho_0 = \text{const.}(eHL/mcv)^2.$$

v is the Fermi velocity in a metal or the mean velocity of the carriers in a semiconductor, and L is the mean free path. This formula suggests that the effect should be small in impurity bands in the metallic range, because L is small, and also in amorphous semiconductors where the current is carried by electrons with energies just above E_C (§ 2.9.2); as we shall see in the next chapter, no magnetoresistance has been observed for such currents.

In general, a small magnetoresistance, which may be significant for impurity-conduction and for narrow bands generally, is to be expected when the current is due to electrons with energies near E_F, whether they move by hopping or not. The effect is as follows. A field H will raise or lower the Fermi energy by $\pm H\mu_B$ according to the spin direction; μ_B is here the Bohr magneton. Then if $\sigma(E)$ is the conductivity at energy E, in a field H the conductivity at $T = 0$ will be

$$\tfrac{1}{2}\{\sigma(E + \mu_B H) + \sigma(E - \mu_B H)\},$$

so that

$$\delta\sigma = \tfrac{1}{2}\sigma''(E_F)(\mu_B H)^2. \tag{6.14}$$

In the hopping range, formula (6.14) has not been compared with experimental data; it should normally give a positive term to the magnetoresistance. There are however many other factors of importance. At high fields, Chroboczek, Prohofsky, and Sladek (1968) find that, for concentrations for which conduction is by hopping, ε_3 can increase with field. They ascribe this effect to spin reversals of the carrier during the hopping process. Chroboczek and Trylski (1970) have calculated the effect of a strong magnetic field on the hopping probability and discussed the dependence on field direction of the positive magnetoresistance for n-type germanium. In general, we may also expect an effect similar to that described in the last section for magnetic semiconductors. An electron in a localized state will have some effect on the spin orientation of electrons in states that are near enough for there to be significant overlap of the orbitals. It will jump to a state where the spins are not affected in this way, and this will increase ε_3 by (say) $\Delta\varepsilon_3$. A magnetic field should decrease $\Delta\varepsilon_3$. Details of this process have not been worked out, but we believe it may be most important in low-temperature conduction in amorphous materials (§ 7.4.7).

Another effect important in Ge, InSb, and other materials where the radius of the donor is large is the contraction of the radius in a strong magnetic field. This was first predicted by Yafet, Keyes, and Adams (1956), and the consequent increase in ε_1, the ionization energy of a centre, was observed by Keyes and Sladek (1956) in InSb. A MNM transition can be produced by a magnetic field (Durkan, Elliott, and March 1968; Yamanouchi 1963; Beckman, Hanamura, and Neuringer 1967; Halbo and Sladek 1970).

Turning now to conduction in an impurity band in the metallic region, we find that a negative magnetoresistance is often observed; typical behaviour is shown in Fig. 6.25 (from Alexander and Holcomb 1968). The effect is strongest just on the metallic side of the MNM transition and is large only as long as the impurity band remains separate from the conduction band. Toyozawa (1962) was the first to

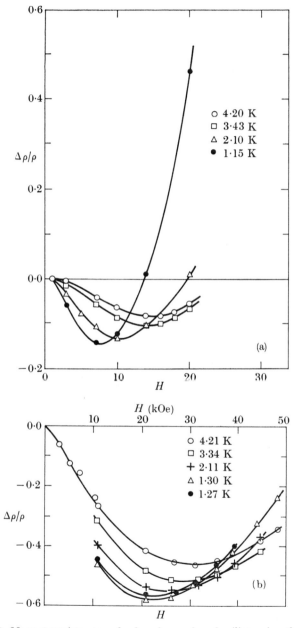

Fig. 6.25. Magnetoresistance of phosphorus-doped silicon in the metallic region (Yamanouchi, Mizuguchi, and Sasaki 1967). H is in kOe; $\Delta\rho/\rho$ is per cent. (a) $N_D - N_A = 4 \cdot 43 \times 10^{18}$ cm^{-3}; (b) $N_D - N_A = 8 \cdot 02 \times 10^{18}$ cm^{-3}.

suggest that the effect was due to localized spins. He thought that these spins might be located at impurity sites that are relatively isolated from other sites, and that they would produce spin-dependent scattering. Further development of these ideas is due to Sasaki (1965).

While we believe that this effect is caused by moments, we think that the moments are not due to fluctuations in density; according to the considerations of § 5.4, moments on *every* donor should persist for concentrations considerably higher than that at which the MNM transition occurs. As long as moments persist, the density of states should consist of two overlapping Hubbard bands, so that the Fermi energy (unless the compensation is high) will be in a pseudogap, where $\sigma''(E_F)$ in (6.14) is positive. Mott and Zinamon (1970) have suggested that this is the cause of the negative magnetoresistance, which can be interpreted in terms of (6.14), rather than spin-dependent scattering. The change of sign of $\Delta\rho/\rho$ at high fields, particularly for low concentrations, is doubtless due to shrinking of the orbits, and the consequent decrease in the widths of the Hubbard bands. The small negative magnetoresistance observed at high concentrations, at which a pseudogap due to overlapping Hubbard bands is unlikely, may also be due to a positive σ'', arising from a mobility increasing rapidly with energy (see note on p. 187).

6.14. Optical absorption and a.c. conduction

In Chapter 2 we deduced that $\sigma(\omega)$, and hence the absorption coefficient α, should vary as $\omega^2\{\ln(I_0/\hbar\omega)\}^4$ for small ω in the limit as $T \to 0$. As far as we know, experiments at frequencies and temperatures low enough to verify this formula have not been made. More detailed formulae, applicable at frequencies where the absorption coefficient passes through a maximum and temperatures such that $\sigma(\omega)$ decreases with temperature, have been proposed by Cumming, Katcoff, Porile, Tanaka, and Wyttenbach (1964) and by Blinowski and Mycielski (1964). Experiments in which comparison is made with these formulae are due to Tanaka and Fan (1963) and Milward and Neuringer (1965).

The effect here, that of direct optical transition, is quite different from the Debye-type loss due to thermally activated hopping discussed in § 2.10. The latter was first observed by Pollak and Geballe (1961) in n-type silicon. Some of their results are reproduced in Fig. 6.26. The theory given by these authors and by Pollak in subsequent papers

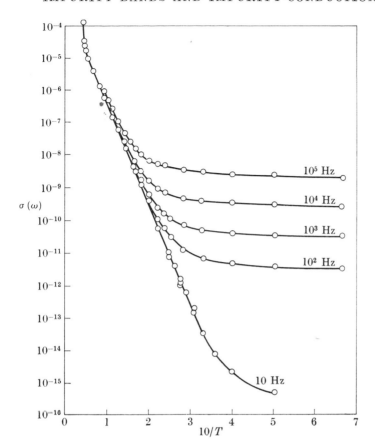

FIG. 6.26. a.c. conductivity $\sigma(\omega)$ in $\Omega^{-1}\,\mathrm{cm}^{-1}$ of n-type silicon with low compensation
(Pollak and Geballe 1961).

(1964, 1965) is similar to that of § 2.10 except that, for low compensation, the assumption of a random distribution of energies is certainly
not valid, and this increases the complexity of the calculation.
Nevertheless, the main results follow, namely that, if σ is the observed
conductivity,

$$\sigma_{\mathrm{a.c.}} = \sigma - \sigma_{\mathrm{d.c.}} = A\omega^{s},$$

with s close to $0\cdot8$ and A independent of T except at very low T. As in
Chapter 2, the loss process is of the Debye type, and the main contribution comes from pairs of centres for which the difference W_{D} in the
energy levels is of order kT, and the distance R between them such that

$$\nu_{\mathrm{ph}}e^{-2\alpha R} \sim \omega.$$

The frequency dependence predicted by the theory is such that

$$\sigma(\omega) \sim \omega\{\ln(\dot{\nu}_{\mathrm{ph}}/\omega)\}^4.$$

The dependence on $\omega^{0\cdot 8}$ is verified, as may easily be seen, if $\nu_{\mathrm{ph}} \sim 10^{12}$ s⁻¹, as it appears to be in silicon and germanium. However, as is shown in § 4.2 the quantity ν_{ph} is extremely sensitive to the parameters

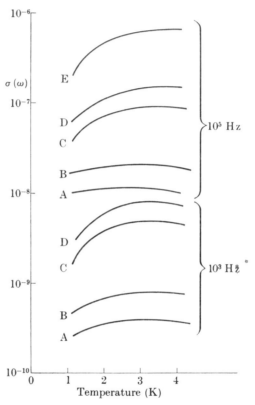

Fig. 6.27. a.c. conductivity $\sigma(\omega)$ of various samples of p-type germanium with high compensation ($K = 0\cdot 4$) plotted against temperature for frequencies 10^3 and 10^5 Hz (Golin 1963). A dependence on T is shown (contrast Fig. 6.26).

involved. Also, if there is strong polarization round the centre, ν_{ph} will contain the factor $\mathrm{e}^{-2\nu}$ at low temperatures,† and the factor $\exp(-W_{\mathrm{H}}/kT)$ must be added when $T > \tfrac{1}{2}\Theta$.

As regards the temperature dependence, the treatment of Chapter 2 supposes that compensation is not small and that kT is small compared with the band width. Thus a fraction proportional to kT of the available

† See § 4.6.

electrons can take part in the hopping, and they can move into a fraction of empty centres also proportional to kT. Since kT comes also in the denominator of the expression for σ, because of the Einstein relationship, $\sigma \propto kT$. In the work of Pollak and Geballe, on the other hand, K was small and the 'holes' non-degenerate; so one of the factors kT falls out, and σ is independent of T.†

Golin (1963) made measurements on p-type germanium, and his work differed from that of Pollak and Geballe in that the compensation K was large (0·4). In this case $\sigma(\omega)$ should be proportional to T. Some results are shown in Fig. 6.27.

† At very low temperatures a drop of σ with T, so that $\sigma \propto T^2$, is to be expected (Pollak 1964).

Note added in proof. The most direct evidence for a pseudogap formed from two overlapping bands, which is the basis of the discussion of the magnetoresistance in §6.14, is the work of Wolf, Losee, Cullen, and Compton (1971) using a barrier tunnelling technique mentioned on p. 31. The question whether a pseudogap can exist without fixed moments on the atoms is discussed by Mott (1971c).

NON-CRYSTALLINE SEMICONDUCTORS

7.1. Introduction
7.2. Preparation and classification of materials
7.3. Studies of the structures of amorphous materials
7.4. Electrical properties of non-crystalline semiconductors
    7.4.1. Summary of theoretical concepts
    7.4.2. Temperature variation of d.c. conductivity
    7.4.3. Drift mobilities
    7.4.4. a.c. conductivity
    7.4.5. Thermoelectric power
    7.4.6. Hall effect
    7.4.7. Magnetoresistance
    7.4.8. Thermally stimulated conductivity

7.5. Photoconductivity and quantum efficiency
7.6. Optical absorption
    7.6.1. Absorption edges and Urbach's rule
    7.6.2. Interband absorption
    7.6.3. Absorption at high energies
    7.6.4. Modulation experiments
    7.6.5. Intraband absorption
    7.6.6. Absorption by phonons
7.7. Other measurements
    7.7.1. Photo-emission from non-crystalline semiconductors
    7.7.2. Electron spin resonance
    7.7.3. Magnetic susceptibility
7.8. Non-ohmic conduction in strong fields
7.9. Switching in non-crystalline semiconductors

7.1. Introduction

THE application of the concepts developed in earlier chapters to non-crystalline semiconductors is one of the main purposes of this book. In this chapter we describe some of the experimental techniques that have been used to characterize these materials, the kinds of results obtained, and the models used to interpret them. More detailed descriptions of specific materials are given in the final three chapters.

Certain phenomena have been observed often enough to appear characteristic of amorphous semiconductors and these will be emphasized in this chapter. However, the relatively small number of materials so far studied makes the identification of such characteristic phenomena somewhat premature. As more extensive measurements become available on a wider variety of substances, it may become clear that, as in crystalline solids, each material has its own individual properties, and a new scheme of generalization will emerge.

This chapter contains sections on preparation and classification of

materials, structural studies, electrical measurements, photoconductivity, optical absorption, and high-field effects. We also summarize
some of the concepts developed in Chapter 2.

7.2. Preparation and classification of materials

The two normal ways of preparing amorphous solids are (i) by
evaporation, sputtering, or similar methods of deposition, or (ii) by
cooling from a melt.† The first method produces thin films and the
second bulk material. If a material can be prepared in the amorphous
phase from a melt, then it is generally also possible to prepare it by
deposition. If a suitable thinning technique, e.g. etching, can be found,
it is frequently possible to bridge the 'thickness gap' between the
two methods of preparation. However, there must be some structural
differences between the same material prepared by different methods,
and care is obviously necessary in any comparison of properties.

Materials that can be obtained by cooling from the molten state are
generally called glasses and have a reduced tendency to crystallize
compared with those that can be prepared only by deposition. In
certain cases this reluctance to crystallize makes it possible to heat the
material through the softening range of temperature into the liquid
state without any discontinuous change in properties. Such stable
glasses may, however, undergo a second-order phase transition at the
so called glass transition temperature T_g. This transition, which
corresponds to the accessibility of new configurational energy states or
degrees of freedom, marks the onset of softening and is accompanied by
an increase of heat capacity and thermal expansion coefficient. Less
stable glasses, for instance those with compositions near the border of
a glass-forming region in a multicomponent system (see Fig. 7.2),
may on heating slowly undergo phase separation and crystallization.
Further heating causes melting, and the properties of the liquid state,
such as the temperature dependence of conductivity, are then similar
to those in the disordered solid at temperatures below crystallization.
In order to prepare such glasses, rather faster quenching techniques
are needed to avoid devitrification. In the case of As_2Te_3, for example,
'splat cooling' is used to prepare the glass. On the other hand, the
crystallization process in As_2Se_3, a stable glass, is so slow as to allow
preparation by cooling the melt at a very low rate. As an example of a
material intermediate between these two extremes, we show in Fig. 7.1

† Other methods include electrolytic deposition from solution, and irradiation of
crystalline material with high-energy particles such as neutrons or ions.

results of differential thermal analysis on $Ge_{16}Te_{82}Sb_2$ reported by
Fritzsche and Ovshinsky (1970). Heating the glass at 25°C/min as
shown in curve (a) produces a small step at T_g, the glass transition
temperature, followed by an exothermic crystallization peak at T_1
and an endothermic melting peak at T_2. Fast cooling (greater than
50°C/min) (curve (b)) shows no reaction, and the high-temperature

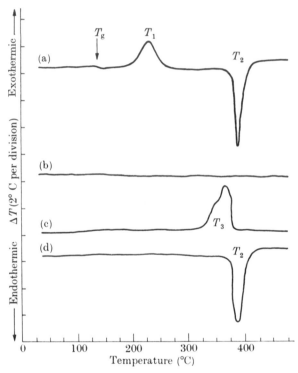

FIG. 7.1. Differential thermal analysis traces of $Ge_{16}Te_{82}Sb_2$ (Fritzsche and Ovshinsky 1970). (a) heating 25°C/min; (b) fast cooling; (c) slow cooling; (d) heating.

disordered state is retained. Slow cooling (less than 10°C/min) shows
(curve (c)) an exothermic transformation at T_3 below which the
material is partially crystallized, subsequent heating of this material
(curve (d)) shows the T_2 endotherm only.

Figure 7.2 illustrates the glass-forming regions in a few ternary
systems. For other examples and more detailed information on the
preparation, stability, and physical properties of glasses the reader is
referred to Rawson (1967) and Turnbull (1969).

The stability or otherwise of glasses can frequently be understood by
structural considerations. Thus, for example, selenium in the hexagonal

crystalline state is composed of helical chains stacked parallel to each other (Chapter 10). The binding in the chains is covalent and strong; between the chains it is weak, perhaps of van der Waals type. In the liquid state the chains can be considered as randomly oriented. Fast cooling of the melt does not allow time for reorientation of these chains before the viscosity becomes too high and the glassy state is formed. Addition of Te to the melt is believed to lead to shorter chains (the

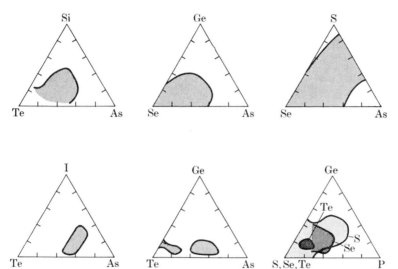

FIG. 7.2. Approximate glass-forming regions in a few ternary systems. (Hilton and Brau (1963); Haisty and Krebs (1969b); Flaschen et al. (1959); Pearson et al. (1962); Krebs and Fischer (1971); Krebs (1969). See also Hilton (1970).)

Se–Te bond being weaker than the Se–Se bond), and devitrification on cooling is much more likely. On the other hand, As tends to act as a cross-linking or branching additive, retarding the reorientation necessary for crystallization.

Generally speaking, most amorphous solids that can be prepared by cooling from the melt are insulators or wide-gap semiconductors, in which the mobility gap (see definition in § 2.9 and in § 7.3) is greater than about 1 eV. Examples include Se, As_2Se_3, and similar chalcogenide compounds or multicomponent systems, $CdGeAs_2$, and the common borosilicate glasses.

Materials such as Te, Ge, Si, B, and GeTe, which cannot be produced in the glassy state by quenching from the melt, can be obtained in an amorphous form by deposition. In the case of Ge and Si it has been established that the coordination numbers in the liquid are 6 or 8 as compared with 4 in the solid. A different coordination in the liquid and solid is the normal rule for this class of materials.[†] The mobility gaps are generally small, less than about 1 eV. For these substances, great care is necessary to avoid unwanted crystallization, and frequently the properties of such films are found to be sensitive to the rates of deposition and to subsequent annealing cycles, indicating structural changes. Keeping the substrate temperature low inhibits crystallization, and many materials have to be deposited at liquid-nitrogen temperatures or below in order to obtain an amorphous state.

For detailed information on the preparation of thin films the reader should consult the references cited in later chapters on individual materials, and the books by Chopra (1969) and Holland (1963).

At the present time, classification of amorphous semiconductors is probably best achieved by division into groups of materials having the same short-range structural coordination. A general rule, first stressed by Ioffe and Regel (1960), which applies to virtually all amorphous semiconductors so far investigated,[‡] is the preservation of the first coordination number of the corresponding crystal. For compositions for which there is no crystalline phase this rule is, of course, meaningless, but it does suggest that, in the As–Se system for example, Se-like structural units might be expected to be dominant at low As concentrations, while at higher As concentrations there may be a tendency to favour As_2Se_3-like units. In Table 7.1 (from Grigorovici 1969) the left-hand column indicates the basic groups, e.g. those elements or compounds that exhibit tetrahedral bonding, those that crystallize in layered structures, those that have ring or other molecular-like character, and so on. The table covers most of the stoichiometric amorphous semiconductors studied in any detail up to the present time but is not intended to be complete. The symbols n and r refer to the first coordination number and nearest-neighbour separations and will be discussed further in the next section.

The above scheme of classification has been used to some extent to divide the experimental results into those described in Chapters 8, 9, and 10. Notable omissions from Table 7.1 include the common silicate borate, and phosphate glasses containing metal ions, transition-metal oxide glasses (Chapter 4), and of course multicomponent glasses containing elements mentioned in Table 7.1 but not in stoichiometric

---

† Tellurium, discussed in Chapter 10, is an exception.
‡ For a possible exception (GeTe) see Betts, Bienenstock, and Ovshinsky (1970) and Chapter 8.

TABLE 7.1

Classification of amorphous semiconductors according to short-range structure and comparison of parameters of the first coordination sphere (coordination number n_1; nearest-neighbour separation r_1) in the amorphous and crystalline states. The numbers printed after a colon (:) are the average number of neighbours of the kind immediately following (from Grigorovici 1969).

Structural type		Amorphous material	n_1 amorphous	n_1 crystalline	r_1 amorphous	r_1 crystalline	Observed
Tetrahedral	Elements $\begin{cases}\end{cases}$	Ge	4	4	2·47–2·54	2·43	
		Si	4	4	2·37–2·41	2·35	
	$A^{IV}B^{IV}$	SiC	4	Si:4C;C:4Si	—	—	
	$A^{III}B^{V}$	GaSb	4	Ga:4Sb;Sb:4Ga	2·65	2·638	
	$A^{III}B^{VI}$	InSe	{In:3·46Se;S₃:3·46In, In:0·95In}	{In:3Se;Se:3In, In:1In}	{In–Se:2·60, In–In:3·15}	{In–Se:2·50, In–In:3·16}	
	$A_2^{III}B_3^{VI}$	(GaIn)₂(Se,Te)₃	{In:(3·91–4·71)Se; Se:(2·59–2·67)In*}	{(Ga,In):4(Se,Te), (Se,Te):2·66(Ga,In)}	2·57–2·60*	2·58*	*in In₂Se₃
	$A^{II}B^{IV}C^{V}_2$	CdGe(P,As)₂	(P,As):2Cd,2Ge	(P,As):2Cd,2Ge	2·50*	{Cd–P:2·55*, Ge–P:2·33}	*in CdGeP₂
	$A_4^{III}B_3^{IV}$	N₄Si₃	Si:4N	Si:4N	~1·7	1·7–1·8	
Layers	Elements $\begin{cases}\end{cases}$	C	3·2–3·4	{4, 3}	~1·50	{1·54, 1·41}	{Diamond, Graphite}
		As	3	3	2·40	2·51	
		Sb	3	3	2·87	2·87	
	$A_2^{V}B_3^{VI}$	(As,Sb,Bi)₂(S,Se,Te)₃ + (A^{III},B^{IV},C^{VI})	{(As,Sb,Bi):(2·9–3·6)(S,Se,Te), (S,Se,Te):(2·0–2·4)(As,Sb,Bi)}	{(As,Sb,Bi):3(S,Se,Te), (S,Se,Te):2(As,Sb,Bi)}	—	—	r_1 amorphous ≈ r_1 crystalline
Chains and rings	Elements $\begin{cases}\end{cases}$	Se	2	2	2·31–2·34	2·32	
		Te	—	2	—	—	
Icosahedra	Elements	B	6	~6	—	~1·8	

proportions. The freedom to depart from stoichiometric proportions is one of the most important features of amorphous semiconductors, and it seems that, particularly for applications, multicomponent systems containing one or more of the chalcogenide elements (S, Se, Te) are likely to be the subjects of the most extensive investigation.

7.3. Studies of the structures of amorphous materials

An amorphous solid is one in which three-dimensional periodicity is absent.† The arrangement of atoms, however, will not be entirely random as in a gas. The binding forces between atoms are very similar to those in the crystal and, although *long*-range order is excluded, *short*-range order of a few lattice constants will generally be present.

A complete theoretical description of the properties of an amorphous solid would need a full knowledge of the structure. Even within the restraints imposed by forces between individual atoms and the tendency towards short-range order, there are an infinite number of allowed structures for any amorphous material. However, in view of the importance of short-range order in determining many physical properties, it is clearly valuable to determine the nature and extent of this as far as possible. If no features greater than about 50 Å (which would indicate crystallization or phase separation) are observable‡, then techniques used for a more microscopic investigation include electron and X-ray diffraction, infrared absorption, and Raman spectroscopy. Neutron diffraction has not been used to any great extent at present, though it has in liquid metals and semiconductors (compare § 3.17). Diffraction patterns from an amorphous solid should consist of broad haloes or rings, without any evidence of spots, which would indicate some degree of crystallinity (see frontispiece).

From the angular dependence of the scattered radiation, the radial or pair distribution function $4\pi r^2 \rho(r)\, dr$ can be obtained by a Fourier inversion. This gives the average number of pairs of atoms separated by a distance lying between r and $r + dr$. Several approximations are involved in obtaining this function, only two of which are mentioned here. First it is normally assumed that the atomic density is uniform over a sphere of a given radius. While this is probably a good approximation for liquid metals, it may not be for amorphous semiconductors,

---

† This definition makes the terms disordered, non-crystalline, amorphous, glassy, or vitreous, synonymous. However, the last two terms are generally restricted to non-crystalline solids prepared by quenching from the liquid state.

‡ In a scanning electron microscope for example—see frontispiece.

in which the presence of voids and cracks is quite likely. Secondly, termination errors in the Fourier integrals can distort the radial distribution function and introduce spurious structure. Considerable care and skill is in fact needed in generating and interpreting plots of $4\pi r^2 \rho(r)$ against r, i.e. radial distribution curves (r.d.c.)

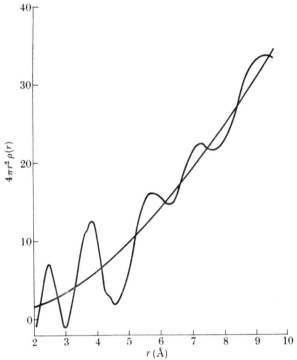

FIG. 7.3. Radial distribution function of amorphous Ge (from Richter and Breitling 1958).

If, however, the first peak of the r.d.c. is well separated from the following ones, measurement of the area beneath the maximum gives the number of atoms contained in the first coordination sphere. The position of the peak gives the average separation between nearest neighbours. Figure 7.3 shows a typical r.d.c. for amorphous Ge (from Richter and Breitling 1958). The curve is seen to be distributed about a parabola, which represents the r.d.c. of a hypothetical amorphous solid of the same density but with matter uniformly distributed in space. Although the first few coordinations are well defined, the width of the peaks indicates some spread in the interatomic distance, and the decreasing amplitude of the oscillations with r shows the lack of

14

long-range order. In the case of germanium, the first two coordination numbers are 4 and 12 as in the crystal. The average interatomic distances are increased, however, by about 3 per cent.

Table 7.1 gives this kind of information for other amorphous semiconductors. In crystalline InSe for example, the first coordination sphere is occupied by atoms of both kinds. Thus each In atom is surrounded by one In and three Se atoms as first neighbours, and each Se atom by three In atoms. In amorphous InSe the first maximum of the r.d.c. is split into two peaks; and the short-range configuration present in the crystal is retained.

In crystalline As_2Se_3, each As atom has three Se atoms and each Se atom two As atoms as their first neighbours. These numbers (not given in Table 7.1) are increased in the amorphous phase but the first distances remain close to the sum of the covalent radii of As and Se. Thus one might infer that the layer structure is conserved to some extent but that the layers are 'wavy' and perhaps attached to one another at some points by cross-linking.

Arsenic and antimony are semi-metals in the crystalline state. In the amorphous state, the first coordination number remains 3 as in the crystal and the radius of the first coordination sphere remains practically unchanged; however, they exhibit semiconducting properties (Krebs 1951). It cannot therefore be assumed that metallic or semiconducting behaviour depends only on coordination number; in the language of Chapter 2, a non-crystalline arrangement of atoms may introduce localization for the states with energies near the Fermi energy E_F, particularly if the density of states $N(E_F)$ is small in the crystalline phase. Examples of this are amorphous alloys of Mg–Bi (§ 3.16.2), and amorphous carbon, prepared by evaporation (Adkins, Freake, and Hamilton 1970).

For a further discussion of the structure of amorphous semiconductors as obtained by X-ray diffraction studies, the reader should consult the review by Grigorovici (1969) and references cited therein. Chapters 8, 9, and 10 contain more detailed accounts of the structures of selected amorphous materials.

Structural models of amorphous solids or liquids can be constructed to give the best fit to the experimental r.d.c., together with any other conditions required by the nature of the bonds surrounding each atom. In most cases knowledge of the structure of the material in its crystalline form, where this exists, is used to determine the basic units, which are then stacked or mixed in an appropriate manner to satisfy experimental observations. This has been attempted with some degree of sophistication for amorphous germanium and silicon, as will be discussed in the next chapter.

The complicated infrared absorption spectra obtained for most amorphous solids makes structural determinations by this method exceedingly difficult, although this may well prove a valuable technique. In conjunction with Raman spectroscopy, however, a good deal of success has been obtained for amorphous selenium and the arsenic selenide–sulphide system. Identification of molecular species (rings and chains) and determination of their relative proportions has been made. This will be described in Chapter 10.

Structural *changes* in an amorphous solid, as a function of temperature for example, can be detected by the method of differential thermal analysis (D.T.A.) (Mackenzie 1970). Studies of switching materials using this technique have been made for example by Fritzsche and Ovshinsky (1970). Measurement of viscosity can also be useful at higher temperatures: Keezer and Bailey (1967) have deduced the extent to which chains in selenium break up with temperature and with addition of various additives.

7.4. Electrical properties of non-crystalline semiconductors

In this section we discuss measurements of d.c. and a.c. conductivity, drift mobilities, Hall effect, thermally stimulated conductivity, thermopower, and magnetoresistance. Generally speaking, the techniques involved in these measurements are the same as or similar to those employed for crystalline materials. On the other hand, the models used in this book for interpreting them are very different. We begin by summarizing the point of view put forward in earlier chapters and developing further some concepts related to electrical properties.

7.4.1. Summary of theoretical concepts

First of all, we emphasize, as in Chapter 2, that the density of states remains a valid concept for non-crystalline as for crystalline materials and can be determined by techniques such as photo-emission. On the other hand, mathematical methods have not as yet been developed for calculating the density of states for real non-crystalline materials.†

---

† See however McGill and Klima (1970); Klima and McGill (1971).

Our discussions are therefore based on the following hypotheses:

(a) The main factors determining the density of states for a given material are the first coordination number and the interatomic distance (§ 2.7). Thus if the former is unchanged, no major change in the density of states is likely except that due to changes in the specific volume. Coordination numbers higher than the first will of course influence the density of states to some extent. In germanium, the third coordination number is different in the crystalline and amorphous forms: the effect of this on the density of states will be discussed in Chapter 8; in crystalline tellurium higher coordinations strongly affect the magnitude of the smallest energy gap and this is very much changed in the amorphous form (Chapter 10).

(b) The wave number k is not a good quantum number for electron states in many non-crystalline materials. Either the mean free path is so short that $\Delta k/k \sim 1$, or else the states are localized. As emphasized in Chapter 3 neither is true near the Fermi energy of most liquid metals, where the density of states is high, nor at the bottom of the conduction band of liquid rare gases where the wave functions are s-like.

(c) In semiconductors that do not have s-like conduction and valence bands, localized states occur at the band extremities in the amorphous phase. Energy values E_C and E_V separate these localized states from non-localized (extended) states, and there is a drop by a factor ~ 1000 in the mobility as the energy crosses these values (the mobility shoulders; see § 2.9.2). The energy difference $(E_C - E_V)$ defines a mobility gap E_g (see Fig. 7.4(a) and (b)).

These are our primary hypotheses. We also have to ask if any states lie in the energy gap and, if so, what is their origin and their distribution in energy. Perhaps the most striking feature of amorphous as compared to crystalline semiconductors is that addition of atoms with valencies different from that of the host does not in general greatly affect the conductivity, i.e. they cannot easily be doped.† The generally accepted explanation is that the disordered structure, including impurities, accommodates itself so that all the electrons are taken up in bonds (§ 2.8). There is evidence that structural defects play a more effective role than do impurities in controlling the conductivity of amorphous semiconductors. A second and equally important observation is that, near room temperature for most of the materials with which we are

† For some exceptions e.g. silver in As_2S_3, oxygen in Se, see Chapters 9 and 10, and for certain semi-metals § 3.16.

concerned, the activation energy for electrical conduction (i.e. the slope of a plot of ln σ against $1/kT$) is approximately equal to one-half of the photon energy corresponding to the onset of strong optical absorption (see for example Fig. 7.31). Furthermore, in cases where a comparison is possible, there is good correspondence between these energies and those occurring in an intrinsic crystalline sample of the same material.

Although, therefore, it seems clear that the Fermi level lies near the middle of the band gap, it is uncertain whether for a given amorphous

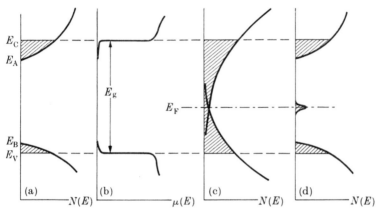

FIG. 7.4. Density of states and mobility as functions of energy in amorphous semi-conductors (see text).

semiconductor the conductivity is intrinsic or extrinsic. By intrinsic we mean that the position of the Fermi level is controlled by the densities of states in the conduction and valence bands. In such a situation the Fermi level moves (linearly) with temperature in such a way as to keep the total concentration of excited electrons equal to that of holes. It should be noted however that even in this case, if the range of localized states at the edge of, say, the valence band is smaller than at the conduction band, the number of holes excited below E_V will exceed the number of electrons excited above E_C and the material can behave as a p-type semiconductor. Cohen, Fritzsche, and Ovshinsky (1969) have suggested that in certain glasses the density of states is as shown in Fig. 7.4(c); the conduction and valence bands have tails of localized states sufficiently extensive to overlap near the centre of the mobility gap. Electrons from states at the top of the valence band are transferred into states at the bottom of the conduction band, ensuring that the Fermi level lies in the region of overlap.

An alternative model suggested by Davis and Mott (1970) is shown in Fig. 7.4(d). A fairly narrow ($<$0·1 eV) band of localized states is assumed to exist near the centre of the gap, of sufficiently high density to effectively pin the Fermi energy over a wide temperature range. Thus conduction is extrinsic rather than intrinsic. The origin of the states is speculative, but they could conceivably arise from some specific defect characteristic of the material, for example dangling bonds, interstitials, etc., the number of which will be dependent on the conditions of sample preparation and subsequent annealing treatments. This model seems more compatible with the high transparency shown by many glasses at photon energies below the fundamental absorption edge (see Fig. 7.31).

Evidence for a fairly high density of states at the Fermi energy comes from a.c. conductivity, d.c. conductivity at low temperatures, thermally stimulated conductivity experiments, and the evidence from contact and field-effect studies that surface (Schottky) barriers are very narrow in amorphous semiconductors. Estimates of $N(E_F)$ from such measurements will be given in later sections. It should be pointed out that at present there is no definite evidence for the existence of such states from optical absorption or photo-emission measurements, although in amorphous germanium there is some evidence for absorption due to defects (§ 8.1.5).

For major portions of this chapter, we shall use the model of Fig. 7.4(d).

7.4.2. Temperature variation of d.c. conductivity

With the above model for the density of states and mobilities in an amorphous semiconductor, three mechanisms of electrical conduction can be distinguished:

(a) Conduction due to carriers excited beyond the mobility shoulders into non-localized or extended states. If the main current is carried by holes we expect, using the notation of Fig. 7.4,

$$\sigma = \sigma_0 \exp\{-(E_F - E_V)/kT\}. \tag{7.1}$$

As discussed in § 2.9.2, the pre-exponential factor σ_0 is expected to be given by

$$\sigma_0 \simeq 0\cdot06e^2/\hbar a_E \tag{7.2}$$

for a coordination number 6. This is $\sim$350 Ω^{-1} cm^{-1} for a value of $a_E = 4$ Å. In general σ_0 may perhaps lie between 100 and 500 Ω^{-1} cm^{-1}

in most materials. It can also be written

$$\sigma_0 = eN(E_V)kT\mu_0, \tag{7.3}$$

and since σ_0 is not expected to be temperature dependent the mobility in extended states μ_0 is proportional to $1/T$ (§ 2.9.2).

A plot of $\ln \sigma$ against $1/T$ will yield a straight line if $(E_F - E_V)$ is a linear function of T over the temperature range measured. If

$$E_F - E_V = E(0) - \gamma T, \tag{7.4}$$

then the slope of such a plot will be $E(0)/k$, and the intercept on the σ axis will be $\sigma_0 \exp(\gamma/k)$. This is illustrated in Fig. 7.5. Experimental

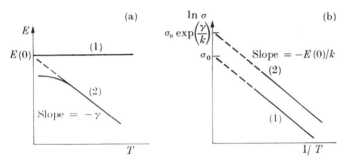

FIG. 7.5. Illustration of the effect of a temperature-dependent energy gap on the slope and intercept of a plot of $\ln \sigma$ against $1/T$. (a) $E = E(0) - \gamma T$, (b) $\sigma = \sigma_0 \exp(\gamma/k) \times \times \exp\{-E(0)/kT\}$. $\gamma = -dE/dT$ and is zero in curves (1).

values of the intercept will be discussed later in this section.

(b) Conduction due to carriers excited into the localized states at the band edges i.e. at E_A or E_B. Again if the main current is carried by holes, and conduction is by hopping, then

$$\sigma = \sigma_1 \exp\{-(E_F - E_B + \Delta W_1)/kT\}, \tag{7.5}$$

where ΔW_1 is the activation energy for hopping and E_B is the energy at the band edge.

An estimate of σ_1 is not easy to make, but it is expected to be a factor of 10^2–10^4 less than σ_0, due partly to an effective density of states lower by a factor $\sim (E_B - E_V)/kT$, but mainly to a lower mobility μ_1. Only if μ_1 does not fall off too rapidly between E_V and E_B will the current be carried at E_B (as opposed to energies between E_B and E_V) and a straight line be obtained on a plot of $\ln \sigma$ against $1/T$ for this mode of conduction.

(c) Conduction due to carriers hopping (tunnelling) between localized states near the Fermi energy. This is the process analogous to impurity-conduction in heavily doped semiconductors, and we may write

$$\sigma = \sigma_2 \exp(-\Delta W_2/kT), \qquad (7.6)$$

where $\sigma_2 \lesssim \sigma_1$ and ΔW_2 is the hopping energy of the order of half the width of the defect band shown in Fig. 7.4(d). Both σ_2 and ΔW_2 will be discussed later in § 7.4.4. We emphasize here that a straight line in a plot of $\ln \sigma$ against $1/T$ is expected only if hopping is between nearest neighbours. As the temperature is lowered, it may become favourable

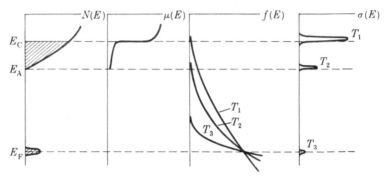

FIG. 7.6. Illustration of the effect of temperature on the mode of conduction.
$$\sigma(E) = eN(E)\mu(E)f(E); \quad T_1 > T_2 > T_3.$$

for the carriers to tunnel to more distant sites, ΔW_2 will fall, and ultimately the conductivity is expected to behave like

$$\ln \sigma = A - BT^{-\frac{1}{4}}, \qquad (7.7)$$

as discussed in § 2.9.1.

The total conductivity for all processes is obtained as an integral over all available energy states. Thus for states above E_{F}, assuming Boltzmann statistics (compare eqn (2.11)),

$$\sigma = e \int N(E)\mu(E)f(E)\, \mathrm{d}E, \qquad (7.8)$$

where $f(E)$ is the Boltzmann distribution function. Figure 7.6 shows schematically the variation of $N(E)$, $\mu(E)$, and $f(E)$ with E for energies above E_{F}, and the manner in which $\sigma(E)$ may vary with temperature. This is also shown on a plot of $\ln \sigma$ against $1/T$ in Fig.7.7. If the density of defect states is high, then process (b) will not dominate in any temperature range and a direct transition from (a) to (c) will result.

Experimental results of the temperature variation of the d.c. conductivity in various amorphous semiconductors will be presented in later chapters. In Fig. 7.8 we show values of C and E for a variety of materials whose conductivity has been reported to obey the relationship $\sigma = C \exp(-E/kT)$. No obvious correlation between C and E exists. Values of C between 10^2 and $10^4\,\Omega^{-1}\,\text{cm}^{-1}$ are observed in many materials (the *Stuke rule*); see for example Fig. 7.21. We believe that in the temperature range measured, conduction in these materials is by carriers in extended states. The spread in values of C ($= \sigma_0 \exp(\gamma/k)$)

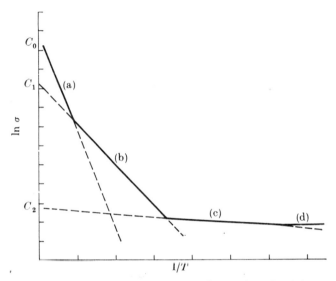

FIG. 7.7. Illustration of the temperature dependence of conductivity expected on the model of Fig. 7.6.

could be due partly to variations in σ_0 but mainly due to differences in γ—the temperature coefficient of $(E_F - E_V)$ (or for n-type conduction $(E_C - E_F)$). It is not possible to obtain γ from experiments on the variation of d.c. conductivity with temperature without a knowledge of σ_0, but it can be estimated either from thermoelectric-power measurements (§ 7.4.5), or from the temperature variation β of the optical gap. Values of β in the range 4–8×10^{-4} eV deg^{-1} are common (Fig. 7.9), so we might assume that γ lies between 2 and 4×10^{-4} eV deg^{-1}, and thus the factor $\exp(\gamma/k)$ between 10 and 10^2.

For the group of materials having a value of C of order $10\,\Omega^{-1}\,\text{cm}^{-1}$, we suggest that conduction is by mechanism (b), that is, due to carriers hopping between the localized states at a band edge. It should be noted that, if the range of localized states $\Delta E = (E_B - E_V)$ (or $(E_C - E_A)$) for electrons) is greater than a few tenths of an eV, then at

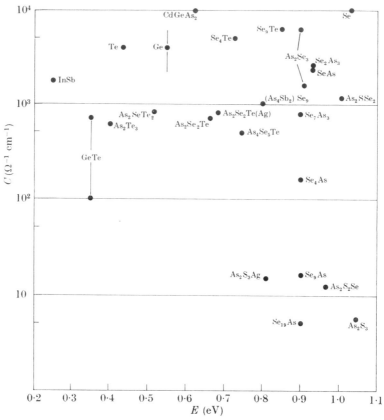

Fɪɢ. 7.8. Values of C and E for amorphous semiconductors whose conductivity near room temperature is given by $\sigma = C \exp(-E/kT)$ (from Davis and Mott 1970).

room temperature the larger number of carriers excited to E_{B} as compared to E_{V} will ensure that the major contribution to the current is carried at E_{B} in spite of the lower mobility and effective density of states there.

In several materials, kinks have been observed in plots of $\ln \sigma$ against $1/T$, which seem to reflect the transition from type (a) to type (b) conduction, and these will be described in later chapters. In particular here we mention results on glow-discharge-deposited silicon (Fig. 8.16); in this material there is also evidence for a simultaneous change in the behaviour of the mobility. The behaviour of $\ln \sigma$ as $A - BT^{-\frac{1}{4}}$ expected under certain conditions for type (c) conduction has been observed over a broad temperature range in evaporated films of silicon and germanium (Chapter 8). In Fig. 7.7 this variable-range hopping behaviour is shown schematically as region (d).

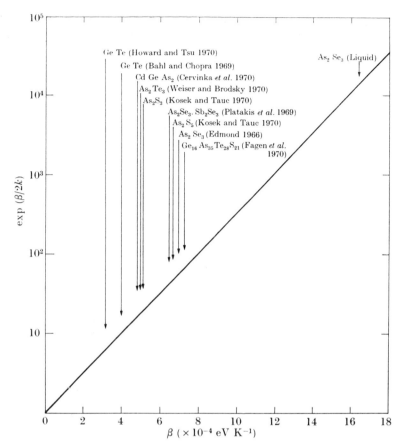

FIG. 7.9. Plot of $\exp(\beta/2k)$ against β and some values of β (the temperature variation of the optical gap) in several materials. (Because of the broadening of the optical absorption edge with increasing temperature, the value for liquid As_2Se_3 is uncertain. Thermoelectric-power data suggest it should be ~ 20 per cent higher than shown.)

Finally in this section we discuss the behaviour of the conductivity of non-crystalline semiconductors on melting. Two classes of materials can be distinguished: (i) For those that cannot be prepared by melt-quenching, e.g. Ge, Te, and (III)–(V) compounds, the liquid state is metallic: the conductivity exhibits a sudden increase on melting: in general, however, crystallization occurs before melting. The coordination number in the liquid state is different from that in the solid. Figure 7.10 (from Ioffe and Regel 1960) shows the transition in a few such materials: the density also increases discontinuously on melting. (ii) For amorphous semiconductors that can be obtained by melt-quenching, there are two sub-cases: stable glasses that do not crystallize even when

heated very slowly, and glasses that do not crystallize on fast heating
but do when heated slowly. There is no sharp distinction between the
two, but the large variation in crystallization times found in practice
makes the distinction a useful one. For both cases, however, the
retention of semiconducting properties in the liquid state seems general.

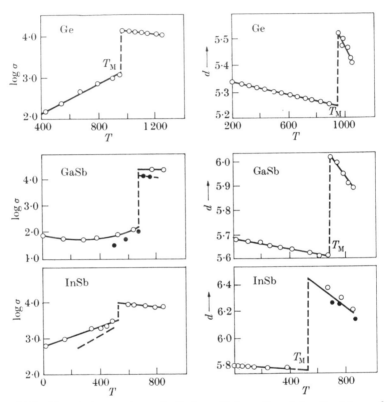

Fig. 7.10. Abrupt changes in conductivity σ (Ω^{-1} cm^{-1}) and density d (g cm^{-3}) in some
non-glass-forming materials on melting (from Ioffe and Regel 1960).

Fig. 7.11 (from Male 1970) gives a few examples. The slope of the ln σ
against $1/T$ plot is frequently higher in the liquid than in the solid. As
the slope gives the activation energy for conduction extrapolated to
$T = 0$, the indication here is that the temperature coefficient of the
gap is higher in the liquid state (see Fig. 7.5); the gap is actually smaller
in the liquid and may close to zero at a sufficiently high temperature.
Some indication of this is seen in the curve for As$_2$Te$_3$, which turns over
at a value of $\sigma \sim 10^3$ Ω^{-1} cm^{-1}. Other examples of this gradual change
towards metallic properties are seen in similar curves for liquid alloys

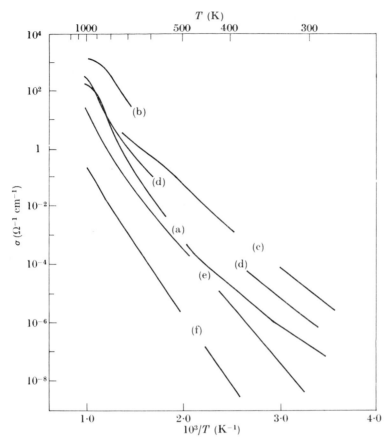

FIG. 7.11. Temperature variation of conductivity in several chalcogenide glasses in the solid and liquid states (from Male 1970). (a) $As_{30}Te_{48}Si_{12}Ge_{10}$; (b) As_2Te_3; (c) $As_2S_3Tl_2Te$; (d) As_2SeTe_2; (e) As_2Se_2Te; (f) As_2Se_3.

of Te–Se (Chapter 3). We presume that in all these cases there is a gradual increase in coordination number as the liquid is heated. Numerous examples of this kind of transition to a metallic state for ternary glasses have been given by Haisty and Krebs (1969a, b).

7.4.3. Drift mobilities

One of the least ambiguous ways of establishing the existence or otherwise of localized states near the extremities of conduction and valence bands is by injecting carriers at one point of a sample and measuring their transit time t_t to another point at a distance d under the influence of an electric field F. The drift mobility is then defined by

$$\mu_D = d/Ft_t.$$

If the dielectric relaxation time ($10^{-12} \rho\kappa/4\pi$ where ρ is the resistivity and κ the dielectric constant) due to carriers already present is much smaller than t_t, then the excess carriers are quickly screened by carriers of opposite sign so that charge neutrality is satisfied locally. Under these conditions it is possible to measure only the drift mobility of minority carriers. Such measurements are described in text books on crystalline semiconductors (see Shockley 1950). In the drift experiments described in this book, the reverse is the case; we are dealing with high-resistance material (typically $\rho > 10^7 \, \Omega$ cm) in which excess

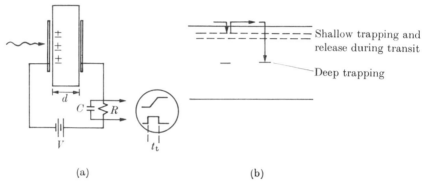

Shallow trapping and release during transit

Deep trapping

(a)   (b)

FIG. 7.12. (a) Experimental arrangement for drift mobility studies; $\mu = d/t_t F = d^2/t_t V$. (b) Schematic representation of shallow and deep trapping processes.

carriers are *not* accompanied during transit by a cloud of carriers of opposite charge. Both hole and electron transits can thus be observed in the sample by proper selection of polarity. For a review of drift-mobility techniques the reader is referred to an article by Spear (1969).

Figure 7.12(a) illustrates a typical 'sandwich' arrangement in which the semiconductor film (perhaps 50 μm thick) is equipped with two blocking electrodes, one of which is semi-transparent if optical injection is used. The carriers can be electrically injected as a pulse (of duration less than t_t) from one of the electrodes, or created in pairs by a flash of strongly absorbed light or by an electron beam. If the injected charge is kept smaller than $C_s V$, where C_s is the capacity of the film, then the internal field remains essentially constant during transit. (For an analysis of transits under the opposite conditions see Many and Rakavy 1962, Papadakis 1967, and Gibbons and Papadakis 1968.) The time for the selected carrier to drift to the opposite electrode is determined by observing either the square-like current transient ($CR \ll t_t$) or the ramp-like charge transient ($CR \gg t_t$).

It is important to ascertain that a well-defined transit time exists and that it scales correctly with field and sample thickness. Problems that commonly invalidate the measurements include spreading of the sheet of charge during transit, either by diffusion or by a large statistical spread in trapping and release times. Shallow trapping levels (Fig. 7.12(b)) with release times short compared to the transit time are responsible for the drift mobility being frequently lower than the microscopic or *conductivity mobility*. If there are deep levels present in the material then carriers can be lost during transit. In this case, the pulse shapes become distorted and transit times become difficult to measure.

When the drift mobility is limited by shallow traps, it is reduced from the conductivity mobility μ_0 by the fraction of time that a carrier on the average spends in the band (or, in the case of amorphous semiconductors, beyond the mobility shoulder). Thus

$$\mu_D = \mu_0\{n_0/(n_0+n_t)\}, \tag{7.9}$$

where n_0 and n_t are the carrier densities in the band and in the traps respectively. Assuming a thermal equilibrium distribution between the free and trapped carriers during transit, this ratio can be expressed in terms of trap parameters. Thus, for a discrete set of traps of density N_t cm^{-3} situated with an energy ε_t below the band edge in a crystalline semiconductor,

$$\mu_D = \mu_0\{1+(N_t/N_c)\exp(\varepsilon_t/kT)\}^{-1}, \tag{7.10}$$

which approximates to

$$\mu_D = \mu_0(N_c/N_t)\exp(-\varepsilon_t/kT), \tag{7.11}$$

except at high temperature where the probability of thermal release is high. Here N_c is the effective density of states at the band edge.

Thus if $\ln \mu_D$ is plotted against $1/T$, the slope yields the trap depth, and, if μ_0 and N_c are known, the intercept yields the trap density. In practice it is difficult to distinguish this relation from that expected when the N_t traps cm^{-3} are uniformly distributed over an energy range extending from the band edge to a depth ε_t. In this case it can easily be shown that

$$\mu_D = \mu_0(N_c/N_t)(\varepsilon_t/kT)\exp(-\varepsilon_t/kT). \tag{7.12}$$

If in an amorphous semiconductor the density of localized states at the band edge is linear with energy over a range ΔE (Chapter 2), then again a temperature-activated drift mobility is expected, of the form

$$\mu_D = \mu_0(\Delta E/kT)\exp(-\Delta E/kT). \tag{7.13}$$

Note that neither the density of localized states nor the density of states at the mobility shoulder enters into this expression.

The number of amorphous semiconductors so far investigated by this technique is relatively small. As mentioned above, the material should have a high resistivity. In amorphous selenium, well-defined transit times have been observed (Spear 1957, 1960; Hartke 1962; Tabak and Warter 1968) for both electrons and holes, and the temperature dependence of the drift mobilities studied. These results are described and discussed in Chapter 10. For As_2Se_3 (Tabak 1971; Owen and Robertson 1970; Kolomiets and Lebedev 1967) and As_2S_3 (Ing and Neyhart, private communication), however, well-defined transit times have not been observed, and it is believed that in thin films of these materials a large fraction of the carriers drift through the sample in the localized states at the band edge (Chapter 9). In glow-discharge-deposited silicon, Le Comber and Spear (1970) find a kink in a plot of ln μ_D against $1/T$ near 200 K. The steady-state d.c. conductivity also shows a change of behaviour at this temperature, suggesting that here a transition from conduction in delocalized (extended) states to conduction in localized states occurs (Chapter 8).

Drift-mobility studies as a function of pressure have been made in amorphous selenium by Dolezalek and Spear (1970). No change in the magnitude or activation energy of the drift mobility was found, providing evidence against hopping conduction at room temperature in this material. Similar measurements on other materials would be valuable.

Although detailed drift-mobility experiments have been made in only a few materials, they are extremely valuable in that they provide the most direct evidence for localized states at the band edges of amorphous semiconductors. Because of the insensitivity of the temperature dependence of the drift mobility to the *distribution* in energy of the localized states, carefully executed experiments over a wide temperature range are needed to determine this distribution. Whatever the distribution, however, the activation energy observed at high T should be an approximate measure of the *range* in energy of the localized states.

Observations of transients under varying conditions of field, temperature, and thickness can be used to determine the carrier lifetime τ, or the time for a carrier to become lost by a deep trapping event. The product $\mu_D \tau$ is the range per unit applied electric field, and is an important material parameter (in the commercial process of xerography for example). Measurement of the total charge collected under conditions where the range is much larger than the sample thickness enables a direct measurement of quantum efficiency to be made. Measurements on selenium as a function of the energy of the incident radiation will be discussed in § 7.5 and in Chapter 10.

7.4.4. a.c. conductivity

As we have seen in § 7.4.2, there are three mechanisms of charge transport that can contribute to a direct current in amorphous semiconductors. They can all contribute also to the a.c. conductivity, as follows:

(a) Transport by carriers excited to the extended states near E_C or E_V. For these we might expect that $\sigma(\omega)$ would be given by a formula of the Drude type,

$$\sigma(\omega) = \sigma(0)/(1 + \omega^2 \tau^2). \tag{7.14}$$

The time of relaxation τ will however be very small ($\sim 10^{-15}$ s) and a decrease in $\sigma(\omega)$ as ω^{-2} (i.e. free-carrier absorption) is not expected until a frequency $\sim 10^{15}$ Hz is reached. This corresponds to an energy quantum lying above the fundamental optical absorption edge in materials of interest here. In any case, as we have seen in § 2.10, the Drude formula is not really applicable for such small values of τ. It is however in excellent agreement with experiment for most liquid metals, but not for liquid tellurium (§ 3.15). Even when τ is large, deviations from the Drude formula are expected if the density of states varies with energy over a range h/τ. In § 7.6.5 we calculate the contribution to $\sigma(\omega)$ due to free carriers (intraband absorption) that is expected in amorphous semiconductors. It is sufficient to state here that in the electrical range of frequencies (up to, say, 10^7 Hz) no frequency dependence of the conductivity due to carriers in extended states is expected.

(b) Transport by carriers excited into the localized states at the edges of the valence or conduction band. Because transport here is by hopping we should expect (see Chapters 2 and 6) the conductivity to increase with frequency as $\omega\{\ln(\nu_{ph}/\omega)\}^4$, i.e. approximately as $\omega^{0.8}$ when $\omega \ll \nu_{ph}$ (Fig. 7.13). In order to estimate the frequency at which such an increase is expected, a comparison with the magnitude of the d.c. hopping conduction is required and will be discussed below. The temperature dependence of this component of the a.c. conductivity should be the same as that for the part of d.c. conductivity involving

15

excitation to the band edge, i.e. for the valence band it should increase as $\exp\{-(E_F - E_B)/kT\}$.

(c) Hopping transport by carriers with energies near the Fermi level (provided $N(E_F)$ is finite). This again should increase with frequency in the same manner as for process (b). However, the exponential dependence on the temperature will be absent, and $\sigma(\omega)$ should be

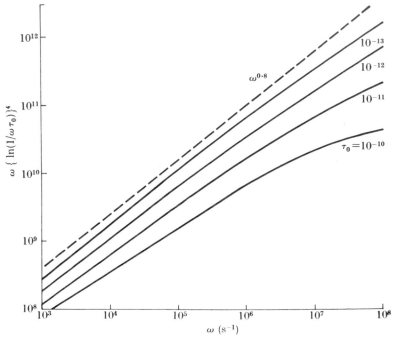

FIG. 7.13. Plot of $\omega\{\ln(1/\omega\tau_0)\}^4$ against ω for various values of τ_0, showing the approximate $\omega^{0.8}$ dependence of the conductivity when $\omega\tau_0 \ll 1$.

proportional to T, if kT is small compared to the width of the occupied part of the defect band; and independent of T otherwise. Davis and Mott (1970) use the formula given by Austin and Mott (1969) (see also § 2.10)

$$\sigma(\omega) = \tfrac{1}{3}\pi e^2 kT\{N(E_F)\}^2\alpha^{-5}\omega\{\ln(\nu_{ph}/\omega)\}^4. \tag{7.15}$$

Assumptions involved in this formula have been discussed by Pollak (1971a, b): the main one is that hopping is between *pairs* of centres i.e. multiple-hopping processes can be neglected. In Pollak's formula the factor $\tfrac{1}{3}\pi$ is replaced by $\pi^3/96$. A more complicated formula should be used if polarons are formed (Chapter 4).

The above formula (7.15) can be compared with that for the d.c. conductivity due to hopping by electrons with energies near E_F (§ 7.4.2),

$$\sigma(0) = \sigma_2 \exp(-\Delta W_2/kT). \qquad (7.16)$$

Writing

$$\sigma_2 = e^2 R^2 \nu_{ph} N(E_F) e^{-2\alpha R}, \qquad (7.17)$$

and putting $N(E_F) = 1/\Delta W_2 R^3$, we find the ratio of the a.c. to d.c. conductivity to be

$$\frac{\sigma(\omega)}{\sigma(0)} = \frac{\pi}{3} \frac{\exp(2\alpha R)}{(\alpha R)^5} \frac{\omega}{\nu_{ph}} \frac{kT}{\Delta W_2} \{\ln(\nu_{ph}/\omega)\}^4 \exp(\Delta W_2/kT). \qquad (7.18)$$

The purpose of writing down this ratio is to estimate the frequency at which the $\omega^{0\cdot8}$ behaviour is expected to take over from the d.c. process.

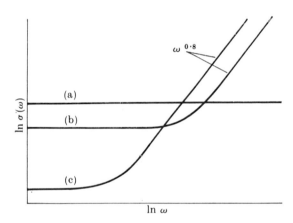

FIG. 7.14. Schematic illustration of the frequency dependence of the three conduction mechanisms described in the text.

Choosing $T = 300$ K, $\alpha^{-1} = 8$ Å, $R = 60$ Å, $\nu_{ph} = 10^{12}$ Hz, and $\Delta W_2 = 0\cdot1$ eV, $\sigma(\omega)/\sigma(0)$ is equal to unity when $\omega \simeq 3$ kHz. The value is sensitive to the parameters chosen, particularly to the product (αR).

In Fig. 7.14 we illustrate schematically the frequency dependence of the conductivity expected for the three conduction mechanisms outlined above. The two hopping processes (b) and (c) should both increase approximately as $\omega^{0\cdot8}$. Experimentally the mechanism giving the highest conductivity at a particular temperature would be observed: in the situation shown this would mean that hopping at the band edge would not be observed at any frequency. Conversely, if the onset of the $\omega^{0\cdot8}$ behaviour for process (b) occurred at a lower frequency, then this would operate to the exclusion of process (c). A distinction between the a.c. conductivity processes (b) and (c) can be made by observing the temperature dependence. As shown above, process (b) will be activated with an energy of approximately half the band gap.

a.c. conductivity measurements in the range 10^2 to 10^5 can conveniently be made using bridge techniques with a sensitive null detector. Experimental difficulties arise when the dielectric loss tan δ is small, and sample geometry is chosen to make the loss as large as possible. A Q-meter can be used up to $\sim 10^7$ Hz, the upper limit for the frequency if electronic circuits are used. For higher frequencies, microwave techniques (slotted-line up to about 10^{10} Hz, wave-guide to 10^{12} Hz) can be employed. The real and imaginary parts of the conductivity are normally determined by regarding the sample as a resistor and capacitor in parallel. From these measurements, the dielectric constant, the dielectric loss, the refractive index, and the optical absorption constant can also be deduced. It is frequently useful to determine the frequency dependence of these parameters when attempting to decide on mechanisms and models.

Data on a.c. conductivity for several amorphous semiconductors will be presented in later chapters. Here we collect together some results on a few chalcogenides (Fig. 7.15). A variation of $\sigma(\omega)$ approximately proportional to $\omega^{0.8}$ is observed in the region of 10^6 Hz. Davis and Mott (1970) have interpreted these results in terms of hopping between localized states near the Fermi level. This mechanism seems preferable to that of hopping at a band edge, because of the weak temperature dependence found by Owen (1967), Owen and Robertson (1970), and Ivkin and Kolomiets (1970) (see Chapter 9). Under the assumption that equation (7.15) is applicable, the density of states at the Fermi energy, $N(E_F)$, can be evaluated. For $T = 300$ K, $\nu_{ph} = 10^{12}$ Hz, and $\omega = 10^6$ s^{-1}, we find

$$\{N(E_F)\}^2 = 6 \cdot 4 \times 10^{49} \sigma(\omega) \alpha^5 \qquad (\omega = 10^6 \text{ s}^{-1}); \qquad (7.19)$$

α is in Å^{-1}, σ in Ω^{-1} cm^{-1}, and $N(E_F)$ in cm^{-3} eV^{-1}. This relationship is displayed graphically in Fig. 7.16 for various values of α^{-1}, the radial extent of the localized wave functions. There is some doubt as to what value to take for this, and it is unlikely to be the same for different materials. Taking $\alpha^{-1} = 8$ Å yields values of $N(E_F)$ for a variety of amorphous chalcogenides that range from 10^{18} to 10^{21} cm^{-3} eV^{-1}.

There is however a surprising correlation between $N(E_F)$ deduced by this method and the band gap of the materials. In Fig. 7.17 the a.c. conductivity at $\omega = 10^6$ s^{-1} is plotted against the d.c. conductivity for a variety of chalcogenides, all data being at 300 K. Also shown are the estimated values of $N(E_F)$ and approximate values of E, the activation energy for conduction (i.e. roughly half the mobility gap). The variation

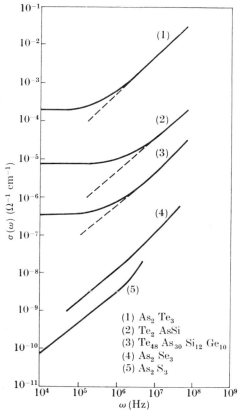

FIG. 7.15. Frequency dependence of conductivity in various chalcogenide glasses. Curves (1)–(3) are from Rockstad (1970), curve (4) from Ivkin and Kolomiets (1970), and curve (5) from Owen and Robertson (1970).

of $N(E_F)$ with the magnitude of E may be considered to support the Cohen–Fritzsche–Ovshinsky model for the density of states in an amorphous semiconductor (Fig. 7.4(c)), the band overlap, and hence $N(E_F)$, being perhaps larger in materials where the band gap is small. However, as stated in an earlier section, the magnitude of $N(E_F)$ would, on this model, imply a very large *total* density of states in the mobility gap, which we believe is incompatible with the good transparency of these materials at photon energies below the fundamental optical absorption edge. If, as suggested by Davis and Mott (1970) and Mott (1971b), the states near $E_{\rm F}$ are confined to a band of width $\sim 0 \cdot 1$ eV, then the total density of states can be much smaller.

A lower limit to the width of the suggested defect band, if it is assumed to be formed from a single kind of point defect, can be

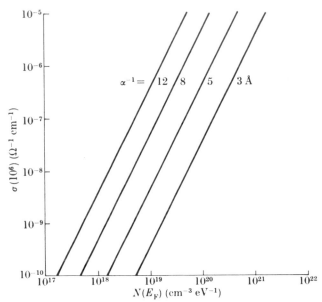

FIG. 7.16. Calculated density of states at the Fermi level $N(E_{\rm F})$ as a function of a.c. conductivity at $\omega = 10^6$ s^{-1} for various values of α^{-1} (the radial extent of the localized wave functions). The plot is for $T = 300$ K and $\nu_{\rm ph} = 10^{12}$ Hz, from equation (7.19).

estimated as follows. As in impurity-conduction ($\S$ 6.2), it should be at least $J \sim e^2/\kappa R$, where R is the average separation between centres. For a density of states $N(E_{\rm F})$ distributed over a band width J, R is given approximately by $(4\pi/3)R^3 N(E_{\rm F})J/2 = 1$, and so

$$ J \sim e^3 \{N(E_{\rm F})\}^{\frac{1}{2}}/\kappa^{\frac{3}{2}}. \qquad (7.20) $$

If $\kappa = 6$ and $N(E_{\rm F}) = 5 \times 10^{19}$ cm^{-3} eV^{-1}, then $J \sim 0 \cdot 04$ eV and $R \sim 60$ Å. The activation energy for d.c. hopping at $E_{\rm F}$ (ΔW_2 in eqn (7.16)) is expected to be about $\frac{1}{2}J$.

The term $\omega\{\ln(\nu_{\rm ph}/\omega)\}^4$ for a.c. hopping conduction comes from averaging the Debye factor $\omega^2\tau/(1+\omega^2\tau^2)$ over the values of τ appropriate to hopping between pairs of centres. The formula should be valid for high frequencies as long as values of τ exist that make $\omega\tau \sim 1$. If τ

cannot drop below a minimum value $\tau_{\min}$, then when $\omega\tau_{\min} > 1$, $\sigma(\omega)$ should saturate to a constant value. However other absorption processes may set in before this is observed.

Results of Shaw on As_2Se_3 films, reported by Davis and Shaw (1970), and of Owen and Robertson (1970) on As_2S_3, show $\sigma(\omega) \sim \omega^n$ with $n \sim 2$ (Shaw), $n \sim 1\cdot5$ (Owen) before any sign of saturation sets in.

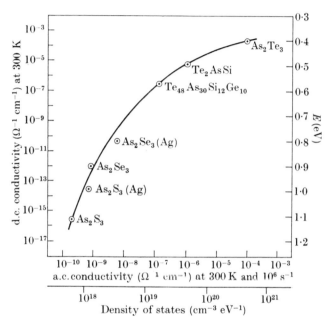

FIG. 7.17. Plot of d.c. against a.c. conductivity at $\omega = 10^6$ s^{-1} in various chalcogenide glasses at room temperature. Also shown are $N(E_F)$, the estimated density of states at E_F, and approximate values of E, the activation energy for d.c. conduction. Note that E is approximately half the mobility or optical gap in these materials (from Davis and Mott 1970).

The ω^2 dependence reported by Davis and Shaw (1970) was later shown to be an experimental artifact related to electrode resistance (Street, Davies, and Ioffe 1971). The measurements of Owen, however, were made (at the higher frequencies) by a slotted-line technique in which no contact to the sample is required. Other authors have reported power dependences larger than expected on the hopping model (see Pollak 1971a, b). It is possible that direct photon absorption (§ 2.11) becomes dominant at high frequencies in some cases. However Pollak estimates that this type of absorption fails to account for the observed magnitude of $\sigma(\omega)$ by several powers of ten. He suggests instead a modification to the hopping theory, which takes into account correlation effects, i.e. the mutual dependence of the occupation probability of neighbouring sites.

Austin and Garbett (1971) suggest a quite different mechanism for the high-frequency conductivity (above 10^6 Hz). In their model it arises from a long low-energy tail to phonon absorption processes. These are normally confined to the near and far infrared (say 10^{12}–10^{14} Hz)

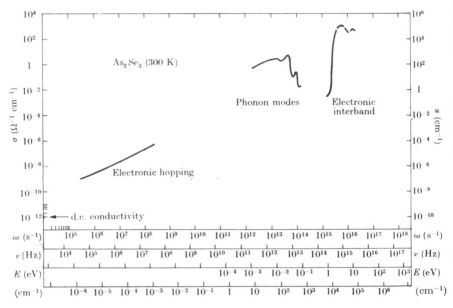

FIG. 7.18. a.c. conductivity and optical absorption over a broad frequency range in amorphous As_2Se_3.

in crystalline materials and are associated with transverse optical modes at $k = 0$. Unless there are more than three atoms per unit cell, optical absorption by a single acoustic phonon is forbidden (Zallen 1968). In an amorphous material, relaxation of the selection rules may allow such absorption, which, with frequency, would follow the acoustic phonon density of states. In materials with a high degree of ionicity or strong electron–phonon coupling, such a process is observed as 'ultrasonic loss'. Amrhein and Mueller (1968) have also suggested that, when the wavelength of the electromagnetic wave is greater than the mean free path, a temperature-insensitive absorption results from interaction with acoustic phonons.

Austin and Garbett's suggestion is reinforced by the magnitude of the a.c. conductivity, which can be converted to an absorption constant by the relationship

$$\sigma(\omega) = n_0\alpha/377.$$

The units here are $\Omega^{-1}\,cm^{-1}$ for σ and cm^{-1} for α; n_0 is the refractive index. This will perhaps be made clearer in Fig. 7.18, in which experimental measurements of optical absorption and a.c. conductivity for amorphous As_2Se_3 are displayed over a wide frequency range in the same diagram, with $n_0 = 4$. For convenience, the frequency scale is shown in terms of several commonly used units. The a.c. conductivity data are from Ivkin and Kolomiets (1970), the phonon absorption data from Austin and Garbett (1971), and the fundamental optical absorption edge data from Edmond (1966). All results refer to room temperature. Data in the large frequency gap between 10^8 and 10^{12} Hz have recently been obtained for As_2Se_3 by Taylor, Bishop, and Mitchell (1970).

7.4.5. Thermoelectric power

In Chapter 2 we have summarized the formulae appropriate to the thermoelectric power. We now discuss further those that are relevant to amorphous and liquid semiconductors and consider some experimental data.

The thermoelectric power or Seebeck coefficient is measured by $\Delta V/\Delta T$ where ΔV is the voltage developed between two points of the material maintained at a small temperature difference ΔT. For an n-type crystalline semiconductor, it is given, with e negative, by

$$S = \frac{k}{e}\left(\frac{E_C - E_F}{kT} + A\right), \tag{7.21}$$

where E_C is the energy of the conduction-band edge and AkT is the average energy of the transported electrons measured with respect to E_C. The value of A depends on the nature of the scattering process and is normally a small constant between 2 and 4. If the current is carried by holes, the sign of S is reversed and $(E_C - E_F)$ is replaced by $(E_F - E_V)$. For ambipolar conduction the thermopower associated with each carrier is weighted according to the contribution each makes to the total current.

In amorphous semiconductors we do not expect major modification to these formulae, mainly because the transport term A makes only a small contribution to S when $(E_C - E_F)$ or $(E_F - E_V) \gg kT$. For current carried in extended states, A is expected to be equal to unity (§ 2.9.3), and E_C or E_V refers to the appropriate mobility shoulder. For current carried in localized states at the band edges, A will again be small and E_C and E_V are to be replaced by E_A and E_B respectively. If there are several parallel mechanisms, a weighted mean must be taken, as in crystalline semiconductors. The sign of S is therefore a much more reliable indication than the Hall effect (§ 7.4.6) of whether the material is n-type or p-type. Measurements of S as a function of temperature provide perhaps the most direct way of determining the temperature coefficient γ of the activation energy for conduction, a quantity of importance, as was shown in § 7.4.2. This is illustrated in Fig. 7.19. As

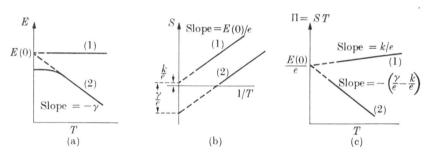

FIG. 7.19. Illustration of the effect of a temperature-dependent energy gap on the slope and intercepts of plots of S against $1/T$ and Π against T. (a) $E = E(0) - \gamma T$, (b) $S = -k/e\{E(0)/kT - \gamma/k + 1\}$, (c) $\Pi = E(0)/e - (\gamma/e - k/e)T$. $\gamma = -dR/dT$ and is zero in curves (1).

before, we assume that over a limited temperature range (for p-type material)

$$E = E_F - E_V = E(0) - \gamma T,$$

giving for S

$$S = -\frac{k}{e}\left\{\frac{E(0)}{kT} - \frac{\gamma}{k} + 1\right\}. \tag{7.22}$$

A plot of S against $1/T$ has a slope that yields $E(0)$ (as does a plot of $\ln \sigma$ against $1/T$, § 7.4.2), and the intercept on the S-axis at $1/T = 0$ yields γ. Alternatively a plot of the Peltier coefficient $\Pi = ST$ against T yields γ from its slope.

Measurements of the thermoelectric power in amorphous chalcogenide semiconductors have shown them to be p-type in the majority of cases reported. Detailed measurements as a function of temperature are at present rather sparse. To some extent this is due to the difficulty of measuring small voltages across high-resistivity material. Some data have been presented by Owen and Robertson (1970), and other results will be given below and in Chapter 9.

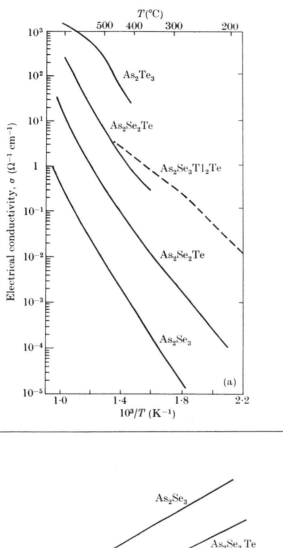

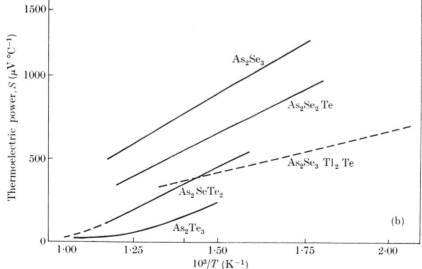

FIG. 7.20. Temperature variation of conductivity and thermoelectric power in various liquid chalcogenides (from Edmond 1966).

Measurements by Edmond (1966) in several liquid chalcogenides are shown in Fig. 7.20(a). Comparison of the slopes of these lines with those obtained from conductivity data, Fig. 7.20(b), is made in Table 7.2. The agreement is not as good as might be expected but it may be within experimental error. It should be pointed out that if an activation energy in the mobility (such as would be expected for hopping conduction, compare Chapter 4) was contributing to the slope of the plot of $\ln \sigma$ against $1/T$, then this would worsen the discrepancy. There is of course the possibility of mixed conduction processes being involved.

TABLE 7.2

Activation energies (in eV) for conduction in various liquid chalcogenides as determined from the data of Fig. 7.20. $E^S(0)$ is the slope of the plot of S against $1/T$, and $E^\sigma(0)$ is the slope of the plot of $\ln \sigma$ against $1/T$. γ is the temperature coefficient of E^S as inferred from the intercepts on the S-axis at $1/T = 0$ of Fig. 7.20(b).

	$E^S(0)$	$E^\sigma(0)$	$\gamma(\text{eVK}^{-1})$
As_2Se_3	1·21	1·06	$1·00 \times 10^{-3}$
As_2Se_2Te	1·04	0·84	$9·80 \times 10^{-4}$
As_2SeTe_2	0·95	0·69	$1·06 \times 10^{-3}$
As_2Te_3	(0·77)	(0·56)	$1·01 \times 10^{-3}$
$As_2Se_3.Tl_2Te$	0·50		$4·05 \times 10^{-4}$

In the case of liquid selenium (Chapter 10), $E^S(0)$ and $E^\sigma(0)$ agree exceptionally well.

Also shown in Table 7.2 is the temperature coefficient of $(E_F - E_V)$, determined from the extrapolated intercept of the plot of S against $1/T$ on the S-axis at $1/T = 0$, under the assumption that $A = 1$. Apart from the liquid containing Tl, the values of γ are all close to 10^{-3} eV deg^{-1}. The value for As_2Se_3 may be compared (see also Chapter 9) with the temperature coefficient of the optical gap, $\beta = 1·65 \times 10^{-3}$ eV deg^{-1}, shown in Fig. 7.9. Although $(E_F - E_V)$ is approximately half the optical gap, it is not necessarily true that $\beta = 2\gamma$. Note that these high-temperature coefficients yield very large values for $\exp(\gamma/k)$, which are consistent with the large values of C (the intercept on the σ-axis of the $\ln \sigma$ against $1/T$ curves shown in Fig. 7.20(b)). As mentioned in § 7.4.2, these high values also explain why the slopes of the $\ln \sigma$ against $1/T$ plots yield higher activation energies in the liquid than in the solid amorphous state.

The temperature at which $S = k/e$ corresponds to that at which

$(E_F - E_V)$ becomes zero. For As_2Te_3 this is, from Fig. 7.20(a), about 770 K (497° C), at which point the conductivity is observed to be about 200 Ω^{-1} cm^{-1} (Fig. 7.20(b)). As the temperature is increased further, the conductivity becomes less dependent on the temperature and appears to saturate at about 2×10^3 Ω^{-1} cm^{-1}. It is tempting to assume that the mobility gap also closes to zero at the same time as $(E_F - E_V)$ vanishes; however there is always the possibility that E_F is moving rapidly towards E_V until the semiconductor becomes degenerate p-type. Similar curves of σ and S for Se–Te liquid alloys have been obtained by Perron (1967) and were discussed in § 3.17.3.

Analysis of thermopower data becomes less simple when S is small ($\leqslant k/e$ i.e. 86 μV deg^{-1}). If it is small not because of ambipolar conduction but because $(E_F - E_V) \sim kT$, the situation is then the same as in a metal, with the current carried by electrons with energies within a few multiples of kT of the Fermi level. In this case the appropriate formula (§ 2.9.3) is

$$S = \frac{\pi^2}{3} \frac{k^2 T}{e} \left(\frac{\partial \ln \sigma}{\partial E} \right)_{E=E_F}, \qquad (7.23)$$

whether conduction is by hopping or not. If it is not, and the current is carried by electrons in extended states, σ is proportional to $\{N(E)\}^2$. Therefore the sign of S will depend on whether the density of states in the vicinity of E_F increases or decreases with energy. There is no indication of S becoming negative in Edmond's data for As_2Te_3. However, a change of sign in S with temperature has been observed in certain amorphous semiconductors, not of the chalcogenide type, at low temperatures. If $N(E_F)$ is finite, then, even when $(E_F - E_V)$ is large, hopping conduction near E_F is expected at low temperatures (§ 7.4.2), and formula 7.23 should be applicable. A change of sign in S is expected as long as the compensation is less than one-half (compare Chapter 6). Thermoelectric-power data on amorphous germanium will be interpreted in this way in Chapter 8. The change of sign of S at high temperatures reported in Chapter 8 for amorphous Si, and in one instance for amorphous Ge, is due to neither of the above effects, but appears to be because the minority carriers are playing an increasingly important part in the conduction.

Thermoelectric power and conductivity data for a few amorphous semiconductors over a limited temperature range are shown in Fig. 7.21(a) and (b) (from Stuke 1970b). The first point to notice here is that for most of this particular group of materials (tetrahedral coordination) the thermopower was found to be strongly n-type† in contrast to the chalcogenides, which are invariably p-type.

In the light of what has already been said in this section concerning the thermoelectric power, we make the following additional remarks concerning the data shown in Fig. 7.21.

(a) The linearity displayed towards high temperatures is as expected according to equation (7.22). However, as shown in Table 7.3, the

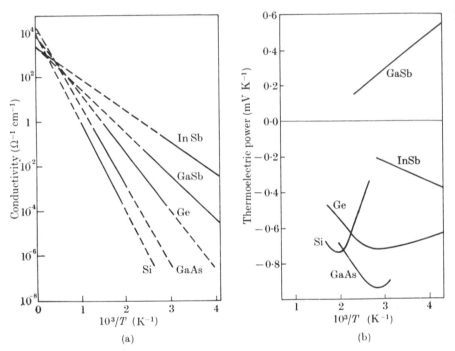

FIG. 7.21. Temperature variation of conductivity and thermoelectric power in various evaporated films of amorphous semiconductors (from Stuke 1970b).

activation energies in all the materials are *less* than the corresponding slopes observed in the conductivity. This difference is in the opposite sense to that observed for the liquid chalcogenide semiconductors (Fig. 7.20), and could be explained in terms of a temperature-activated mobility. However the high values of the extrapolated intercepts on the $1/T$-axis in the conductivity plots, $\sim 10^4 \, \Omega^{-1} \, \mathrm{cm}^{-1}$, do not support

† It should however be pointed out that not all workers agree with these observations. In particular we mention that amorphous Ge has been found p-type by Grigorovici, Croitoru, and Devenyi (1966) and also Chopra and Bahl (1970) As there is also corresponding disagreement on the temperature dependence of conductivity, it seems clear that the properties of this class of materials, which cannot be prepared by melt-quenching, are extremely sensitive to preparative conditions.

such an explanation. Again, effects of two carriers might be involved here.

(b) The decrease in the magnitude of S observed for Ge, Si, and GaAs can be attributed to an increasing contribution to the conductivity from carriers hopping at the Fermi level. Evidence that this is so in the case of germanium (see Chapter 8) comes from a corresponding observation of the $T^{-\frac{1}{4}}$ hopping term in the d.c. conductivity and a change of sign in S at a lower temperature than shown here.

TABLE 7.3

Activation energies (in eV) for conduction as determined from the data of Fig. 7.21. $E^S(0)$ is from the thermopower, $E^\sigma(0)$ from the conductivity.

	$E^S(0)$	$E^\sigma(0)$
InSb	0·12	0·29
GaSb	0·20	0·39
Ge	0·23	0·53
GaAs	0·27	0·70
Si		0·78

7.4.6. Hall effect

In crystalline semiconductors, Hall-voltage measurements are an important complement to conductivity measurements. Interpretation in terms of the microscopic mobility is straightforward for materials in which the mean free path of the carriers is sufficiently long for the Boltzmann equation to be appropriate and in which the energy band structure near the band edges is fairly simple. For carriers with very short mean free path, however, as in an amorphous semiconductor, interpretation in terms of conventional semiconductor theory yields mobilities that are unrealistically low, and, as for some liquid semimetals and certain organic semi-conductors, yields a sign for the carriers that is frequently in contradiction with thermoelectric-power measurements. The recent theory of Friedman (1971) is able to explain this behaviour (see § 2.12).

The Hall voltages observed in amorphous semiconductors are frequently close to the experimental limit of measurement, especially in high-resistivity materials. In these cases special techniques, employing a.c. electric or magnetic fields or both, are necessary. Although the magnitude of the Hall voltage does not seem to be very useful at

present (for determining an absolute mobility), the temperature independence of the Hall mobility commonly observed in amorphous
semiconductors is in accord with Friedman's theory.

Figure 7.22 shows some results on chalcogenide glasses in the solid and
liquid states as obtained by Male (1967). The Hall mobility calculated
from the Hall constant and the conductivity, using the usual formula
for crystalline semiconductors, is seen to be in the region of 10^{-1}
$\mathrm{cm^2\ V^{-1}\ s^{-1}}$, and virtually independent of temperature over a range in
which the conductivity is strongly activated. Furthermore the sign (not

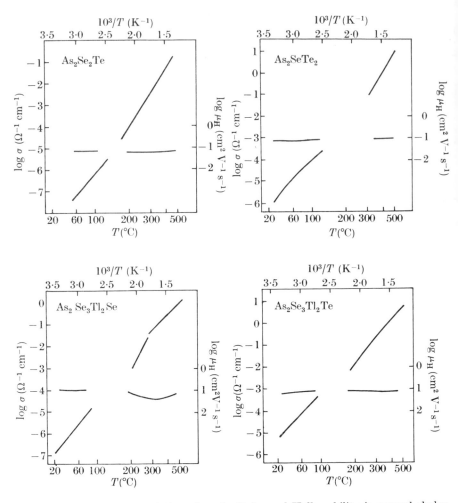

FIG. 7.22. Temperature variation of conductivity and Hall mobility in several chalcogenide glasses in the solid and liquid states (from Male 1967).

indicated) of the Hall effect was found to be negative, in contrast with the thermoelectric power, which is positive in these materials.

In amorphous germanium, Clark (1967) also found a negative Hall effect and estimated a Hall mobility at room temperature of about 10^{-2} cm² V^{-1} s^{-1}. This is close to the experimental limit of measurement using conventional techniques.

7.4.7. *Magnetoresistance*

In crystalline semiconductors measurements of the magnetoresistance, the fractional change $\Delta\rho/\rho$ of resistivity in a magnetic field, can, like the Hall effect, be used to determine carrier mobilities. Normally $\Delta\rho/\rho$ is positive and proportional to the square of the magnetic induction B. For hopping conduction in doped crystalline semiconductors the magnetoresistance can be either positive or negative (see Chapter 6).

Mell and Stuke (1970) have reported magnetoresistance measurements on several amorphous semiconductors using an alternating (1·5 Hz) magnetic field up to 25 kgauss. The magnetoresistance was found to be negative over a wide temperature range. Only at very low magnetic fields and low temperatures was a positive effect found for amorphous germanium (Chapter 8). More recently Mell (private communication) has found a positive effect in amorphous films of InAs and InP. For most materials $\Delta\rho/\rho$ was found to be proportional to B^n, with n being close to unity at high temperatures and falling to a value of the order of one half near room temperature. Figure 7.23 shows the temperature dependence of the magnetoresistance at 25 kG for a number of materials. Following Mell and Stuke (1970), we believe that this negative magnetoresistance is contributed by that part of the current that is carried by electrons hopping with energies near the Fermi level, the fall-off at high temperatures occurring because the current is then mainly due to electrons or holes in extended states where $\Delta\rho/\rho$, like the Hall effect, is small.

At present we do not have a quantitative theory of the nature of this negative magnetoresistance. Any theory ought to be applicable also to impurity-conduction in doped and compensated semiconductors, the difference being that the radii of centres in materials like crystalline germanium is large, so the shrinking of the orbit in a magnetic field, giving a positive magnetoresistance, is important there. Some speculations on the origin of a negative term are given in § 6.13.

16

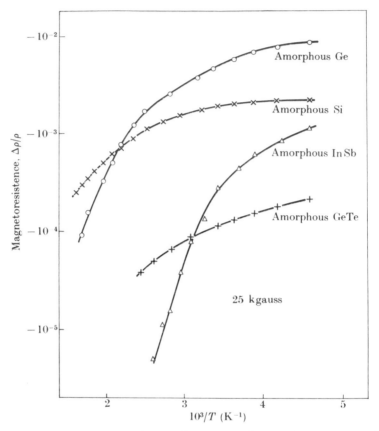

FIG. 7.23. Temperature variation of magnetoresistance in a few amorphous semi-conductors (from Mell and Stuke 1970).

7.4.8. *Thermally stimulated conductivity*

In a semiconductor containing a large density of localized states or trapping levels, considerable storage of charge is likely following termination of a current or light pulse. The rate of decay of this charge will be determined by the rate of release of carriers from their trapping sites, and at low temperatures can be as long as several days. Normally in drift mobility experiments on high-resistivity material, for example, it is essential to work with well-rested samples, which are in a state of true thermal equilibrium. However, by intentionally occupying deep traps at a low temperature and subsequently emptying them during a controlled heating cycle, we can obtain information on the density and depth of trapping levels. The techniques of thermally stimulated conductivity and thermally stimulated emission determine the fraction of released charge that remains available in the conduction or valence band and the fraction that decays radiatively. Theories of these effects are essentially useful approximations to the complex kinetic equations involved. Basically, however, the temperature at which a maximum release occurs yields an estimate for a trap depth, and the area under the curve an estimate of the total density.

Fagen and Fritzsche (1970b) report such measurements on $As_{35}Te_{40}Ge_{11}Si_{11}P_3$, for which glass they estimate $\sim 4 \times 10^{19}$ traps cm^{-3} at a depth 0·43 eV. As this is, within experimental error, equal to the activation energy for d.c. conduction in the dark, it would appear that the experiments detected the high density of levels at E_F, which has been discussed in earlier sections. Similar experiments on amorphous As_2Se_3 by Kolomiets and Mazets (1970) were interpreted in terms of a distribution of levels varying in depth from 0·35 eV to 0·75 eV. It should perhaps be stressed that the technique of thermally stimulated conductivity is not a *precise* method of determining trap parameters, and many assumptions are involved in data reduction.

7.5. Photoconductivity and quantum efficiency

The excess conductivity produced in a semiconductor when exposed to electromagnetic radiation is a function of many parameters. For photoconductivity in the steady state due predominantly to one type of carrier, we can write

$$\Delta\sigma = e\mu \, \Delta n,$$

where Δn is the equilibrium concentration of excess carriers with mobility μ contributing to the conductivity. On our model for amorphous semiconductors, if the photocurrent is carried principally in extended states, the density of carriers effective for photoconductivity will be only a fraction of the total number of excess carriers Δn. This temperature-dependent fraction is given for a particular distribution of localized states later in the section. The total number of excess carriers is given by

$$\Delta n = \tau \eta I_0 (1-R)\{1-\exp(-\alpha d)\}/d \qquad (7.24)$$

for monomolecular recombination characterized by a lifetime τ. The quantity in curly brackets is the number of photons absorbed per second in a sample of thickness d in the direction of the incident radiation. I_0 is the incident flux density, α the absorption coefficient, and R the reflectivity. The quantum efficiency for photogeneration is represented by η. It is normally assumed to be unity for suitable excitation: however it can be measured absolutely.

Many amorphous semiconductors are good photoconductors. Detailed measurements as a function of light intensity, photon energy, and temperature have been made in a few materials. We summarize below some of the principal features observed: detailed results on individual materials will be given in later chapters.

In contrast with most crystalline semiconductors, which exhibit a peak in photoconductivity at a photon energy corresponding to the onset of interband electronic transitions, amorphous semiconductors have a spectral response of photoconductivity that rises at approximately the same frequency as the optical absorption edge and remains relatively constant at higher energies (Fig. 7.24). As the fall-off on the high-energy side of the edge in crystals is attributed to the increased role of surface recombination for carriers generated by strongly absorbed light, this observation presumably implies very similar rates of recombination at the surface and in the bulk. As we shall see in § 7.6.1, the optical absorption edge of nearly all amorphous semiconductors is far from sharp, and in fact is normally characterized by an absorption constant that rises exponentially with photon energy. These two features together make the determination of mobility gaps from photoconductivity data uncertain.

The temperature variation of photoconductivity for strongly absorbed light in a chalcogenide alloy $As_{35}Te_{40}Si_{11}Ge_{11}P_3$ is shown in Fig. 7.25 (from Fagen and Fritzsche 1970b). The maximum exhibited near 250 K is not unique to this material; similar effects have been found by Kolomiets and Lyubin (1960) and by Weiser, Fischer, and Brodsky (1970) in other chalcogenides, and by Tsu, Howard, and Esaki (1970) in GeTe. Following Weiser et $al.$ we suppose that the photocurrent is carried in extended states on either side of the maximum but that the recombination kinetics show a change of character at T_{max}. Below T_{max} the number of thermally generated carriers is assumed negligible and the recombination is bimolecular; above T_{max} the density of thermally generated carriers is larger than that of photo-excited carriers and the recombination is monomolecular. Both processes can be combined in the equation for the rate of change of an excess-carrier density Δp (Blakemore 1962),

$$\mathrm{d}(\Delta p)/\mathrm{d}t = -b\{(\Delta p)^2 + 2n_0\,\Delta p\} + G, \qquad (7.25)$$

where b is the recombination constant, G is the bulk generation rate

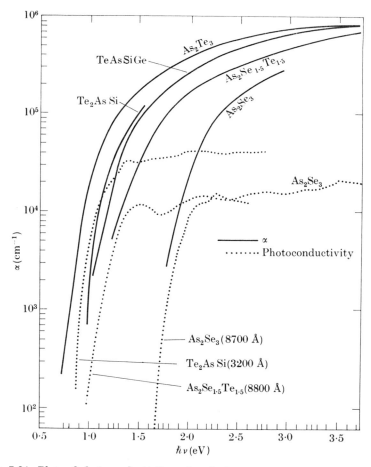

FIG. 7.24. Plots of photoconductivity and optical absorption against photon energy in a few chalcogenide films at room temperature (from Rockstad 1970).

(the quantity in curly brackets in equation (7.24)), and n_0 the density of thermally generated carriers. In the steady state

$$\Delta p = (G/b)^{\frac{1}{2}} \qquad (\Delta p \gg n_0) \qquad \text{bimolecular,}$$
$$\Delta p = G/2bn_0 \qquad (\Delta p \ll n_0) \qquad \text{monomolecular.}$$

Using the notation of Fig. 7.4 and assuming densities of states that are linear with energy, we have for thermally generated electrons

$$n_0 = \int_{E_A}^{\infty} A(E - E_A) \exp\{-(E - E_F)/kT\}\,dE$$
$$= A(kT)^2 \exp\{-(E_A - E_F)/kT\}.$$

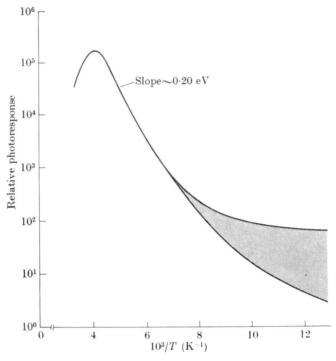

FIG. 7.25. Temperature dependence of photoconductivity in an evaporated film of $As_{45}Te_{30}Si_{11}Ge_{11}P_3$. At the peak, $\Delta\sigma/\sigma \sim 0.1$ in a flux of 2×10^{14} photons $cm^{-2}s^{-1}$ at $1.06\ \mu m$. The shaded area indicates sample-to-sample variations (after Fagen and Fritzsche 1970b).

Thus Δp is temperature dependent only for the case of monomolecular recombination.

The density of excess carriers Δp_{free} contributing to the photocurrent will be that at energies just below E_V. It is easily shown that for Boltzmann statistics

$$\Delta p_{free}/\Delta p = (1+\Delta E_V/kT)\exp\{-\Delta E_V/kT\}.$$

Thus for bimolecular recombination the photocurrent will be proportional to

$$\Delta p_{free} = (G/b)^{\frac{1}{2}}(1+\Delta E_V/kT)\exp(-\Delta E_V/kT), \qquad (7.26)$$

and for monomolecular recombination to

$$\Delta p_{free}$$
$$= (G/2bAk^2T^2)(1+\Delta E_V/kT)\exp\{(E_A-E_F)/kT\}\exp\{-\Delta E_V/kT\}.$$
$$(7.27)$$

From these two equations we expect the photoconductivity at low temperatures to be proportional to the square root of the incident light intensity and to exhibit a negative temperature coefficient such that

$$d(\ln \Delta\sigma)/d(1/T) \sim -\Delta E_V.$$

At high temperatures the photoconductivity should be proportional to the first power of the light intensity and exhibit a positive temperature coefficient, such that $d(\ln \Delta\sigma)/d(1/T) \sim (E_A - E_F) - \Delta E_V$.

Weiser, Fischer, and Brodsky's results on $2As_2Te_3 . As_2Se_3$ are reproduced in Fig. 7.26(a) and (b). Under conditions (low T, high intensity) where the photoconductance displays a square-root dependence on light intensity, the slope on a plot of $\ln \Delta\Sigma$ against $1/T$ is -0.18 eV, and under conditions (high T, low intensity) where the dependence on light intensity is linear, it is 0.13 eV. A value for ΔE_V of 0.18 eV is of the same order as estimated in other materials by, for example, drift mobility studies. Combined together, these energy values yield $(E_A - E_F) = 0.31$ eV. If the Fermi energy is assumed to be mid-way between E_A and E_B, a value for $(E_F - E_V)$ of 0.49 eV is obtained. This is in good agreement with the value 0.47 eV obtained from dark-conductivity measurements (the material is p-type). It should be mentioned that Weiser et al. (1970) suggest a somewhat different interpretation of ΔE_V. They believe that it represents the depth of a 'recombination edge' on the Cohen–Fritzsche–Ovshinsky (1969) model.

Monomolecular and bimolecular recombination processes have also been observed at temperatures respectively above and below the photoconductivity maximum in the material studied by Fagen and Fritzsche (Fig. 7.25). Interpretation of this data in the way described above suggests $\Delta E_V \sim 0.2$ eV. The decrease in activation energy at low temperatures suggests that here the photocurrent is carried in localized states, but we have not attempted an analysis.

Studies of transient photoconductivity in several amorphous semiconductors indicate that the response is fast, with rise times to be measured in microseconds at low temperatures and fractions of a microsecond at high temperatures. Measurements on GeTe have been reported by Tsu, Howard, and Esaki (1970). The decay of photoconductivity following cessation of excitation exhibits a similar fast component followed by a much slower process. For bimolecular recombination in films of $2As_2Te_3 . As_2Se_3$ Weiser et al. (1970) find the expected logarithmic dependence on time for the fast component. The slow decay

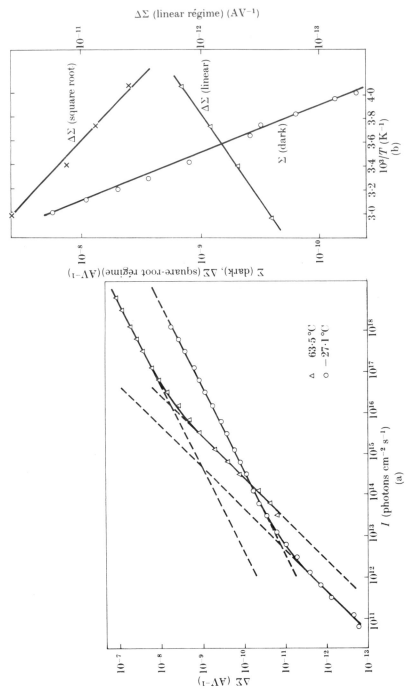

Fig. 7.26. Photoconductivity in amorphous $2As_2Te_3.As_2Se_3$. (a) Photoconductance $\Delta\Sigma$ against photon flux at two temperatures using He–Ne laser (6328 Å) excitation. (b) Photoconductance $\Delta\Sigma$ (linear and square-root régimes of (a)) and dark conductance Σ against inverse temperature. Cross-sectional rea $0.6 \times 200\ \mu m$, distance between electrodes $10\ \mu m$ (from Weiser, Fischer, and Brodsky 1970).

process indicates considerable deep trapping for some of the photo-generated carriers, a feature that is also born out by the thermally stimulated conductivity experiments described in § 7.4.8.

Photoconductivity experiments are normally made with coplanar electrodes in a surface cell geometry. If a sandwich cell, of the type described for drift mobility studies, is used, it is possible to make direct measurements of quantum efficiency, that is of the number of free electron–hole pairs generated per absorbed photon. The technique involves the use of strongly absorbed, pulsed excitation and sufficiently high electric fields to ensure that the drifting carriers do not suffer a range limitation due to deep trapping during their passage across the film. Extensive measurements of this kind have been made on amorphous Se by Tabak and Warter (1968) and Pai and Ing (1968), and on amorphous As_2S_3 by Ing and Neyhart (private communication). Several new and interesting features arise from these studies: the quantum efficiency is found to depend on photon energy, temperature, and electric field, reaching unity only for high values of these parameters.

Figure 7.27 (from Hartke and Regensburger 1965) compares the quantum efficiency and optical absorption edges in amorphous selenium at room temperature. The quantum efficiency does not saturate at unity until a photon energy $\sim$3 eV is reached. Although it is not obvious where exactly to locate the optical absorption edge (this problem will be discussed in § 7.6), it is clear that there is considerable absorption at 2·1 eV, at which energy the quantum efficiency has fallen to very small values.

Hartke and Regensburger offered an explanation for the gap between the optical absorption and quantum efficiency edges in amorphous selenium that depended on the assumption that the predominant mode of optical absorption near the edge is into exciton states. The lack of any sharp feature in the absorption spectra that could be associated with excitons was supposed to arise from a considerable broadening of the line due to the disordered nature of the lattice. If the component that gives rise to photoconductivity was subtracted from the optical absorption, it was found possible to 'extract' an exciton peak from the absorption curve and to calculate its parameters. A hydrogen-like exciton of radius $\sim$13 Å and binding energy $\sim$0·08 eV was postulated.

An alternative explanation has been suggested by Chen (1970) and by Lucovsky (1970) who believe that the non-photoconducting absorption results from the creation of *localized* excited states of Se ring molecules.

Se$_8$ rings are known to be present in the amorphous phase. The observation that a similar phenomenon occurs in orthorhombic sulphur (see Cook and Spear 1969 and references cited there) lends support to this model. The model therefore regards the non-photoconducting absorption in amorphous Se as arising from the molecular rather than the disordered nature of the material; it does not explain the fall in

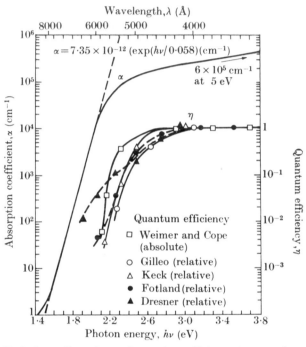

FIG. 7.27. Optical absorption edge and quantum efficiency in amorphous selenium at room temperature (from Hartke and Regensburger 1965).

quantum efficiency with photon energy observed in amorphous As$_2$S$_3$ and As$_2$Se$_3$ (Felty and Myers, private communication) unless molecular units exist in these materials also.

Even in the absence of localized excitations one might expect in amorphous semiconductors a reduced probability for separation of photogenerated carrier pairs. Initially, the two carriers share an excess kinetic energy equal to $(\hbar\omega - E_0)$, where E_0 is the optical gap. The rate of loss of this energy is expected to be high in view of the high frequency of scattering events, and thermalization can occur in a time so short that the carriers trying to diffuse apart find themselves still under the influence of their mutual Coulomb attraction. This idea is the basis behind the explanation proposed by Davis (1970) and Davis and Mott (1970) for a wavelength dependence of quantum efficiency. The quantum efficiency for the generation of free pairs cannot reach unity unless the pair diffuse apart a distance R such that $e^2/\kappa R$ is, say, $2kT$. The distance R can be written $(Dt)^{\frac{1}{2}}$ where D is the diffusion constant of order $\hbar/6m$ (§ 2.9) and t is the thermalization time. Assuming that the rate of emission of phonons during thermalization is of the same order as the phonon frequency ν_{ph} itself, t is given by

$$t = (\hbar\omega - E_0)/h\nu_{ph}. \tag{7.28}$$

The quantum efficiency therefore reaches unity when the photon energy exceeds E_0 by

$$3\pi m e^4 (\nu_{ph}/\kappa kT)^2.$$

At room temperature, for $\kappa = 6$ and $h\nu_{ph} = 0\cdot04\,\text{eV}$ (values appropriate for Se), this is $\sim 0\cdot5\,\text{eV}$.

The electric-field dependence of quantum efficiency observed in amorphous selenium (Chapter 10) can be explained by an extension of these ideas. In an electric field F the Coulomb potential is modified so that the effective barrier for escape is lowered by an amount proportional to $F^{\frac{1}{2}}$ (just as in the Poole–Frenkel mechanism § 7.8). Details of the calculation are given in Davis (1970).

7.6. Optical absorption

In Fig.7.18 the optical absorption in amorphous As_2Se_3 was shown over a very wide frequency range. This section is concerned with those absorption processes that occur at the higher end of the frequency spectrum, particularly those associated with interband electronic transitions. In § 7.6.1 we consider the fundamental absorption edge, which lies in the materials with which we are mainly concerned between $0\cdot3$ and $2\cdot5\,\text{eV}$. The absorption at slightly higher energies ($\alpha \geqslant 10^4$ cm^{-1}), which may provide information on the combined density of states at the valence-band and conduction-band edges, is discussed in § 7.6.2. Interband absorption involving valence and conduction states lying deeper in their respective bands is the subject of § 7.6.3. The recent use of synchrotron radiation extends the range normally covered by ultraviolet spectroscopy (6–15 eV) out to several hundred eV and enables the observation of absorption due to transitions from deep-lying atomic-like levels to the conduction band.

Reference to Fig. 7.18 shows a region of the spectrum in the range

10^{14}–10^{15} s^{-1} in which no measurements are presented for As_2Se_3. It is in this range that intraband or free-carrier absorption could be detected if it were not for impurity and structure-dependent absorption, which frequently dominates the spectrum of materials on the low-energy side of the fundamental edge. There is, however, some evidence for intraband absorption in As_2Se_3 at high temperatures (liquid phase) when the d.c. conductivity is greater than 10^{-2} Ω^{-1} cm^{-1}, and at room temperature in chalcogenides with a smaller band gap. Intraband absorption will be the subject of § 7.6.5.

Absorption by phonons (infrared and Raman absorption) will be discussed in § 7.6.6.

Perhaps the most important feature of optical absorption processes in amorphous semiconductors is that certain selection rules (particularly that of k conservation), which apply to optically induced transitions in crystalline materials, are relaxed.

7.6.1. Absorption edges and Urbach's rule

Before discussing the optical absorption edges observed in amorphous semiconductors, it may be useful to review briefly the types of edges that have been found in crystals and their interpretation.

Basically there are two types of optical transition that can occur at the fundamental edge of crystalline semiconductors, direct and indirect. Both involve the interaction of an electromagnetic wave with an electron in the valence band, which is raised across the fundamental gap to the conduction band. However, indirect transitions also involve simultaneous interaction with lattice vibrations. Thus the wave vector of the electron can change in the optical transition, the momentum change being taken or given up by phonons. (The radiation imparts negligible momentum to the electron.)

If exciton formation or electron–hole interaction is neglected for the moment, the forms of the absorption coefficient α as a function of photon energy $\hbar\omega$ depend on the type of energy bands containing the initial and final states. For simple parabolic bands they are:

For direct transitions

$$\alpha n_0 \hbar\omega \sim (\hbar\omega - E_0)^n, \tag{7.29}$$

where $n = \frac{1}{2}$ or $\frac{3}{2}$ depending on whether the transition is allowed or forbidden in the quantum-mechanical sense. E_0 is the optical gap and n_0 the refractive index. This type of absorption, shown schematically in Fig. 7.28(a), is independent of temperature apart from any variation in E_0.

For indirect transitions

$$\alpha n_0 \hbar \omega \sim \frac{(\hbar\omega - E_0 + h\nu_{\mathrm{ph}})^n}{\exp(h\nu_{\mathrm{ph}}/kT) - 1} + \frac{(\hbar\omega - E_0 - h\nu_{\mathrm{ph}})^n}{1 - \exp(-h\nu_{\mathrm{ph}}/kT)}. \tag{7.30}$$

The two terms here represent contributions from transitions involving phonon absorption and emission respectively, and have different coefficients of proportionality and temperature dependences. For allowed transitions $n = 2$ and for forbidden transitions $n = 3$ (Fig. 7.28(b)). In each case, multiple-phonon processes can occur, leading to additional pairs of terms.

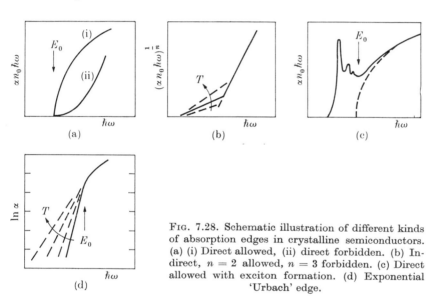

FIG. 7.28. Schematic illustration of different kinds of absorption edges in crystalline semiconductors. (a) (i) Direct allowed, (ii) direct forbidden. (b) Indirect, $n = 2$ allowed, $n = 3$ forbidden. (c) Direct allowed with exciton formation. (d) Exponential 'Urbach' edge.

In general, both direct and indirect transitions can occur in a crystalline semiconductor. However, in materials in which the smallest gap is a direct one, indirect transitions, which are associated with smaller absorption coefficients, are not observed. An exception to this is the special case of vertical transitions involving absorption of a phonon of very small wave vector.

All the above types of optical transitions are modified in materials in which the electron–hole interaction cannot be ignored. The mutual attraction allows bound states of the electron and hole, namely excitons, to be formed, with energy less than that of the free pair. For direct allowed transitions, absorption into these exciton states is in the form of a hydrogenic spectrum below the continuum at E_0. Moreover the continuum itself is modified in shape. For direct forbidden transitions the $n = 1$ line is missing and the continuum absorption, although increased above the edge, starts at $\alpha = 0$.

For allowed and forbidden indirect transitions, inclusion of electron–hole interaction does not lead to a series of absorption lines, transitions into bound exciton states giving rise to a continuous absorption. However, additional terms similar to those in equation (7.30) will occur, corresponding to the transitions into bound exciton states. For these the power n is $\frac{1}{2}$ and $\frac{3}{2}$ for allowed and forbidden transitions respectively. For transitions into the continuum the corresponding power laws are $\frac{3}{2}$ and $\frac{5}{2}$.

Examples of most of the above relationships have been observed in crystalline semiconductors, and detailed investigations on certain materials have yielded considerable information concerning the electronic structure at the band extrema.

A completely different type of optical absorption edge is observed in several materials, in particular the alkali halides, CdS, and trigonal selenium. It is an absorption constant that increases as the exponential of the photon energy. Thus, in contrast with 'direct allowed' edges, for example, which lead to a rather rapid rise in the absorption coefficient over several decades within a few tenths of an eV near the forbidden gap, one observes in this case a gradual increase in the absorption extending over perhaps several eV. This so-called Urbach edge (Urbach 1953; Dexter and Knox 1965) frequently obeys the empirical relationship

$$\alpha = \alpha_0 \exp\{\gamma'(\hbar\omega - E_0)/kT\}, \tag{7.31}$$

where γ' is a constant and T is the absolute temperature down to a critical value T_0 ($\sim$100 K) and equal to T_0 for lower temperatures. Thus the edge becomes broader as the temperature rises above T_0 (Fig. 28(d)).

No single explanation has been accepted for this behaviour in crystalline materials, which is unfortunate in view of the fact that, as we shall see, it appears to be the type of edge most characteristic in amorphous semiconductors. A short review of the theoretical situation has been given by Hopfield (1968). We shall briefly summarize the various models that have been proposed.

(a) *Bound exciton interacting with lattice vibrations.* Toyozawa (1959, 1964) first proposed that the normal Gaussian shape of an exciton line becomes exponential in its leading edge when quadratic terms in its interaction with phonons are considered. This theory seems to account for the exponential tails observed in alkali halides particularly well. The difficulty seems to be in justifying the fact that the quadratic terms outweigh the linear terms in the interaction. For other theoretical treatments based on the same ideas the reader should see Mahr (1963), Mahan (1966), and Keil (1966).

(b) *Electric-field broadening of the absorption edge.* In the presence of an electric field, the absorption coefficient associated with direct allowed transitions between parabolic bands is modified in the manner shown in Fig. 7.29. At photon energies below the onset of absorption without the field, an approximately exponential tail is introduced, and

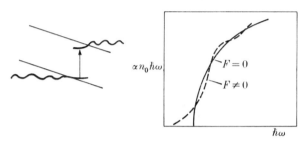

FIG. 7.29. Schematic illustration of Franz–Keldysh effect and the effect on a direct allowed optical absorption edge.

at higher energies the absorption coefficient oscillates. The 'red shift' at low energies is the Franz–Keldysh effect and is due to a finite probability for tunnelling of the band Bloch states into the energy gap. Clearly, if this explanation is invoked to explain Urbach behaviour, then the origin of the electric field has to be considered. In principle this could arise from charged impurity states (Redfield 1963). However, the temperature dependence of the slope must be taken into account in any proposed model. Dexter (1967) introduces this by postulating that the electric field arises from the vibrating atoms in the material. In ionic solids optical phonons are involved; in the more covalent materials instantaneous changes in electronic charge clouds have to be invoked. The magnitude of the effect depends on the electron–phonon interaction, which is strong in piezoelectric solids like CdS and trigonal Se.

(c) *Electric-field broadening of an exciton line.* Dow and Redfield (1970) treated the problem of absorption for direct excitonic transitions in a uniform electric field. A numerical study of the shape of the absorption showed that, in contrast with the Franz–Keldysh results, its variation with photon energy is *accurately* exponential. These authors therefore propose that the 'spectral' Urbach rule arises from an electric-field broadening of an exciton line. Fig. 7.30(a) shows the results of the calculations. The parameter f is the electric field strength expressed as the ratio of the potential-energy drop due to the field across the radius of the exciton to the exciton binding energy. The Bohr radius a of the exciton ground state and the Rydberg constant R are given by

$$a = \hbar^2\kappa/m^*e^2, \qquad R = e^2/2\kappa a = m^*e^4/2\kappa^2\hbar^2,$$

where m^* is the reduced mass of the electron–hole pair. Thus

$$f = F|e|a/R$$
$$= 3\cdot89 \times 10^{-10}(m/m^*)^2\kappa^3 F,$$

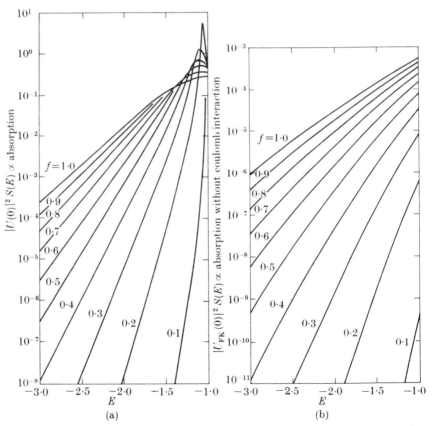

FIG. 7.30. Dow and Redfield's theory for optical absorption in the presence of an electric field: (a) exciton effects included; (b) exciton effects not included (Franz–Keldysh result). The parameter f is a measure of the strength of the electric field. The energy E is measured from the energy gap in units of the binding energy of the unperturbed exciton (from Dow and Redfield 1970).

where m is the free-electron mass and F is in V cm^{-1}. For $m^* = m$ and $\kappa = 6$, the line marked $f = 0\cdot6$ corresponds to a field $\sim 7 \times 10^6$ V cm^{-1}. It is interesting that a classical criterion for direct field ionization of an exciton ($F_c = \kappa R^2/4e^3$) corresponds to $f = 0\cdot125$. As seen from the curves, a discernible exciton peak remains for fields almost an order of magnitude larger than this. The influence of the electron–hole interaction on the shape of absorption curves can be seen by comparing with Fig. 7.30(b) in which the Coulomb interaction has been 'turned off', giving the normal Franz–Keldysh result

$$\alpha = \alpha_0 \exp\{C(\hbar\omega - E_0)^{\frac{3}{2}}\}.$$

If Dow and Redfield's model is a correct description of Urbach's rule, it is of course still necessary to consider the origin of the internal electric field and the temperature dependence of the slope. This point will be returned to later.

As mentioned above, the fundamental absorption edge in most amorphous semiconductors follows an exponential law, i.e. ln α is proportional to $\hbar\omega$. At the time of writing, only thin films of Ge and Si and perhaps InSb stand out as notable exceptions. (Absorption edges in these materials will be presented in Chapter 8.) However, because of the experimental difficulties associated with measuring small values of the absorption constant in thin films, it is not easy to test for exponential behaviour in those amorphous semiconductors that can be prepared only in this form. Verification of exponential behaviour is thus established with certainty only for those amorphous semiconductors that can be obtained as a glass by melt quenching, even though of course thin films of these materials are used for transmission measurements at high values of α. Figure 7.31 shows the room-temperature absorption edges of a few amorphous semiconductors. Exponential behaviour is observed up to $\alpha = 10^2$ cm^{-1} in some materials, up to 10^4 cm^{-1} in others.

As discussed above there are several plausible explanations for the existence of an exponential absorption edge. In amorphous semiconductors there is an additional possibility, which has been suggested by many authors, namely that it arises from electronic transitions between (localized) states in the band-edge tails, the density of which is assumed to fall off exponentially with energy (Tauc 1970a; Lanyon 1963). We think that this explanation is unlikely (see Davis and Mott 1970). The main evidence against such an interpretation is that, as shown in Fig. 7.31 and Table 7.4, slopes of the observed exponential

17

absorption edges are very much the same in a variety of materials: it would seem unlikely that the state tailing is so similar. It seems more likely that any contribution to the absorption due to transitions from or into any density-of-states tails in amorphous semiconductors must contribute only a small part to the observed absorption.

In view of the likely presence of strong internal fields in amorphous semiconductors and the accurately exponential behaviour predicted by

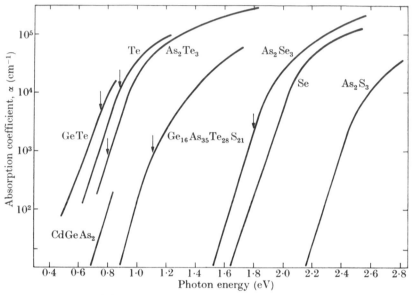

FIG. 7.31. Exponential absorption edges in amorphous semiconductors at room temperature (references as for Table 7.4). The arrows mark the value of $2E$ for those materials in which the electrical conductivity has been observed to obey the relation

$$\sigma = C \exp{(-E/kT)}.$$

Dow and Redfield's theory for field broadening of an exciton line, this model is obviously attractive as an explanation for the type of edge shown in Fig. 7.31. If the average of the observed slopes (Table 7.4) is taken as 17 eV^{-1}, the corresponding value of the parameter f in Fig. 7.30(a) is ~ 0.5 for $\kappa = 6$ and ~ 1.0 for $\kappa = 8$ (assuming $m^* = m$). Before proceeding further we should pay attention to the following questions:

(a) Do excitons exist in amorphous semiconductors?

(b) What possible sources are there of internal electric fields?

(c) If the fields are random and have a spatial variation in magnitude, do they average to give the same result as a constant uniform field?

With regard to (a) we do not know of any theoretical treatment, but it is obvious that the Coulomb field $e^2/\kappa r^2$ between electron and hole exists as in crystals and should lead to bound states. Furthermore, the dielectric constants of most chalcogenide glasses are not high, and, unless the effective mass of either carrier is very small, fairly large binding energies are possible. However, even in the absence of an electric field, strong scattering of the exciton should occur leading to

TABLE 7.4

Approximate values of Γ for the amorphous semiconductors of Fig. 7.31 in the region where $\alpha = \alpha_0' \exp(\Gamma\hbar\omega)$, and values of the photon energy $\hbar\omega$ corresponding to $\alpha = 10^2$ cm^{-1} ($T = 300$ K).

	Γ(eV^{-1})	$\gamma' = \Gamma kT$	$\hbar\omega(\alpha = 10^2$ cm^{-1}) (eV)	Reference
GeTe	15	0·38	0·50	Bahl and Chopra (1969)
Te	18	0·47	0·61	Stuke (1970a)
As$_2$Te$_3$	19	0·49	0·70	Rockstad (1970)
CdGeAs$_2$	19	0·49	0·80	Cervinka et al. (1970)
Ge$_{16}$As$_{35}$Te$_{28}$Si$_{21}$	22	0·57	0·99	Fagen et al. (1970)
As$_2$Se$_3$	20	0·52	1·64	Edmond (1966) (from Owen 1970)
Se	17	0·44	1·77	Hartke and Regensburger (1965)
As$_2$S$_3$	19	0·49	2·28	Kosek and Tauc (1970)

a breakdown in the k selection rule, so no *sharp* absorption lines would be expected.

As regards the origin of internal electric fields in amorphous semiconductors we may consider longitudinal optical phonons (as Dexter (1967) did in crystalline materials); or static spatial fluctuations in potential due to the lack of long-range order or variations in density; or charged defect centres. It is not easy to calculate the magnitude of the electric fields produced by these possible sources without knowledge of specific parameters (Tauc 1970b).

With regard to (c), general calculations are difficult (Bonch-Bruevich 1970a,b; Lukes and Somaratna 1970; Redfield 1963). It is relevant to note that experimental evidence has been obtained for exponential broadening of absorption edges by electric fields created by charged impurities in crystals (Afromowitz and Redfield 1968).

Any model that is invoked to explain exponential absorption edges in amorphous semiconductors should consider the effect of temperature.

Experimentally it is observed that there is only a slight change of slope with temperature below room temperature. There is, as might be expected, a displacement towards lower photon energies as the temperature is raised, but this presumably simply reflects the temperature coefficient of a gap. Above room temperature (from data on a limited number of materials) the slope decreases as the temperature is raised. However, it appears necessary to reach the liquid state before the temperature dependence predicted by Urbach's empirical rule (equation (7.31)) is obeyed. Thus, for amorphous semiconductors, T_0 is considerably higher than in crystalline materials obeying Urbach's rule. Results on specific materials will be presented in later chapters. If the exciton model with electric-field broadening is appropriate, then the temperature dependence of the dielectric constant will certainly be involved, although probably not to the third power as in Dow and Redfield's theory, because F itself will probably be proportional to at least $1/\kappa$. If the field is considered to arise from longitudinal optical phonons, then it may be possible to account for the high value of T_0 by regarding the amorphous state as one that contains a large concentration of frozen-in phonons.

The effect of hydrostatic pressure on exponential absorption edges has been measured in only a few materials (see Chapter 9). In these, a parallel shift to lower energies with increasing pressure has been found. Presumably this displacement merely reflects the pressure coefficient $(\partial E_0/\partial P)_T$ of some gap E_0. It is interesting that in the materials studied, the sign of this quantity is opposite to that expected from the sign of the temperature coefficient $(\partial E_0/\partial T)_P$ referred to above. Either an increase in temperature or an increase in pressure shift the edge to lower energies. The coefficients are related by the thermodynamic relationship

$$\left(\frac{\partial E_0}{\partial T}\right)_P = \left(\frac{\partial E_0}{\partial T}\right)_V - \frac{\alpha_V}{K_s}\left(\frac{\partial E_0}{\partial P}\right)_T, \qquad (7.32)$$

where α_V is the volume expansivity $(\mathrm{d}V/\mathrm{d}T)_P/V$ and K_s the compressibility $-(\mathrm{d}V/\mathrm{d}P)_T/V$. The second term is the contribution to $(\partial E_0/\partial T)_P$ due to dilation and, with the negative sign in front, makes a positive contribution. As $(\partial E_0/\partial P)_T$ is negative, $(\partial E_0/\partial T)_V$ must make a sizeable negative contribution. However it appears that this behaviour, not common in most crystalline materials in which $(\partial E_0/\partial T)_V$ is normally rather small and attributable to electron–phonon interaction (Fan 1951), is not characteristic of the amorphous state. In Chapter 9 we show that a similar behaviour occurs in crystalline As_2Se_3 and similar materials.

In view of the uncertainties concerning the nature of the exponential absorption edges in amorphous semiconductors, we may ask whether it is possible to define an *optical gap*. In crystalline materials obeying Urbach's rule, a gap is normally determined by locating the *focal point* of the family of edges obtained as a function of temperature. Thus, allowing E_0 in equation (7.31) to be a linear function of temperature, so that $E_0 = E_0(0) - \beta T$, we obtain

$$\alpha = \alpha_0 \exp[\gamma'\{\hbar\omega - E_0(0) + \beta T\}/kT].$$

The absorption coefficient is thus independent of T when $\hbar\omega = E_0(0)$, and this is the focal point. In trigonal selenium for example (Roberts, Tutihasi, and Keezer 1968), it lies at $\alpha = 10^5$ cm^{-1}. As the temperature dependence of Urbach's rule is not normally seen in solid amorphous semiconductors, this procedure cannot be used. In the next section we shall show how the form of the absorption above the exponential edge may be extrapolated to give an optical gap. This energy frequently turns out to lie close to the 'knee' of the absorption edge, i.e. the energy where ln α ceases to be linear with $\hbar\omega$. However, this is a very crude marker, and as we shall see it is expected to give values less than the mobility gap.

It has been pointed out by Stuke (1970a) that the mobility gap in many amorphous semiconductors corresponds to a photon energy at which the optical absorption coefficient has a value $\sim 10^4$ cm^{-1}. The assumption here is that the mobility gap is equal to twice the acti-vation energy for electrical conduction (or twice the slope of a plot of ln σ against $1/kT$), i.e. that conduction is truly intrinsic. If this is not the case then the value twice the activation energy observed in electrical conduction is not a quantity of particular significance. In addition, one should correct the slope of a curve plotting ln σ against $1/kT$ for any temperature variation of the mobility gap in order to compare it with a room-temperature absorption curve. Applying this correction would lead to the positioning of the mobility gap for values of the absorption coefficient near 10^3 cm^{-1}.

As mentioned above, both amorphous Ge and amorphous Si have been reported to exhibit sharp absorption edges, and of course there is then no problem in defining an optical gap. Results on these materials will be presented in Chapter 8. We point out here that if field-broadened exciton lines are responsible for exponential edges, then there are two possible reasons for their non-occurrence. Firstly, the excitons could have small binding energies because of high dielectric constants; secondly, if the field is assumed to arise from longitudinal optical phonons, this will be negligible in materials like Ge and Si in which the dipole moment of such phonons is zero (Tauc 1970b). The form of the absorption edges should then be as calculated in the next section.

7.6.2. Interband absorption

In this section we discuss the form of the optical absorption edge expected in amorphous semiconductors in the absence of any electric-field or exciton effects. The results should be appropriate for those amorphous semiconductors that do not exhibit the exponential edge (e.g. Ge and Si) and for other materials at photon energies above the exponential tail. The following assumptions are also made:

(a) The matrix elements for the electronic transitions are constant over the range of photon energies of interest.

(b) The k-conservation selection rule is relaxed. This assumption is made in amorphous semiconductors because, near the band edges at least, $\Delta k \sim k$ and thus k is not a good quantum number. There is evidence (Berglund and Spicer 1964) for a relaxation of the k-conservation rule for some interband transitions even in certain crystalline materials. In an E–k diagram such transitions would be non-vertical. However, no phonon absorption or emission processes are invoked to conserve energy: all the energy required is provided by the incident photons. Such transitions are termed *non-direct* as opposed to *indirect*. Interaction with the lattice is, of course, required to satisfy momentum conservation, but the momentum is thought to be transferred to the solid as a whole rather than to phonons.

The conductivity at frequency ω was given in § 2.3:

$$\sigma(\omega) = \frac{2\pi e^2 \hbar^3 \Omega}{m^2} \int \frac{N(E)N(E+\hbar\omega)\,|D|^2\,\mathrm{d}E}{\hbar\omega}, \qquad (7.33)$$

where Ω is the volume of the specimen and D the matrix element of $\partial/\partial x$. The corresponding absorption coefficient is given by

$$\alpha = (4\pi/n_0 c)\sigma(\omega),$$

where n_0 is the refractive index.

The matrix element D for transitions between states in different bands will be taken to be the same as that for transitions between extended states in the same band, without the factor m/m^* (§ 2.5), so that

$$D = \pi(a/\Omega)^{\frac{1}{2}},$$

where a is the average lattice spacing. It should be pointed out that we are taking the matrix element to be the same whether or not either the initial or final state, or both, are localized. This is an assumption that needs justifying. The argument given in Davis and Mott (1970) is that the smaller value of D that may be expected when the wave functions are localized is compensated by the increased value of the normalization factor. However, when both initial and final states are localized the lack of spatial overlap between states may cut down D to small values.

Neglecting for the moment this last possibility, we find for interband transitions (ignoring the variation of n_0 with $\hbar\omega$)

$$\alpha(\omega) = \frac{8\pi^4 e^2 \hbar^2 a}{n_0 c m^2 \omega} \int N_V(E) N_C(E+\hbar\omega)\, dE, \qquad (7.34)$$

where the integration is over all pairs of states in the valence and conduction bands separated by an energy $\hbar\omega$.

Without knowledge of the form of $N(E)$ at the band edges it is speculative to take the calculation further. Tsu, Howard, and Esaki (1970) have used an integral expression of the above kind and derived $N(E)$ from measured absorption data. This of course involves the assumption that $N_C(E) = N_V(-E)$ (only the product of the densities of states is determined in an optical absorption experiment). In amorphous GeTe they found that, above the exponential tail, $N(E) \sim E^{\frac{1}{2}}$ and thus

$$\alpha(\omega) = \text{const.}\,(\hbar\omega - E_0)^2/\hbar\omega.$$

This relation, which is of a form similar to that for indirect transitions in crystalline semiconductors, had been given previously by Tauc (1970a) under the assumption of parabolic bands. The absorption in many amorphous semiconductors is observed to obey this relation above the exponential tails. A few examples are shown in Fig. 7.32. The constant E_0 can be used to define an optical gap, although it may represent an extrapolated rather than a real zero in the density of states.

The same relation has been derived by Davis and Mott (1970). Their assumptions are different from those used by Tauc. Using the notation

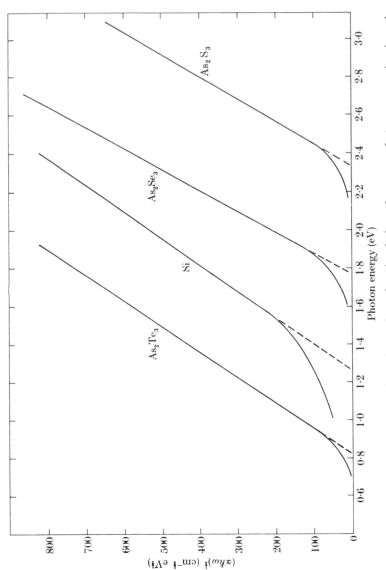

Fig. 7.32. Examples of absorption edges whose functional dependence on photon energy is given by $\alpha\hbar\omega = B(\hbar\omega - E_0)^2$. Data for As_2Te_3 from Rockstad (1970); Si from Brodsky, Title, Weiser, and Pettit (1970); As_2Se_3 and As_2S_3 from Felty and Myers (private communication). Not all authors agree precisely on the values of the slope and intercept for these materials—see Chapters 8 and 9 for other examples.

of Fig. 7.4(a) and assuming that the density of states at the band edges are linear functions of the energy, also that

$$N(E_C) = N(E_V), \qquad E_C - E_A = E_B - E_V = \Delta E,$$

and that transitions in which both the initial and final states are localized can be neglected, we find from equation (7.34)

$$\alpha(\omega) = (4\pi/n_0 c)\sigma_0(\hbar\omega - E_0)^2/\hbar\omega \, \Delta E. \qquad (7.35)$$

Here, E_0 is $(E_A - E_V)$ or $(E_C - E_B)$, whichever is the smaller, and

$$\sigma_0 = (2\pi^3 e^2 \hbar^3 a/m^2)\{N(E_C)\}^2$$

is the quantity discussed in Chapter 2 and in § 7.4.2. We can make a rough estimate of the magnitude of the absorption coefficient

TABLE 7.5

Room-temperature experimental values of E_0 and B for a few amorphous semiconductors whose optical absorption coefficient α obeys the relation $\alpha\hbar\omega = B(\hbar\omega - E_0)^2$ in a range of photon energies above the exponential edge.

	E_0 (eV)	B (cm^{-1}eV^{-1})	Reference
GeTe	0·70	$2·1 \times 10^5$	Tsu, Howard, and Esaki (1970)
As$_2$Te$_3$	0·83	$4·7 \times 10^5$	Weiser and Brodsky (1970)
	0·82	$5·4 \times 10^5$	Rockstad (1970)
Si	1·26	$5·2 \times 10^5$	Brodsky, Title, Weiser, and Pettit (1970)
As$_2$Se$_3$	1·76	$8·3 \times 10^5$	Felty and Myers (private communication)
As$_2$S$_3$	2·32	4×10^5	Felty and Myers (private communication)

by taking $\Delta E \sim 0·2$ eV, $n_0 = 4$, and $\sigma_0 \sim 200 \, \Omega^{-1}$ cm^{-1}. Thus, if energies are in eV,

$$\alpha(\omega) \sim 10^5(\hbar\omega - E_0)^2/\hbar\omega \text{ cm}^{-1}. \qquad (7.36)$$

In Table 7.5 values of B and E_0 are given for a few amorphous semiconductors whose optical absorption obeys the relationships $\alpha\hbar\omega = B(\hbar\omega - E_0)^2$. In certain cases the above relationship holds over a much larger range of photon energies than is consistent with our estimate of ΔE. At higher photon energies, Tauc's assumption of parabolic bands may therefore be more appropriate.

There are some notable exceptions to the quadratic frequency
dependence of the absorption coefficient, and it should not therefore
be regarded as a characteristic phenomenon of amorphous semiconductors. The absorption coefficient in amorphous Se exhibits, above the
exponential tail, a relation of the form (see Chapter 10)

$$\alpha(\omega)\hbar\omega = \text{const.}(\hbar\omega - E_0).$$

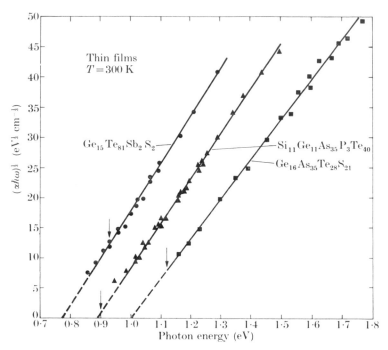

FIG. 7.33. Absorption edges in three multicomponent glasses which obey the relationship
$\alpha\hbar\omega \sim (\hbar\omega - E_0)^3$. The arrows mark the values of $2E$ in the formula $\sigma = C \exp(-E/kT)$
(Fagen, private communication).

Some speculations regarding this behaviour have been made by Davis
and Mott (1970). Certain multicomponent materials have been found
by Fagen (private communication) to have an absorption coefficient
that obeys the relation

$$\alpha(\omega)\hbar\omega = \text{const.}(\hbar\omega - E_0)^3.$$

These are shown in Fig. 7.33. This relationship can be derived by
relaxing one of the assumptions used above in obtaining the quadratic
relation, namely that transitions between localized states can be
neglected, and assuming instead that they have the same matrix

elements as all other transitions. In this case we find (Davis and Mott 1970)

$$\alpha(\omega) = (4\pi\sigma_0/3n_0c)(\hbar\omega - E_0)^3/\hbar\omega(\Delta E)^2. \tag{7.37}$$

Here E_0 is equal to $(E_A - E_B)$, where we use again the notation of Fig. 7.4(a).

Amorphous germanium was reported in early papers to have an exponential absorption edge followed at higher energies by the quadratic variation. More recent measurements by Donovan, Spicer, and Bennett (1969) have revealed a sharp absorption edge, but no simple power law is capable of describing its spectral shape (see Chapter 8). Presumably the density of states at the band edges is not given by a simple power law either.

In summary, it appears that the absorption edge of many amorphous semiconductors can be described by a simple power law, at least over a limited range of absorption coefficients, which enables an optical gap E_0 to be defined. However, without independent knowledge of the density of states and matrix elements as a function of energy, we can only speculate on whether this is a real gap in the density of states or some other characteristic energy related to the mobility gap.

7.6.3. Absorption at high energies

Beyond the fundamental absorption edge both crystalline and amorphous semiconductors continue to absorb strongly. Measurements up to about 20 eV can be made most conveniently using an ultraviolet diffraction-grating reflectometer. The optical constants are then derived from a Kramers–Kronig analysis of the reflectivity.

In crystalline semiconductors, the interband absorption in this range is characterized by a succession of peaks related to structure in the density of states of both the valence and conduction bands. As an example, Fig. 7.34 shows (dotted curve) the experimentally determined absorption spectrum of crystalline germanium above the edge (at 0·7 eV). Note that the imaginary part of the dielectric constant is related to α by the relation $\epsilon_2 = n_0 c\alpha/\omega$. The structure shown here has been interpreted as arising principally from the transitions marked by arrows in Fig. 7.35(a), which is a theoretical calculation of the electronic band structure of crystalline Ge in two principal directions of the Brillouin zone. It should be stressed that these assignments are not unambiguous; in particular it is now considered that the transition X_4–X_1 is not truly representative of the large peak at 4·5 eV but that a much larger region of the zone is involved. However, it serves to illustrate the principles of interpretation of optical absorption spectra of crystals in this range of photon energies. These are:

(a) Vertical transitions (corresponding to no change in the electron wave vector) at critical points in the zone contribute strongly to the absorption. Critical points occur where the valence and conduction

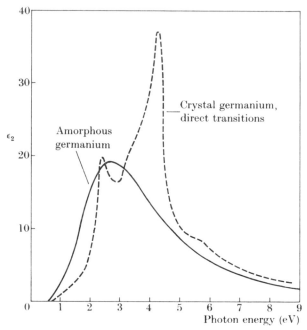

Fɪɢ. 7.34. Spectral dependence of the imaginary part of the dielectric constant ϵ_2 as determined by Kramers–Kronig analysis of reflectance data for amorphous Ge (solid line) and crystalline Ge (dashed line) (from Spicer and Donovan 1970a).

bands are parallel in k-space because the joint or combined densities of states thus have maximum values.

(b) The joint density of states is not the only parameter of importance. Certain transitions are forbidden by symmetry requirements. Others are damped or enhanced by a matrix element, which may have considerable structure as a function of energy. For example, the 4·5 eV transition in Ge referred to above is Umklapp-enhanced (Phillips 1966).

The density of states determined optically can thus be considerably different from the actual density of states obtained by integrating all the various over-lapping bands over the whole Brillouin zone (Fig. 7.35 (b)).

Amorphous semiconductors show far less structure in their absorption spectra. The solid line of Fig. 7.34 is the experimentally determined spectrum for amorphous Ge. Other materials show a similar lack of structure although, as will be seen in later chapters, gross features are frequently preserved.

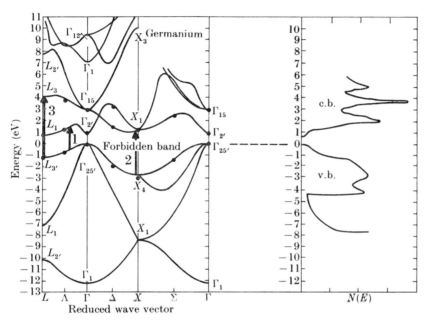

FIG. 7.35. Electronic band structure of crystalline Ge (from Herman *et al.* 1967), showing the principal interband transitions contributing to the ϵ_2 spectrum of Fig. 7.34, and the density of states in the valence and conduction bands.

There are two approaches to an understanding of the ϵ_2 spectra of amorphous semiconductors, both of which are of fundamental importance as far as the future of the theory of amorphous semiconductors is concerned. The first approach is to start with the crystalline band structure and introduce modifications as seem appropriate. Thus we might attempt to generate the ϵ_2 spectrum by first relaxing the k-conservation selection rule, allowing all states in the conduction band to be accessible from all states in the valence band. In amorphous Ge, this procedure results in a smoothed-out absorption curve (Fig. 7.36(a)), which peaks at too low an energy to account for the experimental results, as shown by Herman and Van Dyke (1968). A second step is to determine by X-rays or by density measurements what difference, if any, exists between the nearest-neighbour separation in the crystalline and amorphous forms, and to use a density of states appropriate to the dilated lattice. Again using Ge as an example, this procedure does shift the peak to lower energies, but even if an increase of 10 per cent in the length of the Ge–Ge bond is assumed, corresponding to the density change, this is not enough to bring the result in line with experiment. Thirdly, we can try to refine the calculations further by

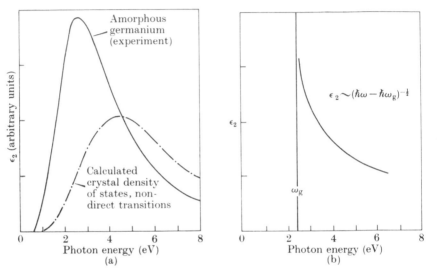

Fig. 7.36. (a) The imaginary part of the dielectric constant ϵ_2 in amorphous germanium as determined experimentally (solid line) and as calculated from the crystalline density of states, assuming non-direct transitions and constant matrix elements (dashed and dotted line). (b) Expected form of ϵ_2 on the Penn model.

considering the effect on the density of states of differences of co-ordination numbers higher than the first in the amorphous and crystalline forms. This 'perturbed-crystal' approach will be described in more detail for amorphous Ge in Chapter 8.

The second approach to understanding the optical spectra of amorphous semiconductors has been described by Phillips (1970, and unpublished work), who also concentrated on the results presented above for Ge. Phillips's model retains only the energy gap associated with the tetrahedral coordination, which is taken to be essentially undisturbed in the amorphous form. He assumes that the absence of long-range order causes the energy spectrum $E(k)$ to become isotropic, with the gap ($\sim 2 \cdot 5$ eV) at the edge of a spherical zone. This is essentially the Penn model (Penn 1962; Bardasis and Hone 1967), the absorption according to which has the form shown in Fig. 7.36(b). By introducing Lorentzian broadening, Phillips demonstrates how the experimentally determined ε_2 spectrum of amorphous germanium can be approximated.

A very high-energy (50–70 eV) absorption experiment on selenium by Cardona, Gudat, Sonntag, and Yu (1970), in which electrons were

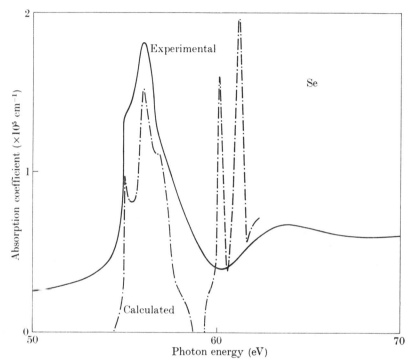

FIG. 7.37. Optical absorption in amorphous Se using synchrotron radiation (from Cardona *et al.* 1970).

excited from a narrow low-lying d level into the conduction band, revealed a spectrum (Fig. 7.37) that was, within experimental error, the same in both the crystalline and amorphous forms. Furthermore, good agreement was obtained with a theoretical calculation using the density of states appropriate to the crystal. This result demonstrates that, in selenium at any rate, the total width of the conduction band is approximately unchanged on going to the amorphous state.

7.6.4. Modulation experiments

The modulation techniques used to enhance the sensitivity and resolution of conventional optical spectroscopy have been applied to amorphous semiconductors by a few workers (Weiser and Stuke 1969; Piller, Seraphin, Markel, and Fischer 1969; Kolomiets, Mazets, Efendiev, and Andriesh 1970). The technique involves the application of a periodic perturbation (e.g. electric field, temperature, stress) to the sample and detection of induced changes in the optical properties at the same frequency (or in some cases twice the frequency). In crystalline semiconductors the method of electroreflectance in particular has revealed fine structure not resolved by static methods. For a full description of the experimental techniques the reader should consult Cardona (1969).

Results obtained on amorphous Ge, As_2S_3, and Se are described in Chapters 8, 9, and 10 respectively.

7.6.5. Intraband absorption

Figure 7.38 shows the absorption near the fundamental edge in amorphous As_2Se_3 as measured by Edmond (1966). In the solid glassy state (curves (1)–(3)) the absorption coefficient obeys the spectral Urbach rule (§ 7.6.1) and there is a parallel shift to lower photon energies as the temperature is raised. The absorption in the neighbourhood of 10^{-1} cm^{-1} is presumed to be residual and depends on the conditions of sample preparation. In the liquid state (curves (4)–(11)) strong absorption occurs at much lower energies, and it may be considered that the absorption edge is broadening (as well as shifting) as the temperature is raised, in accordance with Urbach's rule. However, the magnitude of α at a fixed photon energy (0·5 eV $\sim$ 4000 cm^{-1}) was found to be proportional to the d.c. electrical conductivity, at least for temperatures above about 450°C. This is shown in Fig. 7.39. There is thus a strong possibility that free-carrier absorption is being observed.

It should be noted that free-carrier absorption in crystalline semiconductors is normally observed on the low-energy side of the absorption edge as a component that, at a fixed temperature, increases with decreasing photon energy, i.e. α is proportional to λ^2. This of course simply derives from the Drude formula for a.c. conductivity:

$$\sigma(\omega) = \sigma(0)/(1+\omega^2\tau^2), \qquad \alpha(\omega) = (4\pi/n_0c)\sigma(\omega).$$

The application of this formula to free-carrier absorption in semiconductors relies essentially on the existence of a relaxation or scattering time τ, as intraband transitions are quantum-mechanically forbidden. As discussed in § 7.4.4 the equation is not applicable for amorphous semiconductors with very small values of τ.

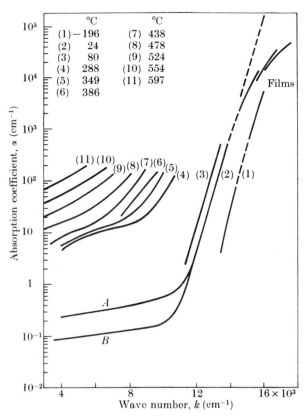

°C	°C
(1) −196	(7) 438
(2) 24	(8) 478
(3) 80	(9) 524
(4) 288	(10) 554
(5) 349	(11) 597
(6) 386	

FIG. 7.38. Optical absorption in liquid and glassy As₂Se₃ as a function of temperature (from Edmond 1966).

We suggest that the increase in absorption with increasing photon energy shown in Fig. 7.38 arises from an increasing density of available final states. Using the notation of Fig. 7.4(a) we calculate this absorption as follows. Following the arguments of § 2.13 we write

$$\sigma(\omega) = \frac{2\pi^3 e^2 \hbar^3 a}{m^2} \int_{E_A}^{\infty} N(E - \hbar\omega) N(E) \{ f(E - \hbar\omega) - f(E) \} \, \mathrm{d}E / \hbar\omega.$$

With $f(E) = \exp\{ -(E - E_F)/kT \}$ and $N(E) = N(E_C)(E - E_A)/\Delta E$, the maximum of $f(E)N(E)$ occurs at $E = E_A + kT$. Thus

$$\sigma(\omega) = \frac{2\pi^3 e^2 \hbar^3 a}{m^2} \left\{ \frac{N(E_C)}{\Delta E} \right\}^2 \frac{kT(kT + \hbar\omega)}{\hbar\omega} \int_{E_A}^{\infty} \{ f(E - \hbar\omega) - f(E) \} \, \mathrm{d}E,$$

18

which for $\hbar\omega > kT$ becomes

$$\sigma(\omega) = \sigma_0(kT/\Delta E)^2\exp\{-(E_A-E_F)/kT\}\exp(\hbar\omega/kT), \quad (7.38)$$

where (compare eqn (2.29))

$$\sigma_0 = (2\pi^3e^2\hbar^3a/m^2)\{N(E_C)\}^2. \tag{7.39}$$

Equation (7.38) predicts an absorption that is proportional to the d.c. conductivity and increases exponentially with photon energy. Assumptions that are made here are that the density of states is linear with

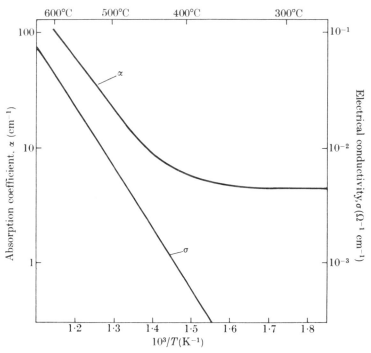

FIG. 7.39. Absorption coefficient at 40 000 cm^{-1} from Fig. 7.38 and electrical conductivity as functions of inverse temperature in liquid As$_2$Se$_3$ (Edmond, private communication).

energy, and that the matrix elements for transitions from the localized states at the bottom of the band to extended states higher in the band are the same as those used earlier in this book. A similar expression has been obtained by Hindley (1970). It should be noted that eqn 7.38 does not predict correctly the slope of the curves shown in Fig. 7.38, and further work on this problem is necessary.

    Edmond (private communication) has subsequently observed similar behaviour to that reported above in solid glasses of the system

$As_2(Se, Te)_3$. In all cases, the high-frequency conductivity at $\sim 7 \times 10^{14}$ s^{-1} was found to be about twenty times the d.c. value. Bishop, Taylor, Mitchell, and Slack (1971) have also reported similar observations in $Tl_2SeAs_2Te_3$.

7.6.6. Absorption by phonons

The limited number of investigations of the optical properties of amorphous semiconductors in the infrared region of the spectrum makes

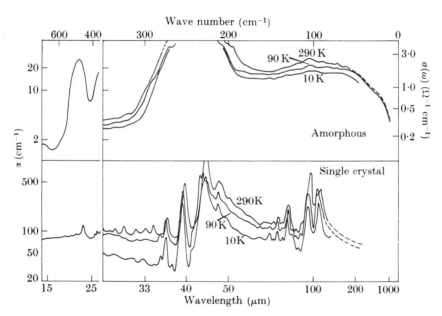

FIG. 7.40. Vibrational spectra of glassy and crystalline As_2Se_3 (from Austin and Garbett 1971).

it difficult to generalize about the effects of disorder on vibrational spectra. Some experimental observations will be given in later chapters: they can be summarized as follows.

(a) In molecular-type materials there is little qualitative change in the spectrum of the crystal on disordering. In amorphous Se, almost the whole infrared absorption spectrum can be correlated with that in monoclinic Se and attributed to vibrational modes of Se_8 molecules (Chapter 10).

(b) In As_2Se_3 and similar chalcogenide alloys the vibrational spectrum is preserved in essence but much fine structure is lost. This is shown in Fig. 7.40 (from Austin and Garbett 1971).

(c) In $CdGeAs_2$, and presumably other predominantly covalently bonded materials, vibrational bands characteristic of the crystal are virtually absent in the amorphous phase (Fig. 8.41). This could be because of excessive dampening or broadening due to a statistical distribution of oscillator frequencies.

Raman spectra of Se confirm that molecular-like vibrations are retained on disordering. For Ge and Si, there is also considerable similarity between the Raman spectra of the crystalline and amorphous forms (Smith, Brodsky, Crowder, and Nathan, private communication).

The far-infrared absorption in amorphous SiO_2 and similar glasses has been discussed by Stolen (1970) and by Wong and Whalley (1971). Bell, Bird, and Dean (1968) and Bell and Dean (1971) have computed the vibrational spectra for various disordered lattices and have shown the importance of localized modes in SiO_2 for example.

7.7. Other measurements

7.7.1. Photo-emission from non-crystalline semiconductors

Photo-emission is one of the most valuable experimental techniques available in the study of the electronic band structures of semiconductors. The method involves the photo-injection of carriers from valence states through conduction states into the vacuum. An analysis of the energy distribution of the emitted electrons as a function of photon energy completes the experimental data. Unfortunately the experiments are relatively difficult to perform properly, and a great deal of skill is needed in their interpretation. As far as amorphous semiconductors are concerned, only Ge has been studied thoroughly by this technique at the time of writing.

For photons of energy $\hbar\omega$, the energy distribution of emitted electrons is given by

$$N(E, \hbar\omega) \, \mathrm{d}E = \{K(\hbar\omega)/\alpha(\hbar\omega)\} T(E) S(E, \hbar\omega) N_\mathrm{c}(E) N_\mathrm{v}(E - \hbar\omega) \, \mathrm{d}E,$$

where K is a scale factor which includes parameters of the experimental apparatus, α the absorption coefficient, T an escape function, and S the fraction of excited electrons of energy E lost because of scattering. Thus, like optical absorption measurements, photo-emission gives the combined or joint density of states in the valence and conduction bands. The above formula assumes that the k-conservation selection rule is not important.

There are, however, two major advantages that photo-emission measurements have over optical absorption. The first is that the energy at which a peak in $N_C N_V$ occurs can be related to some fixed point in the band structure, such as the top of the valence band. In optical absorption experiments only *energy differences* are determined. In photo-emission a determination of absolute energies can, in principle, be made with a knowledge of the electron affinity of the semiconductor and, if a retarding-potential method is used to measure the energy

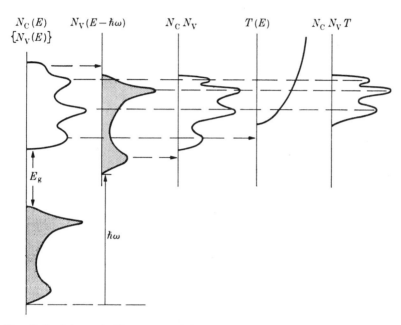

FIG. 7.41. Schematic illustration of the principles involved in photo-emission experiments.

distributions, of the collector. In practice, however, the measured retarding potential can be related to the energy at the top of the valence-band by noting the maximum value of the retarding potential, for a given $\hbar\omega$, at which electrons appear in the energy distributions. The second advantage can be seen by considering the schematic density of states shown in 7.41, in which the valence-band density of states is shown raised by $\hbar\omega$ to obtain the produce $N_C(E)N_V(E - \hbar\omega)$. Multiplication by the escape function T yields, if S is constant, a spectrum proportional to the measured energy distribution of emitted electrons. For another value of $\hbar\omega$, a different spectrum results. Peaks in the distribution that do not vary their position with $\hbar\omega$ are to be associated with maxima in the conduction-band density of states; those peaks in the distribution that do vary their position with the photon energy originate from maxima in the valence-band density of states. Thus one can, in principle, determine both N_C and N_V separately. However, as conduction-band states below the vacuum level of the semiconductor are inaccessible to the technique, it is normally not easy to obtain much information on $N_C(E)$. In practice a layer of, say, caesium can be evaporated

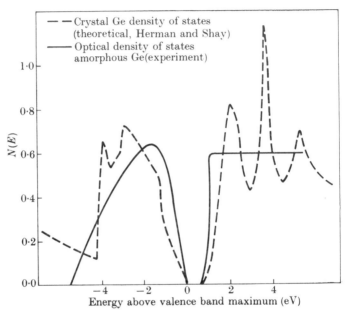

FIG. 7.42. Optical density of states for amorphous Ge as determined by photo-emission, and calculated density of states for crystalline Ge (from Donovan and Spicer 1968).

on to the surface in order to lower its work function and hence increase the accessible range.

The optical density of states in amorphous germanium as determined from photo-emission data by Donovan and Spicer (1968) is shown in Fig. 7.42. This result will be discussed in Chapter 8.

7.7.2. Electron spin resonance

Brodsky and Title (1969) have reported e.s.r. signals from amorphous films of silicon, germanium, and silicon carbide. From a comparison of the g value, line width, and shape of the signal with those detected on freshly cleaved, single-crystal surfaces of silicon, these authors suggest that the signals arise from dangling bonds. Table 7.6 summarizes their results. The high density of spins ($\sim 10^{20}$ cm^{-3}) was found to be a true bulk density. Annealing studies on amorphous silicon showed (see § 8.1.4) that this density could be reduced by a factor of 10–100 on heating to a temperature close to the amorphous–crystalline transformation temperature (~450°C). The observed line width suggests exchange or motional narrowing, implying that the unpaired electron at the dangling bond samples the environment at several similar sites, i.e. is free to move from site to site.

TABLE 7.6

e.s.r. results on amorphous films compared with similar resonances in crystalline materials. The densities of spins are estimated to be accurate within a factor of two. Data for the amorphous films from Brodsky and Title (1969), for the crystals from Walters and Estle (1961); see also Haneman (1968).

Material	Amorphous films (77K)			Crystalline surfaces		Neutron-irradiated crystals	
	g value	Line width (G)	Density of spins (cm⁻³)	g value	Line width (G)	g value	Line width (G)
Si	2·0055 ±0·0005	4·7	2×10^{20}	2·0055 ±0·002	7–8	2·0055	16–20
Ge	2·021 ±0·001	39	1×10^{20}	2·023 ±0·003	50		
SiC	2·003 ±0·001	6	3×10^{20}	2·0027 ±0·002	5·5		

Similar studies on chalcogenide glasses (Fritzsche, private communication) indicate a much smaller density of such centres.

7.7.3. *Magnetic susceptibility*

Magnetic susceptibility measurements as a function of temperature have been reported by Cervinka *et al.* (1970) on $CdGe_xAs_2$ glasses (see Chapter 8). In contrast with crystalline $CdAs_2$ and $CdGeAs_2$, which exhibit a virtually temperature-independent diamagnetic susceptibility, the glasses show a temperature-dependent contribution that obeys the Curie law. Writing the total susceptibility as

$$\chi = \chi_0 + A/T, \tag{7.40}$$

then χ_0 represents the lattice susceptibility, and A can be expressed as

$$A = n\mu^2/3\rho k, \tag{7.41}$$

where n is the concentration of magnetic moments μ, and ρ is the density of the material. Using this relation, Cervinka *et al.* estimate a concentration of paramagnetic centres in $CdGeAs_2$ glass of 10^{20} cm^{-3}.

Similar measurements by Tauc, Menth, and Wood (1970) on As_2S_3 glass suggest a concentration in this material of 6×10^{17} free spins cm^{-3}. The diamagnetic component (χ_0) of the magnetic susceptibility of As_2S_x glasses has been measured and discussed by Cimpl, Kosek, and Matyas (1970).

7.8. Non-ohmic conduction in strong fields

Many observations show that the current in thin films of amorphous semiconductors increases more rapidly than the field, as indeed it does

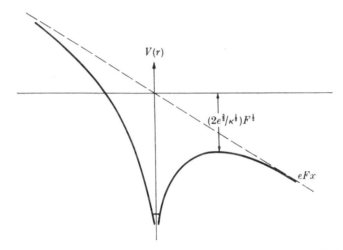

Fig. 7.43. Potential energy of an electron in a Coulomb centre under the influence of an electric field F, illustrating the Poole–Frenkel effect.

in many crystalline materials. We shall not attempt a survey of the experimental material; many observations are recorded in the *Journal of Non-Crystalline Solids* (volume 4), which contains the papers read at the 1969 conference at Cambridge on the subject. We shall, however, summarize some of the possible mechanisms and refer to a few experiments that seem to illustrate them.

(a) *The Poole–Frenkel effect.* If a semiconductor, crystalline or amorphous, contains donors in which the binding energy of an electron is E, then it was first shown by Frenkel (1938), following earlier work by Poole (1916, 1917), that a field F lowers the ionization energy of the centre by $\beta F^{\frac{1}{2}}$, where β is given by

$$2e^{3/2}/\kappa^{\frac{1}{2}}. \qquad (7.42)$$

The potential energy of the electron is shown in Fig. 7.43, and in the derivation of this formula it is assumed that there is no tunnelling through the barrier. The model from which formula (7.42) is obtained is one-dimensional; three-dimensional versions have been given by Jonscher (1967) and Hartke (1968). As the temperature is lowered, however, tunnelling through the barrier, at any rate through the top of the barrier, can be important. Hill (1971) has worked out formulae taking into account the lowering of the barrier due to tunnelling, and has applied them in detail to experimental results by various authors on amorphous films of SiO. Good agreement with experiment is obtained. It is envisaged that electrons, once freed, are pulled out of the film.

As pointed out by Simmons (1967) and Mark and Hartman (1968), a strong field can also affect the quasi-equilibrium within a semiconductor. The analysis is as follows: for intrinsic or non-compensated extrinsic semiconductors in which there are n free carriers, the number generated per unit time will be of the form

$$\nu_{\rm ph}\exp\{-(E-\beta F^{\frac{1}{2}})/kT\}, \qquad (7.43)$$

and the number recombining will be proportional to n^2. Thus the number of carriers should depend on the field as $\exp(\frac{1}{2}\beta F^{\frac{1}{2}}/kT)$. For an extrinsic *compensated* semiconductor the number recombining is proportional to n, so that in equilibrium n is now proportional to $\exp(\beta F^{\frac{1}{2}}/kT)$.

For an intrinsic semiconductor, Fig. 7.43 refers to the mutual potential energy of an electron and hole. This mechanism has been discussed by Mott (1971b), who points out that for non-elements there is some uncertainty about the appropriate value of κ.

There are many examples in the literature of a linear relationship between the logarithm of the current and $F^{\frac{1}{2}}$. Yeargan and Taylor (1968) compare the results of theory, which they develop in some detail, with experiments on silicon nitride. Croitoru *et al.* (1970) have made measurements on As–Te–Ge–Si and obtained agreement with the Poole–Frenkel formula, assuming the value of κ to be 5. Moorjani and Feldman (1970) report results on silicon and boron; for boron they obtain for β twice the Poole–Frenkel value. At the time of writing, a comparison between experimental and theoretical values of β seems premature, particularly in view of the possibility that the temperature in the material passing the current is higher than the ambient temperature. Müller and Müller (1970) have investigated amorphous selenium films and obtained a good relationship between $\log j$ and $F^{\frac{1}{2}}$, and have shown that their results are bulk controlled, and not an electrode (Schottky) effect. Their value of κ, however, is half the Poole–Frenkel value, and these authors suggest, following Simmons (1967), that this is due to the presence either of non-compensated donors or of intrinsic conduction. Other authors quoted in this paper have attributed non-ohmic behaviour to space-charge limited currents, a phenomenon that will not be discussed here.

(b) *Effect on the mobility.* We know of no analysis of the effect of strong fields on the mobility of electrons or holes in extended states; we should not expect it to be large. We have, however, given reasons in Chapter 4 for expecting that a field satisfying the criterion

$$e\mu F^2 > \sim\hbar\omega^2$$

would give energy to an electron faster than it can lose it to phonons, so that such fields may lead to acceleration of electrons, the formation of secondaries, and an avalanche. Here ω is the maximum phonon frequency and the formula is valid if the coupling constant is not too small (Mott 1971*b*). We refer again to this prediction in the next section.

For electrons in localized states, on the other hand, the effect of a field may be large. Consider first the weakly localized states near the extremities of the conduction and valence bands. If the field ionizes such states in a time comparable with the time taken for recombination, then every time a carrier is produced it will be pulled out into an extended state. Such an effect has been predicted by Dussel and Böer (1970). This may possibly be the reason for the rapid increase in current observed in chalcogenide glasses prior to switching (Fritzsche and Ovshinsky 1970).

If the hopping mobility is of the form

$$\mu = (eR^2\nu_{\mathrm{ph}}/kT)\exp(-2\alpha R)\exp(-W/kT), \qquad (7.44)$$

hopping being to nearest-neighbour sites, a field should reduce W to $W-eRF$. It should also increase the tunnelling factor $\mathrm{e}^{-2\alpha R}$, but calculations of the effect to be expected have not been made. The effect of a field under conditions when $\ln \rho \propto 1/T^{\frac{1}{4}}$ has not been worked out either; Mott (1970) has, however, pointed out that, at the absolute zero of temperature, hopping is possible with the emission of a phonon each time an electron moves; he obtains the relationship

$$\ln j \propto -A/F^{\frac{1}{3}}. \qquad (7.42)$$

7.9. Switching in non-crystalline semiconductors

The realization that thin films of certain amorphous semiconductors can exhibit a very fast and reversible conversion from a high-resistance to a low-resistance state under the influence of an applied field is one reason for the very rapid growth of interest in amorphous materials that took place in the last years of the decade 1960–70. Switching occurs in a wide variety of materials and even in liquid Se, S, and Te alloys (Busch, Güntherodt, Künzi, and Schweiger 1970), and it is unlikely that the same mechanism is responsible in all cases. We shall not attempt to assess the very wide range of papers that has appeared on this subject.

One mechanism that is relatively well understood is the instability that arises when heating of the material, with consequent increase in the conductivity, leads to a negative resistance. Discussions on this effect go back to Lueder and Spenke (1935) and Ridley (1963), and recent treatments are due to Fritzsche and Ovshinsky (1970), Warren (1970a,b), Stocker, Barlow, and Weirauch (1970), and Mott (1971b). Applied to a thin film, the phenomenon can be described in the following way. For a film of thickness L the heat produced per unit area is $\sigma V^2/L$. The rate at which heat is conducted away will depend on the geometry, but apart from constant factors will vary as $K(T-T_0)/L$, where T_0 is the ambient temperature and K the heat conductivity. A negative resistance will occur if σV^2 rises with temperature faster than $K(T-T_0)$, the condition for which is that

$$V/L \sim \{K/L(\mathrm{d}\sigma/\mathrm{d}T)\}^{\frac{1}{2}}. \tag{7.45}$$

$(T-T_0)$, the rise in temperature when this occurs, is of the order of $20°$ only. Several authors have solved the equation for heat conduction, assuming that current and heat flow remain perpendicular to the film and do not vary over its surface; the curve shown in Fig. 7.44 is obtained. But it is doubtful if this ever happens in practice; any instability will lead to a conducting channel. One would expect eqn (7.45) to give the condition for channel formation, but the precise conditions for the process are not understood. Perhaps the major uncertainty is the width of the hot channel; Mott (1971b) has suggested that with certain boundary conditions it should normally be of order L, but this is not proved.

Warren (1970a,b) has looked at the behaviour of a thin cylindrical conductor and makes the important point that when condition (1) is fulfilled the temperature of the axis of the cylinder rises rapidly to a very high value, probably melts, and then cools down rapidly as heat conduction raises the temperature throughout the cylinder. We think this probably happens in the channel through a thin film. An important feature of the thermal mechanism is, then, that the temperature along the axis of the channel cools down after switching.

Many investigations of thermal switching exist, which have established the existence of a hot channel; thus Pearson (1970), using

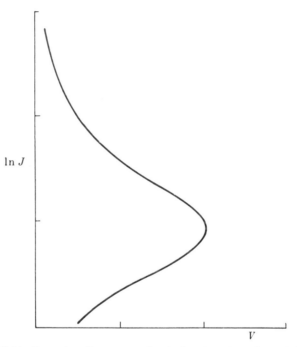

FIG. 7.44. Current–voltage curve due to heating of specimen (schematic).

a film 10 μm thick of glassy As_2SeTe, has established the existence of a liquid filament, and a hot filament in silicon has been observed by Fulenwider and Herskowitz (1970). Whether the thermal theory can account for the behaviour of the much thinner films ($\sim$1 μm) developed as switches by Ovshinsky (1968) and his co-workers is more controversial. Stocker *et al.* (1970), Chen and Wang (1970), and Warren (1970*a,b*) claim that it is so, but in our view there is up till now some uncertainty in these treatments about the channel width and its dependence on current.

It will be noted that, according to formula (7.45), the field (V/L) for thermal breakdown increases for small values of the thickness L of the film. If the considerations of § 4.1 and the preceding section are correct, a fast electronic process, dependent on V/L and independent of film thickness, ought to occur first for thin enough films. Mott (1971b) has given a model to show how this could lead to a current-controlled 'on' state.

This book will not attempt a review of the formation of 'memories'—that is to say the creation after threshold switching of a filament that has transformed, probably by crystallization, into a state with much higher conductivity. At the time of going to press, the subject is developing too rapidly for a review to be worth while.

PROPERTIES OF AMORPHOUS GERMANIUM, SILICON, AND OTHER SEMICONDUCTORS WITH TETRAHEDRAL COORDINATION

8.1. Amorphous germanium and silicon
  8.1.1. Methods of preparation
  8.1.2. Structure of amorphous germanium and silicon
  8.1.3. Electrical properties of amorphous germanium
  8.1.4. Electrical properties of amorphous silicon
  8.1.5. Optical properties of amorphous germanium

8.1.6. Optical properties of amorphous silicon
8.2. InSb and other III–V compounds
8.3. CdGeAs$_2$ and similar ternaries
  8.3.1. Electrical properties of glasses of the type CdGeAs$_2$
  8.3.2. Optical properties of glasses of the type CdGeAs$_2$

8.1. Amorphous germanium and silicon

AMORPHOUS semiconductors that cannot be prepared as a glass by quenching (supercooling the liquid state) are usually obtained in the form of thin films by some method of deposition. It has already been stated that the properties of such films are dependent on the method and conditions of preparation, and this will be very much in evidence in the first sections of this chapter, where results of different workers are compared. However, recent attempts at characterizing the amorphous phase of these materials by correlating, for example, temperature of deposition with density and other properties, have gone some way towards reconciling these results.

8.1.1. Methods of preparation

In the liquid state, germanium and silicon have six-fold coordination and are metallic. They cannot therefore be prepared in the amorphous solid state by cooling from the melt. Methods that have been used to prepare films of germanium are as follows:

(a) *Vacuum evaporation* (Tauc, Grigorovici, and Vancu 1966; Clark 1967; Walley and Jonscher 1968; Walley 1968*a,b*; Croitoru and Vescan 1969; Spicer and Donovan 1970*a*; Chopra and Bahl 1970). Evaporation in high vacuum (preferably $<10^{-6}$ torr) can produce films up to 20 μm in thickness. However, such thick films tend to break up because of internal strains, and most measurements have been made on films of a few μm. Either resistive or electron-beam heating of intrinsic crystalline germanium from molybdenum or tungsten boats is used, and the substrate, for instance KCl or fused silica, is normally kept at room temperature or below. Evaporation rates from 1–15 μm per hour ($\sim$3–45 Å s^{-1}) are common. Film uniformity and parallelism obtained by this method are good, and with special care (for example, use of very smooth rotating substrates) can be considerably better than 1 per cent. The films can be annealed up to 200°C or higher without loss of their non-crystalline nature but with definite changes in their properties, as will be described below. Heating to about 450°C produces poly-crystalline material. Tauc has reported preparation of unsupported films, following evaporation on to copper or collodion substrates. The density of films prepared by vacuum evaporation has been reported to be up to 30 per cent lower than that of the crystal (5·35 g cm^{-3}), but, on the average, densities are perhaps 15 per cent lower. Donovan, Ashley, and Spicer (1970) report that evaporation on to a quartz substrate held at 250–300°C produces amorphous films of density close to that of the crystal.

(b) *Sputtering*. Films prepared by sputtering in argon at a deposition rate of 1 μm per hour on to NaCl substrates have been described by Tauc, Abraham, Zallen, and Slade (1970). The films were not as uniform as those prepared by vacuum evaporation and contained from 3–7 per cent of oxygen.

(c) *Electrolytic deposition* (Szekely 1951; Tauc, Abraham, Zallen, and Slade 1970). Thick ($\sim$30 μm) films of amorphous germanium can be prepared by deposition on to a copper cathode immersed in an electrolytic solution of $GeCl_4$ in $C_3H_6(OH)_2$. Such films, which contain a few per cent of oxygen and copper as impurities, can be obtained unsupported by subsequently dissolving the copper substrate in chromic–sulphuric acid.

(d) *Glow-discharge deposition* (Chittick, Alexander, and Sterling 1969, and references cited therein). This method employs an electrode-less radio-frequency (1 MHz) glow discharge in germane gas. The reaction takes place at a pressure of $\sim$0·1 torr, and deposition rates are limited to $\sim$2–12 Å s^{-1} in order not to affect the glow discharge. Substrates used by Chittick *et al.* were optically flat glass (Corning 7059) and cleaved KBr. The method should result in a low concentration of oxygen in the films but this has not been confirmed. The variation in thickness across the films has been reported to be about 5 per cent and their density to be about 4·6 g cm^{-2}.

Amorphous silicon films can be prepared by methods very similar to those employed for germanium (Grigorovici, Croitoru, and Devenyi 1967a; Walley 1968; Chittick, Alexander, and Sterling 1969). However, it appears to be difficult to obtain samples free from oxygen, and this leads to strong silicon–oxygen vibrational absorption bands in the infrared.

8.1.2. Structure of amorphous germanium and silicon

The radial distribution curve for amorphous germanium derived from X-ray diffraction data is shown in Fig. 8.1, the shaded area covering all known measurements. The dashed curve is that appropriate to crystalline germanium. The radius of the first coordination sphere (2·47–2·54 Å) is, on the average, about 3 per cent larger than that in crystalline germanium (2·43Å). From the area under the first maximum, the coordination number is 4, showing unambiguously that the same nearest-neighbour tetrahedral bonding is retained in the amorphous form. The second coordination number (12) is also equal to that in the crystal. The most striking difference is the absence in the amorphous form of the third coordination maximum. Richter and Breitling (1958) emphasized the sensitivity of the radial position of this and other faint maxima to slight rotations of neighbouring tetrahedra in the lattice.

Grigorovici and Manaila (1968), and Coleman and Thomas (1968) have suggested models for amorphous germanium and silicon that are built by packing closely together Voronoi polyhedra (or Wigner–Seitz cells) of the diamond-like lattice (Fig. 8.2(a)). For convenience, they used simplified polyhedra (Fig.8.2(b)), which have the form of truncated tetrahedra. Such units can be stacked as shown in Fig. 8.2(c), which corresponds to neighbouring sets of tetrahedral bonds being in the staggered position, with a 60° relative rotation about their common bond (d). This leads to a folded ring of six atoms (e) and eventually to the diamond lattice. An alternative stacking arrangement, Fig. 8.2(f), however, corresponds to bonds in the eclipsed positions (g) leading to a ring of five atoms (h). Such stacking results in a slight angular mismatch (109° 28' instead of the pentagonal angle 108°). Twelve pentagonal rings form a pentagonal dodecahedron (i) containing 20 atoms, which Grigorovici and Manaila have called an *amorphon*. Because of non-crystallographic five-fold symmetry, this yields an amorphous-like diffraction pattern with broad maxima. Although energetically unfavourable in crystalline germanium, the eclipsed configuration seems plausible in the amorphous form; atomic arrangements with large

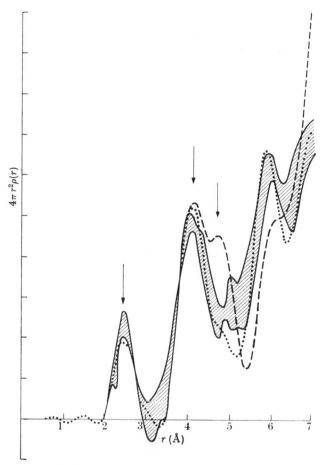

FIG. 8.1. Radial distribution curve of amorphous germanium: shaded area covers all known measurements. $----$ Theoretical curve based on the diamond lattice and broadened by a parameter so as to produce agreement with the first peak in amorphous germanium. $\ldots\ldots$ Theoretical curve based on a 50 % amorphonic plus 50 % diamond-like structure. $\rho(r)\,\mathrm{d}r$ is the number of pairs of atoms separated by a distance lying between r and $r+\mathrm{d}r$. (From Grigorovici and Manaila 1968.)

internal energy can clearly occur in such frozen structures. It is worth recalling that the wurtzite (hexagonal) structure of ZnS and other (II)–(VI) compounds consists of tetrahedral units with a quarter of the bonds in the eclipsed configuration. Because pentagonal dodeca-hedra can fill only small regions of space on account of angular misfit, it has been proposed that amorphous Ge and Si contain a mixture of such units and diamond or wurtzite regions.

Table 8.1 shows the radii, number of atoms, and broadening param-eters of twenty-six coordination spheres for the diamond, wurtzite, and

19

amorphonic structures of germanium. The radii are increased by 3 per cent as compared with those in crystalline germanium. The parameter c is equal to $\sqrt{2}$ times the standard deviation of a Gaussian distribution of distances associated with each coordination sphere, and refers to the amorphonic structure only.

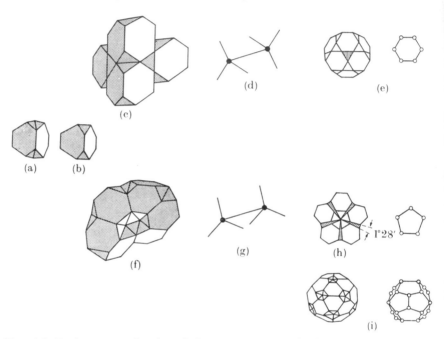

FIG. 8.2. Basic structural units of diamond and amorphonic structures. (a) Exact Voronoi polyhedra of diamond lattice. (b) Simplified Voronoi polyhedra. (c), (d) Simplified polyhedra stacked in the staggered-bond configuration. (e) Six polyhedra in diamond structure—folded six-atom ring. (f), (g) Simplified polyhedra stacked in the eclipsed-bond configuration. (h) Five polyhedra in amorphonic structure—plane five-atom ring. (i) Twenty polyhedra forming an amorphon. (From Grigorovici and Manaila 1968; Grigorovici 1969.)

The radial distribution curve appropriate to a structure based on a fifty–fifty mixture of units of diamond and amorphonic type is shown in Fig. 8.1. A pure wurtzite structure yields a curve (not shown) similar to that for the fifty–fifty mixture, and in fact the presence of wurtzite-type regions is a necessary part of the mixed structure. Grigorovici and Manaila conclude that amorphous germanium has a structure most like that represented by the mixture, i.e. a connected linkage of tetrahedra, half being in the eclipsed and half in the staggered configuration. Although such structures can be made 'ideal' in the sense that all bonds are satisfied, some radial and angular distortions are expected to favour a certain number of unsatisfied bonds or local defects.

For amorphous silicon a structural model composed of 60 per cent diamond and 40 per cent amorphon-like units provides the best fit to the experimental radial distribution curve (Coleman and Thomas 1968).

TABLE 8.1

Radii, numbers of atoms, and broadening parameters c of the coordination spheres for diamond-like, wurtzite-like and amorphonic structures (from Grigorovici and Manaila 1968)

No.	Diamond-like		Wurtzite-like		Amorphonic		
	$r(\text{Å})$	N	$r(\text{Å})$	N	$r(\text{Å})$	N	$c(\text{Å})$
1	2·50	4	2·50	4	2·50	4	0·30
2	4·09	12	4·09	12	4·09–4·10	12	0·35
3			4·17	1			0·35
4	4·80	12	4·80	9			0·40
5	5·80	6	5·80	6	5·80	24	0·40
6			5·85	6			0·40
7	6·31	12	6·31	8			0·45
8			6·39	1			0·45
9			6·69	2	6·68–6·70	12	0·45
10	7·08	24	7·08	18	7·08–7·10	4	0·45
11	7·53	16	7·53	9			0·45
12			7·83	12			0·50
13			7·89	3			0·50
14					8·00–8·02	24	0·50
15	8·17	12	8·17	6			0·50
16			8·25	6			0·50
17			8·50	10			0·50
18	8·55	24	8·55	13			0·50
19			8·85	3			0·50
20	9·15	24	9·15	8	9·15	24	0·50
21			9·20	7			0·50
22	9·50	12	9·50	2			0·55
23					9·67–9·70	28	0·55
24			9·75	12			0·55
25			9·80	60			0·55
26	10·00	8	10·00	4			0·55

An alternative structure that has been proposed for amorphous germanium and silicon is based on the random network concept (Zachariasen 1932). Polk (1971) has constructed a model in which each atom has a first coordination number equal to 4 and only a small variation in nearest-neighbour separations is allowed. However, rather than restricting neighbouring triads to be in either the eclipsed or staggered configuration, the random network model allows *all* possible angles of rotation about the common bond. To construct such a model without any dangling bonds requires departures from the tetrahedral bond angle by up to $\pm20°$. However, this again would be an 'ideal' structure and actual films are expected to have a large concentration of unsatisfied bonds. Polk's ideal structure would have a density only 3 per cent less than that of the crystal and, like Grigorovici's model, produces a radial distribution curve (r.d.c.) in good agreement with experiment.

Accurate electron-diffraction data from films of amorphous silicon have been obtained by Moss and Graczyk (1969, 1970). These authors decide that the experimentally determined angular distribution of scattered intensities cannot be reconciled with a 'small-crystallite' model for amorphous silicon. In addition they also report an appreciable low-angle scattering component, which they associate with 'voids' or 'pores', small enough to escape detection under high-resolution electron microscopy. Furthermore, when the films were annealed this low-angle scattering decreased, suggesting a densification of the structure due to removal of the voids.

Moss and Graczyk (1970) have compared the r.d.c. of an amorphous silicon film and that of the same film after crystallization has been allowed to take place (by heating to over 500°C). Their results are shown in Fig. 8.3. The following features are noteworthy:

(a) From the first peak, an interatomic spacing (2·35 Å) and a coordination number (4·0±0·1) are obtained which are the same in both the crystalline and amorphous film. The breadth of the peak yields a value for the mean square amplitude of atomic displacement of 0·010 Å² in the crystal and 0·014 Å² in the film (compare 0·019 Å² as determined from the Debye–Waller factor for an independently vibrating atom in crystalline Si).

(b) From the second peak an interatomic spacing (3·86 Å) and a coordination number (11·6±0·5) are obtained which again are the same in the crystal and film. However, for this shell, the mean square displacement is 0·020 Å² in the crystal and 0·051 Å² in the film. Thus, when the effects of phonons are filtered out, a static mean square displacement $\sim$0·031 Å² is left. Moss and Graczyk assign this to bond-angle distortions, which can be estimated to be $\sim$20° off the normal tetrahedral angle of 109° 28'.

(c) The dramatic loss of the third coordination peak present in the curve for the crystal (this was also shown in Fig. 8.1 for Ge) marks the most striking departure point from the diamond structure.

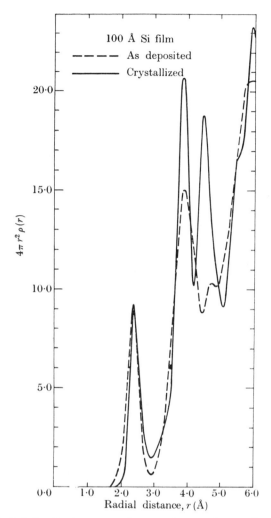

FIG. 8.3. Radial distribution curves for amorphous and crystalline silicon as determined from analysis of electron diffraction data (from Moss and Graczyk 1970).

8.1.3. Electrical properties of amorphous germanium

In view of the structural changes that accompany annealing of amorphous films of germanium, it is not surprising to find in the literature conflicting results on the electrical characteristics. Apart from clear differences between films prepared by different methods and under different conditions, most workers report a change of properties with time after deposition. Annealing at temperatures above that of deposition can lead to an increase in the room-temperature resistivity by a factor of three or more. This is accompanied by an increase in the activation energy for electrical conduction. There is also disagreement concerning the magnitude and, what is more important, the sign of the Seebeck coefficient.

These differences should not be allowed to overshadow one of the principal features of this and other amorphous semiconductors, namely that impurities play a relatively minor role. Evaporation of a material that is initially a degenerate n-type or p-type semiconductor produces films of high resistivity in which the Fermi level is located near the centre of the gap. We assume that differences between samples and differences resulting from annealing arise from a wide range of concentrations of specific types of defects present in the films. In general, one might expect both donor-like and acceptor-like defects,[†] and perhaps it is not too unreasonable to suppose that in some samples acceptors outnumber donors and in others the reverse is true. Alternatively, the relative ranges of localized states at the band edges could determine whether a given sample was n-type or p-type (see § 8.3.1).

The room-temperature resistivity of amorphous germanium prepared by evaporation lies between 10^2 and 10^3 Ω cm. Glow-discharge-deposited films have a higher value ($\sim 7 \times 10^3$ Ω cm). Silver or aluminium electrodes have been found to give ohmic characteristics. Non-ohmic behaviour above 10^4 V cm^{-1} has been studied by Croitoru and Vescan (1969), Walley and Jonscher (1968), and Chopra and Bahl (1970).

The variation of resistivity with temperature has been measured by several workers (Clark 1967; Grigorovici, Croitoru, and Devenyi 1966; Walley and Jonscher 1968; Chopra and Bahl 1970; Chittick 1970; Stuke 1970a). Compared with the linear behaviour for an intrinsic crystal (for which the slope $\frac{1}{2}E_g$ is ~ 0.4 eV), the behaviour most frequently reported is that a plot of ln ρ against $1/T$ follows a smooth curve. Clark (Fig. 8.4(a), curve (1)) finds a slope of the resistivity plot of 0.15 eV at room temperature and of 0.02 eV at 30K (the low-temperature portion of Clark's curve is not shown here). Walley and Jonscher find similar smooth curves, but they stress the sensitivity of the shape and absolute magnitude of the resistivity to the method of preparation and the amount of annealing. Their films were about 100 times thinner than those measured by Clark. Chopra and

† As a possible example of such a defect, we remark that an unsatisfied or dangling bond is expected, by attracting an additional electron, to act as an acceptor level.

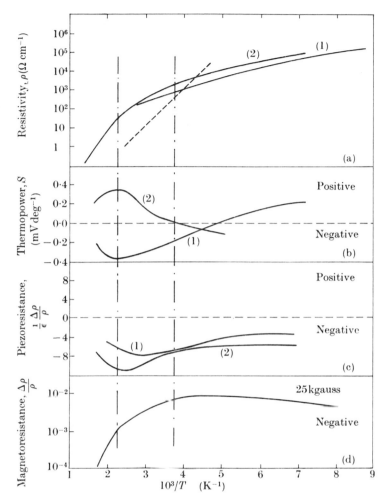

FIG. 8.4. Resistivity, thermoelectric power, piezoresistance, and magnetoresistance in amorphous germanium as functions of temperature, according to various authors. (a) (1) Clark (1967), (2) Grigorovici *et al.* (1966) – – – – intrinsic crystal. (b) (1) Stuke (1970*a*), (2) Grigorovici *et al.* (1966). (c) (1) Fuhs and Stuke (1970), (2) Devenyi *et al.* (1970). (d) Mell and Stuke (1970).

Bahl also report an activation energy that increases with temperature; they take their measurements up to several hundred degrees Kelvin, where the limiting slope is 1·45 eV.

In contrast, Grigorovici *et al.* reported a variation of resistance with temperature that they suggest can be represented by three approximately linear portions (Fig. 8.4(a), curve (2)). The activation energies, which are 0·55 eV, 0·20 eV, and 0·09 eV, are attributed by these authors to the following conduction mechanisms: if $T > 450K$, intrinsic activation across a thermal gap of 1·1 eV; if $450K > T > 250K$, extrinsic hole conduction by carriers released from acceptor levels 0·2 eV above the valence band; if $T < 250K$ electron-hopping processes between these acceptor levels. Stuke (1970a) also reports a value for the activation energy of 0·55 eV, followed at lower temperatures by a smooth curve. The data of both Grigorovici *et al.* and Stuke were obtained with annealed films. The division into

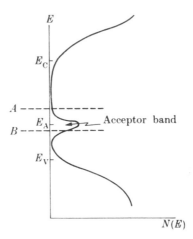

FIG. 8.5. Density-of-states model used by Grigorovici *et al.* (1966)—see also Mott (1969c)—to explain the temperature variation of resistivity and thermoelectric power in amorphous Ge. As T is lowered the Fermi energy moves from A (near mid-gap) to B (in a band of acceptor levels).

different regions is supported to some extent by measurements of thermoelectric power shown in Fig. 8.4(b).

According to Grigorovici (Fig. 8.4(b), curve (2)), the Seebeck coefficient exhibits a maximum at a temperature corresponding to the first inflexion in the resistivity curve, and a change of sign at the second inflexion. A possible model for this behaviour is then as shown in Fig. 8.5. At low temperatures the Fermi level lies at B, conduction is by hopping in the acceptor band, and S is negative according to equation (7.23). As the temperature is raised, the current is carried predominantly by holes excited into the valence band and S becomes positive. At high temperatures, the Fermi level moves to A, the electron contribution to the current becomes important, and S falls to smaller values due to an increasingly larger negative component. We shall, however, suggest an alternative model below.

Stuke (1970a) also reports the temperature variation of the thermo-electric power in amorphous germanium. Figure 8.4(b) incorporates these results. The curve is very nearly a mirror image of that due to Grigorovici et al. Ignoring the possibility of an error in sign deter-mination, we must conclude that some germanium films are n-type at room temperature and that a model similar to that proposed by Grigorovici et al. but with the acceptor band replaced by a donor band is possible. Chopra and Bahl (1970) report a very small value for the thermoelectric power below room temperature, which increases to a positive value at higher temperatures. Thus, qualitatively at least, Chopra and Bahl agree with Grigorovici et al.

Fig. 8.4 shows, on the same temperature scale as the resistivity and thermoelectric power, measurements of the piezoresistance (Grigorovici and Devenyi 1968; Devenyi, Belu, and Korony 1970; Fuhs and Stuke 1970) and of the magnetoresistance (Mell and Stuke 1970). The piezo-resistance is negative over the whole temperature range investigated, in contrast with a positive effect found in polycrystalline material. Interpretation of the piezoresistance can perhaps be made by con-sidering what information the curves of Fig. 8.4(c) give concerning the effect of uniaxial tension or elongation on the resistivity curves of Fig. 8.4(a). Firstly, they yield a decrease with tension in the activation energy observed above 450K. This decrease is from three to four times smaller than that observed for the electrical gap of crystalline german-ium ($\sim -6 \times 10^{-6}$ eV kg^{-1} cm^{-2}). In the low-temperature region (below about 250K), a lowering of the resistance under tension takes place without a change in the curvature. At first sight, this would seem to contradict the hopping model for this temperature region, the effect of an elongation being expected to decrease the overlap between neighbouring sites. However, Devenyi et al. point out that, since a longitudinal elongation leads to a transverse contraction, the net effect of the distortion of the initially isotropic wave functions by the uniaxial tension could be an effective increase in the overlap. They find a transverse coefficient about one half of the longitudinal coefficient. In the intermediate temperature range, the behaviour of the piezo-resistance suggests an increase in the activation energy with strain. Devenyi et al. associate this with an increase in the energy range of localized states in the valence band.

The magnetoresistance of amorphous germanium at 25 kG is negative over the temperature range shown in Fig. 8.4(d). Mell and Stuke (1970) report a sign reversal below 120K at very low fields (of the order of a few kG) but in view of the limited data available this will not be discussed. At 535K the dependence of the magnetoresistance on field is approximately linear; with decreasing temperature this dependence changes monotonically to a square-root behaviour below ~200K. As discussed in Chapter 6, a negative magnetoresistance can occur for hopping conduction. It is not known what sign of magnetoresistance is expected for conduction with short mean free path in extended (delocalized) states. (For band conduction in crystals the magnetoresistance is always positive; and it is also observed to be positive in polycrystalline germanium.) Figure 8.4 (d) shows a rapid fall in the magnitude of $\Delta\rho/\rho$ in the temperature range where such conduction in extended states is expected to dominate. Mell and Stuke claim that the absence of a positive magnetoresistance at high temperatures suggests that the mobility in extended states must be less than 50 cm^2 V^{-1} s^{-1}. Without a theoretical treatment of the magnetoresistance in amorphous semiconductors, the results do not provide much information about the conduction mechanisms prevailing in the different temperature regions.

On the basis of the evidence that we have summarized, we can, however, make some speculations concerning conduction mechanisms in amorphous germanium. Firstly, it seems evident that conduction at low temperatures (say below 200K) occurs by hopping. Apart from some indications shown in Fig. 8.4 and already discussed, amorphous germanium provides a good example of the relation of $\ln \sigma$ to $1/T^{\frac{1}{4}}$ expected for hopping and derived in Chapter 2. Fig. 8.6 shows Clark's data plotted against $1/T$ and against $1/T^{\frac{1}{4}}$. Resistivity data obtained by Walley and Jonscher (1968) also plot linearly on a $T^{-\frac{1}{4}}$ basis (see Mott 196Ja), as do Chopra and Bahl's results[†]. It should be pointed out that the linearity extends to rather higher temperatures than expected; it would not seem reasonable to consider hopping at the Fermi level an appropriate description above, say, 200K ($T^{-\frac{1}{4}} = 0.27$), so this agreement may be partly fortuitous.

The most plausible explanation of the behaviour of the resistivity at higher temperatures (above ~300K) is that the carriers are electrons (or holes, depending on the preparation of the specimen) excited into localized states at the band edge. It seems that in amorphous germanium deposited at room temperature it is not normally possible to reach a temperature where the current is controlled by carriers excited into

[†] From the analysis presented in § 2.9.1, the slope of the plot of $\ln \sigma$ against $1/T^{\frac{1}{4}}$ is approximately $2\{\alpha^3/kN(E_F)\}^{\frac{1}{4}}$. The data of Fig. 8.6 yield a value of $N(E_F) \sim 5 \times 10^{18}$ cm^{-3} eV^{-1} for $\alpha^{-1} = 8$ Å or $\sim 10^{20}$ cm^{-3} eV^{-1} for $\alpha^{-1} = 3$ Å.

delocalized states, without causing irreversible structural changes that occur on heating; otherwise the plot of ln ρ against $1/T$ should be linear. The results of Grigorovici *et al.* discussed above were made on annealed samples, and the high-temperature activation energy is in fact rather better defined in such samples.

A careful study of the effect of annealing on glow-discharge deposited films of amorphous germanium has been made by Chittick (1970).

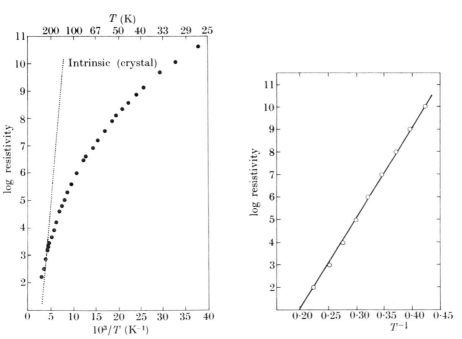

Fig. 8.6. Temperature variation of resistivity in amorphous Ge as determined by Clark (1967), plotted as log ρ against $1/T$ and log ρ against $1/T^{\frac{1}{4}}$.

Fig. 8.7 shows his results on two samples. The general behaviour agrees with that observed by other workers, namely that annealing increases the resistivity below about 300K. At high temperatures the activation energy for conduction also increases, while at low temperatures the effect of annealing is a parallel shift of the curve. The latter observation suggests simply a reduction in the number of defect centres (perhaps dangling bonds) at which hopping is occurring. Direct evidence that annealing reduces the number of defect centres in amorphous *silicon* has been obtained by electron spin resonance studies (§ 8.1.4).

The increase in the high-temperature slope of the ln σ against $1/T$ plot on annealing can be accounted for in the following way. We have

suggested that, in amorphous germanium deposited at room temperature, conduction, except at low temperatures, is by hopping in localized
states at a band edge. Annealing is expected to reduce this range of
localized states and to make conduction by carriers excited beyond a
mobility shoulder a more likely possibility (see § 7.4.2). If this model is

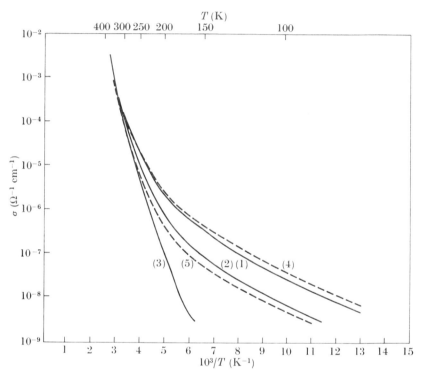

FIG. 8.7. Temperature variation of conductivity in two samples of glow-discharge-
deposited amorphous Ge before and after annealing (from Chittick 1970). Solid curve,
sample deposited at room temperature, thickness $1\cdot 6\ \mu$m: (1) cooled to 77K from 295K;
(2) heated to 336K, then cooled; (3) heated to 384K, then cooled. Dashed curve, sample
deposited at room temperature, thickness $1\cdot 0\ \mu$m: (4) cooled to 77K from 292K; (5)
heated to 354K and cooled.

correct, then the increase of activation energy should be accompanied
by an increase in C, the extrapolated intercept on the $1/T$ axis of a
plot of ln σ against $1/T$. Evidence that this happens is provided by data
obtained by Chittick and shown in Fig. 8.8. Here is plotted the value of
$\rho_0\ (= 1/C)$ and $E(\rho = \rho_0\ \exp(E/kT))$ as a function of deposition
temperature. Films deposited at room temperature have a value of
$C \sim 10\ \Omega^{-1}\ \mathrm{cm}^{-1}$, which is about as expected for hopping at a band
edge (see Chapter 7). As the temperature of deposition is increased, C

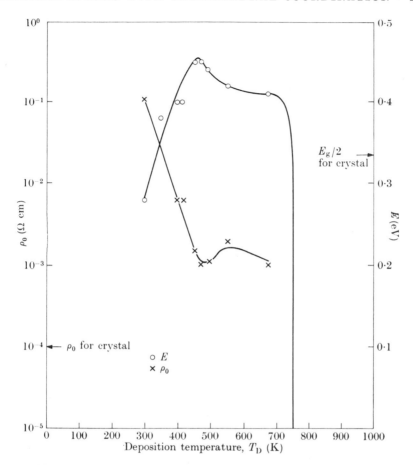

FIG. 8.8. Variation of ρ_0 and E defined by $\rho = \rho_0 \exp{(E/kT)}$ as a function of deposition temperature for glow-discharge-deposited Ge (from Chittick 1970).

increases to a value $\sim 10^3\ \Omega^{-1}\ \text{cm}^{-1}$, as expected for conduction in extended states. The rise in C is accompanied by an increase of about $0 \cdot 17$ eV in E. Note that for a deposition temperature of 750K the films are polycrystalline and E falls dramatically. Chittick measured the optical absorption edge of his samples but not to low enough values of the absorption coefficient α to observe whether or not the edge was sharp, as found by Donovan, Spicer, and Bennett (1969) in evaporated films. Optical properties of amorphous germanium are to be discussed in § 8.1.5. We shall use the data presented there that the absorption edge of germanium occurs at about $0 \cdot 6$ eV in films deposited at room temperature and at about $0 \cdot 75$ eV (i.e. close to that in crystalline Ge) in films deposited near to the amorphous–crystalline transition temperature. Our suggested model for the effect of annealing on the electronic states in amorphous germanium is therefore as shown in Fig. 8.9 (assuming n-type conduction).

In the remainder of this section, which will describe other electrical measurements on amorphous germanium, we shall assume that annealing effects have been recognized by the workers concerned, and that

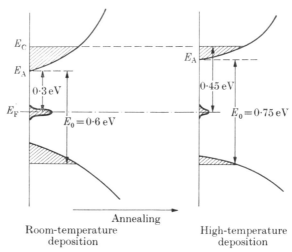

Annealing

Room-temperature deposition

High-temperature deposition

FIG. 8.9. Suggested model for the density of states in amorphous Ge and the effects of annealing (reduction in the density of defect centres at E_F and in the extent of localized states at the band edge). The predominant conduction mechanism changes from being at localized states near E_A to extended states at E_C. The values for the electrical activation energy, $(E_A - E_F)$ before annealing and $(E_C - E_F)$ after annealing, are from Chittick (1970). Grigorovici *et al.* (1966) and Stuke (1970a) find 0·55 eV in annealed samples. Optical gaps E_0 are from Donovan, Ashley, and Spicer (1970). Corrections for the hopping energy at E_A and for temperature variations of the gaps have been ignored.

the films have been 'stabilized', at least up to the highest temperature at which measurements have been reported.

It would of course be extremely useful to know to what extent (if at all) the variation of resistivities shown in Fig. 8.4, 8.6, and 8.7 were due to a change in carrier mobility with temperature. Unfortunately, as with other amorphous semiconductors, measurements of the Hall effect are difficult because of the small magnitude of the Hall voltage, and furthermore are not easy to interpret. Thus Clark (1967) observed a negative Hall effect (i.e. with sign opposite to the sign of the thermoelectric power normally found in amorphous germanium at room temperature) which could be measured with an accuracy of only ∼100 per cent. Its temperature dependence could not be followed. Interpreting Clark's data using the conventional one-carrier relationship $R = 1/nec$, we obtain an electron-carrier concentration of about 10^{18} cm^{-3}, which in conjunction with the conductivity data implies a Hall mobility at room temperature of about 10^{-2} cm^2 V^{-1} s^{-1}. In view of the uncertainty concerning interpretation, these figures give little firm information. However, the value for the Hall mobility is not inconsistent with the recent theoretical treatment of the Hall effect for conduction in extended states near the mobility edge as developed by Friedman (1971) and described in § 2.12.

From measurements of the voltage dependence of the capacitance of a p–n junction formed between amorphous germanium and single-crystal n-type germanium, Grigorovici, Croitoru, Devenyi, and Teleman (1964) deduce a hole density of about 10^{19} cm^{-3} with a mobility of $\sim 10^{-3}$ cm^2 V^{-1} s^{-1}. Junctions formed between amorphous germanium and p-type germanium crystals were only weakly rectifying. The procedure used to determine μ by this method has been criticized by Walley and Jonscher (1968).

If conduction is by carriers hopping between localized sites a decrease of the resistivity with frequency of the applied field is to be expected (see Chapters 2, 6, and 7). Walley and Jonscher report no decrease up to 20 kHz at room temperature. Chopra and Bahl (1970) report the results shown in Fig. 8.10. A decrease in resistivity with increasing frequency occurs above 50K Hz at room temperature. The frequency at which the decrease first sets in is smaller at lower temperatures. At 77K, a variation with frequency to a power close to 2 is observed from about 5×10^3 to 10^5 Hz. According to the theory presented in Chapter 2 and discussed in Chapter 7, hopping conduction should, above a certain frequency, follow a dependence on frequency to a power somewhat less than unity. Above 300K the reduced temperature dependence shown in Fig. 8.10 suggests hopping at the Fermi level, and, under the same assumptions as used in § 7.4.4, an estimate for the density of states $N(E_F)$ can be made. It is $\sim 5 \times 10^{21}$ cm^{-3} eV^{-1}.

This high value is not unreasonable in view of the e.s.r. results of Brodsky and Title (1969). By comparing the g value ($2 \cdot 021 \pm 0 \cdot 001$) and line width (39 G) of an e.s.r. signal detected from amorphous germanium with that observed on mechanically damaged surfaces of crystalline germanium, Brodsky and Title suggest that dangling bonds are present with a total density $\sim 3 \times 10^{20}$ cm^{-3} (see § 7.7.2).

Studies of the tunnelling current from a metal electrode through an oxide barrier into amorphous germanium as a function of bias have been reported by Osmun and Fritzsche (1970). Their results are shown in Fig. 8.11. The tunnelling current is almost exactly symmetric with respect to zero bias, and furthermore this symmetry is unchanged as the temperature is lowered to 78K. These experimental results, which differ from earlier measurements by Nwachuku and Kuhn (1968), provide strong evidence for a Fermi level that, at the film surface at least,

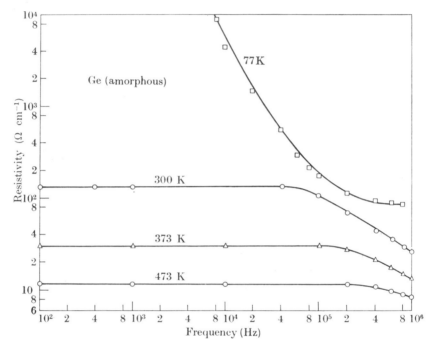

FIG. 8.10. Frequency dependence of resisitivity in evaporated films of Ge at various temperatures (from Chopra and Bahl 1970).

is pinned close to the centre of a gap in the density of states. They thus contradict the model shown in Fig. 8.5, but support the alternative model described in this section. Unfortunately it does not appear possible to assign a value for the size of the energy gap from the shape of the tunnelling curves.

Photoconductivity in amorphous germanium has been measured by Grigorovici, Croitoru, and Devenyi (1967b) and by Clark (1967). The magnitude of the photoconductivity is very small and as the results from the two laboratories are in disagreement they will not be discussed here.

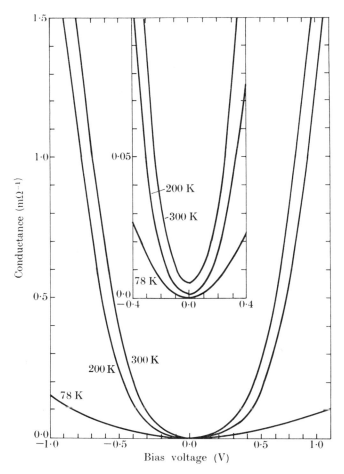

FIG. 8.11. Differential tunnelling conductance of an Al–Al$_2$O$_3$–amorphous Ge tunnel junction (from Osmun and Fritzsche 1970).

8.1.4. Electrical properties of amorphous silicon

There have been fewer electrical measurements made on amorphous silicon than on germanium. Qualitatively the properties of the two materials are similar, as is seen, for example, in Fig. 8.12 due to Walley (1968*b*), which compares the temperature variation of resistance of annealed samples; if resistivity had been plotted, Walley claims that the curves could be superimposed. Brodsky and Title (1969) find from e.s.r. studies on amorphous silicon deposited at room temperature a density of unpaired spins $\sim 2 \times 10^{20}$ cm^{-3}, i.e. equal within experimental error to that found in amorphous germanium.

20

As for amorphous germanium, annealing effects are observed at temperatures above that of deposition. Results from Brodsky, Title, Weiser, and Pettit (1970) are reproduced in Fig. 8.13 for a silicon film sputtered on to a substrate held at 77K. The reduction in conductivity (at least for temperatures below 300K) with annealing is accompanied by a fall in the strength of the e.s.r. signal. The signal is shown as a function of annealing temperature in Fig. 8.14(a), which also includes the simultaneous decrease in refractive index. It should be

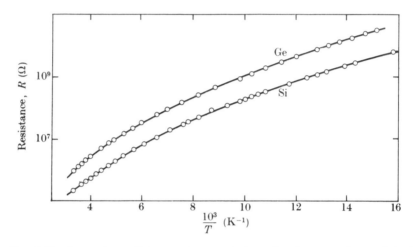

FIG. 8.12. Comparison of temperature variation of resistance of annealed films of amorphous silicon and germanium (from Walley 1968*b*).

noted that there is good evidence that crystallization does not occur until an annealing temperature of above 500°C and that changes *below* this temperature are considered to arise from structural modifications to the films, which remain amorphous. Figure 8.14(b) gives some X-ray diffraction results that support this idea, although the sensitivity of these measurements is such that more than 10 per cent of the film would have to be crystalline to be observable over the amorphous background. Similar *electron* diffraction patterns have been obtained by Moss and Graczyk (1969).

Annealing studies by Chittick (1970) on silicon films prepared by r.f. decomposition of silane are presented in Fig. 8.15 in the same manner as were his results for amorphous germanium, i.e. plots of ρ_0 and E against deposition temperature ($\rho = \rho_0 \exp(E/kT)$). The rapid decrease of ρ_0 between deposition temperatures of 300 and 400K suggests, as for germanium, that the predominant conduction mechanism changes

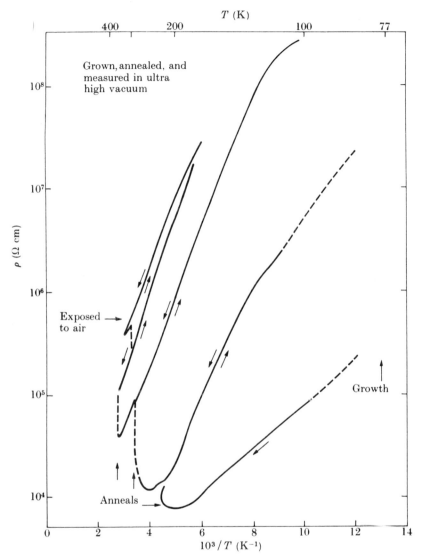

FIG. 8.13. Temperature variation of resistivity of amorphous silicon grown at about 80K and subsequently annealed (after Brodsky *et al.* 1970).

from hopping in localized states at the band edge to conduction beyond a mobility edge. The very low value of E for the film deposited at room temperature arises because Chittick measured the slope on a curved portion of the curve of $\ln \rho$ against $1/T$, where the relation $\rho = \rho_0 \exp(E/kT)$ was not obeyed. A more striking difference between Fig. 8.15 and Fig. 8.8 is the steady decrease of E for deposition

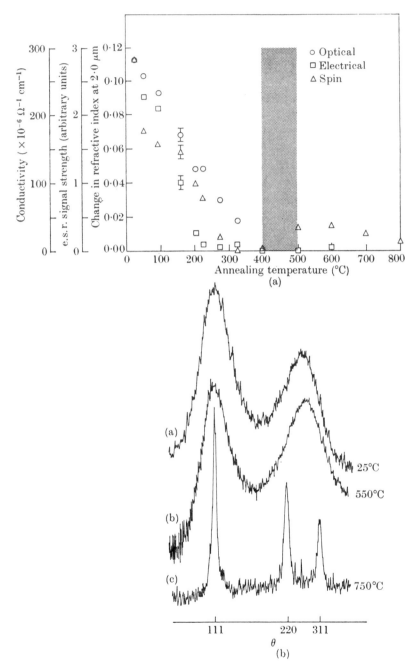

FIG. 8.14. (a) The dependence on annealing temperature of the room-temperature conductivity, strength of e.s.r. signal, and change in refractive index of amorphous Si. The shaded region separates the amorphous from the polycrystalline material. (b) Normalized microdensitometer traces of X-ray diffraction patterns of Si. The film remains amorphous even after three hours at 550°C but crystallizes (bottom trace) after an anneal at 750°C (from Brodsky et al. 1970).

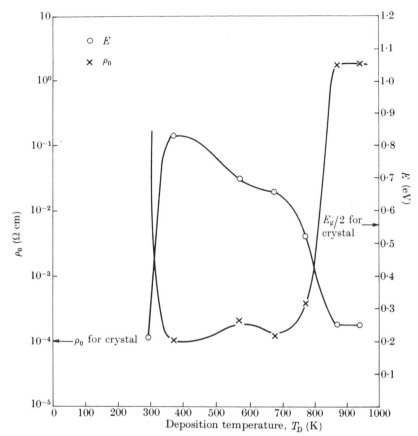

FIG. 8.15. Variation of ρ_0 and E defined by $\rho = \rho_0 \exp(E/kT)$ as a function of deposition temperature for glow-discharge deposited Si (from Chittick 1970).

temperatures from 400K to the temperature of crystallization ($\sim$800K). Because of the constancy of ρ_0 in the same range, this decrease of E leads to a decrease in ρ. Thus Chittick's films behave on annealing in exactly the opposite sense to those of Brodsky et al. Clearly the different methods of preparation are responsible for this apparent contradiction.

The r.f. discharge method of preparing amorphous silicon leads to a higher room-temperature resistivity than any other method. For a deposition temperature of about 400K the resistivity is (from Fig. 8.15) $\sim$10^{-4} exp(0·84/kT), i.e. $\sim$10^{10} Ω cm at room temperature. We can speculate that this arises from a larger energy range of localized states at the band edge than in evaporated films and, following Chittick, suppose that the fall in E with annealing towards the value 0·65 eV arises from delocalization of states in this range. From Fig. 8.15 we can estimate therefore that the range of localized states is $\sim$0·2 eV for samples deposited at 400K. For samples deposited at room temperature the range of localized states must be even greater; the increase of ρ_0 suggests that, in the temperature range concerned, conduction is by hopping at the band edge.

The high resistivity of amorphous silicon prepared in this way makes the measurement of drift mobility (§ 7.4.3) a feasible proposition. Le Comber and Spear (1970) have performed such measurements. In view of their importance the results will be described in some detail. Fig. 8.16 summarizes the observations. The temperature dependence of drift mobility for electrons (hole transport could not be detected) exhibits a kink at about 250K, above which the activation energy is 0·19 eV and below which it is 0·09 eV. The plot of d.c. conductivity against inverse temperature also exhibits a change of slope at about the same temperature (240K). Above T_C the transport of injected electrons is assumed to occur in extended states, the activation energy in the drift mobility arising from trapping in the shallow localized states at the conduction-band edge. According to equation (7.13) a range of localized states can be estimated $\sim$0·2 eV wide, and a mobility in extended states equal to $\sim$9–10 cm^2 V^{-1} s^{-1}. These values are certainly of the magnitude predicted by theory and so justify interpretation in this way. Below T_C it is conjectured that transport occurs by hopping through the localized states at the band edge and that the slope of the plots of ln σ against $1/T$ represents a hopping energy of 0·09 eV. According to § 7.4.2 we expect the slopes of the plots of ln σ against $1/T$ to be $(E_C - E_F)$ above the kink and $(E_A - E_F + \Delta W_1)$ below the kink. Using the observed difference in the slopes of 0·11 eV we find

$$(E_C - E_A - \Delta W_1) = 0·11\text{eV}.$$

Thus if the range of localized states $E_C - E_A$ is 0·19 eV, then $\Delta W_1 = 0·08$ eV, which is in good agreement with the value obtained directly from the low-temperature drift mobility.

Measurements of the thermoelectric power of amorphous silicon prepared by evaporation have been made by Stuke (1970b) and were shown in Fig. 7.21. Similar measurements have been reported over a broader temperature range by Grigorovici, Croitoru, and Devenyi (1967a) and are shown in Fig. 8.17. Qualitatively the behaviour is similar to that in amorphous germanium.

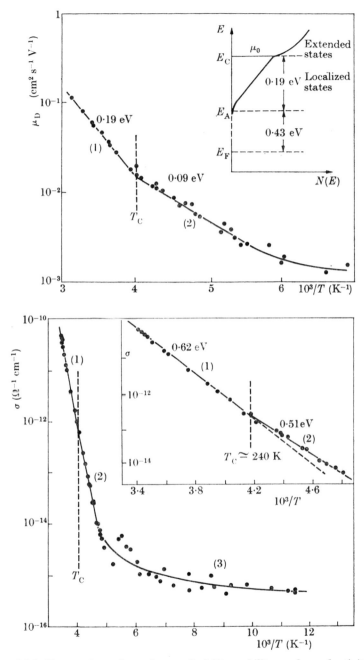

FIG. 8.16. Temperature dependence of drift mobility and conductivity in glow-discharge-deposited silicon (from Le Comber and Spear 1970).

The magnetoresistance of amorphous silicon (Mell and Stuke 1970) is negative and shows a variation with temperature from 200 to 500K similar to that in amorphous germanium (see Fig. 7.7).

Considerable photoconductivity (three decades increase for white illumination of 220 lux) was observed by Chittick in glow-discharge-deposited silicon. The spectral response of films deposited at various temperatures gave, on Fowler plots, thresholds for photoconduction

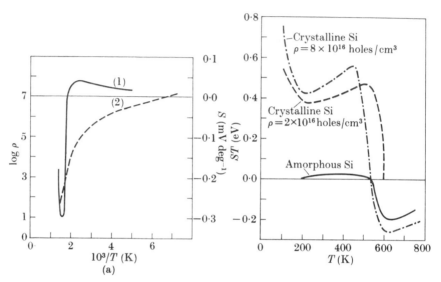

FIG. 8.17. Resistivity ρ and thermoelectric power S of evaporated silicon. (a) Plot of (1) log ρ and (2) S against $1/T$. (b) Plot of ST against T. Also shown in (b) is the variation of thermoelectric power for two p-type silicon crystals (from Grigorovici et al. 1967a).

approximately equal to twice the high-temperature slope of the ln ρ against $1/T$ plots.

8.1.5. Optical properties of amorphous germanium

It would be hard to find in the whole of the published literature on amorphous semiconductors a greater disparity than exists for the form of the optical absorption edge in amorphous germanium. Fig. 8.18 collects together room-temperature data of Tauc (1970a), Clark (1967), Spicer and Donovan (1970a), Chopra and Bahl (1970), and Chittick (1970). Before attempting to discuss these results we point out that the edge in crystalline germanium, shown as a dashed curve (Dash and Newman 1955), is produced by transitions across an indirect gap of 0·66 eV and a direct gap of 0·8 eV corresponding (see Fig. 7.35) to the transitions $\Gamma_{25'} \to L_1$ and $\Gamma_{25'} \to \Gamma_{2'}$ respectively.

All the measurements shown in Fig. 8.18 agree in one respect, namely that the absorption coefficient at a photon energy corresponding to indirect transitions in the crystal is high. Thus, if an understanding of the optical properties is sought on the basis of a density of states that is only slightly different in the amorphous and crystalline forms, we might

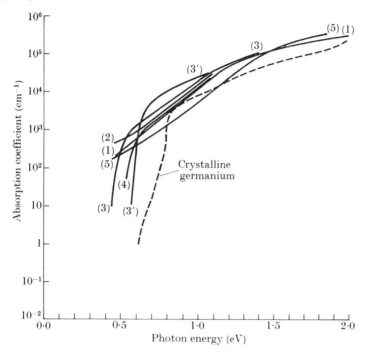

Fig. 8.18. Room-temperature optical absorption edges in amorphous germanium as reported by various authors. (1) Chittick (1970); (2) Clark (1967); (3) and (3′) Spicer and Donovan (1970a); (4) Chopra and Bahl (1970); (5) Tauc (1970a). The dashed curve for the crystal is from Dash and Newman (1955).

infer that the k-conservation selection rule, which reduces the probability for optical transitions near 0·6 eV in the crystal, is no longer operative in the amorphous state. In any event, the optical absorption edge occurs at lower photon energies in the amorphous than in the crystalline phase. As was shown in § 8.1.4 the electrical gap is increased, which is a consequence of localized states at the band edges.

Some of the curves shown in Fig. 8.18 show an absorption constant that obeys a spectral Urbach rule over a limited range (§ 7.6.1). However, the slope observed is about one half of that normally found in the majority of amorphous semiconductors and it seems unlikely to arise from the same mechanism.

There seems little doubt that most of the discrepancies between the results in Fig. 8.18 arise from differences in methods of preparation and annealing treatments of the films, as discussed in earlier sections. The most important point of difference lies in the behaviour of the absorption constant for low photon energies. Whilst most workers have found a gradual tailing of the edge, Spicer and Donovan (curves 3 and 3') and Chopra and Bahl (curve 4) report sharp falls in α near 0·5 eV. It should be emphasized that the thickness limitations imposed on films prepared by vacuum evaporation make it exceedingly difficult to obtain accurate absorption data below 10^2 cm^{-1}. Spicer and Donovan (see also Donovan, Spicer, Bennett, and Ashley 1970) were able to measure to 10 cm^{-1} using extremely parallel films up to 2 μm in thickness. Although the position of the sharp edge was found to be sensitive to evaporation conditions and to the nature of the substrate, they found no evidence for any absorption above 10 cm^{-1} in the photon energy range from 0·1 eV up to the sharp edge. Later measurements (Donovan, Ashley, and Spicer 1970) confirmed these observations and correlated the position of the sharp edge with temperature of deposition and also film density. For substrate temperatures less than 250°C, Donovan *et al.* found that the position of the edge was always below 0·6 eV and the film density $\sim$4.7 g cm^{-3}, while for substrate temperatures in the range 250–300°C the edge shifted abruptly to 0·7–0·8 eV and the film density increased, within experimental error, to the value for the crystal (5·35 g cm^{-3}). It should be stressed that these authors do not regard the existence of the sharp edge or its shift to higher energies on annealing as arising from any form of crystallization in their films.

On our model for the density of states in amorphous germanium shown in Fig. 8.9, a sharp absorption edge is expected, and the optical gap is marked on this figure, on the assumption that it occurs at the onset of transitions from extended to localized states. We have already discussed (§ 7.6.1) possible reasons for the non-existence of sharp edges in most other amorphous semiconductors.

Figure 8.19 shows the variation of the refractive index n_0 and the imaginary part of the dielectric constant ϵ_2 with photon energy as obtained by Donovan, Spicer, Bennett, and Ashley (1970) on films of amorphous germanium, the average absorption edge of which was shown as curve (3') in Fig. 8.18. The low-energy value for n_0 equal to 4 was found to be independent of any annealing treatment. The variation of ϵ_2 with $\hbar\omega$ cannot be described by any of the simple power relationships discussed in § 7.6.2. Included in Fig. 8.19(b) are the results of

Tauc, Grigorovici, and Vancu (1966), which these authors fitted to a relation of the type

$$\epsilon_2(\hbar\omega)^2 \sim \alpha\hbar\omega \sim (\hbar\omega - 0\cdot88)^2.$$

The structure in the energy range $0\cdot2$–$0\cdot3$ eV reported by Tauc *et al.* (1966) was originally interpreted as due to transitions between branches of the valence band. In later work (Tauc, Abraham, Zallen, and Slade 1970) this interpretation was discounted, following measurements on thicker evaporated films, which did not exhibit this structure

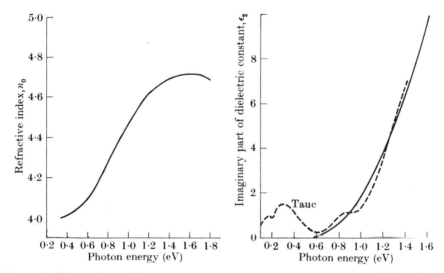

FIG. 8.19. Spectral dependence of the real part of the refractive index and the imaginary part of the dielectric constant, as determined from transmission and reflection data near the edge in amorphous germanium by Donovan *et al.* (1970). The variation of ϵ_2 as determined by Tauc *et al.* (1966) is also shown.

nor that near $0\cdot9$ eV. However in the same paper Tauc *et al.* report an absorption band at $0\cdot23$ eV in sputtered and also in electrolytically deposited germanium. The results are shown in Fig. 8.20. Interference fringes dominate the transmission spectra, especially in the more nearly optically perfect evaporated films. The band at $0\cdot23$ eV is interpreted by Tauc *et al.* (1970) as arising from transitions from the valence band to a defect level in the gap (radiation damage in crystalline germanium introduces an acceptor level $0\cdot24$ eV above the valence band). The other strong absorption band that can be seen near $0\cdot07$ eV (Fig. 8.20) is attributed by Tauc *et al.* to an oxygen-defect complex. Bands in almost exactly the same location have been observed by Chittick (1970) in glow-discharge-deposited

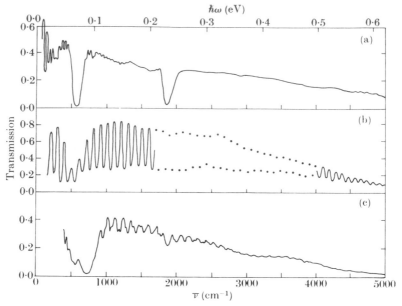

Fɪɢ. 8.20. Infrared transmission spectra of amorphous germanium prepared by three different methods (from Tauc *et al.* 1970). (a) Electrolytic amorphous Ge, thickness = 27μm; (b) evaporated amorphous Ge, thickness = 12 μm; (c) sputtered amorphous Ge thickness = 35 μm.

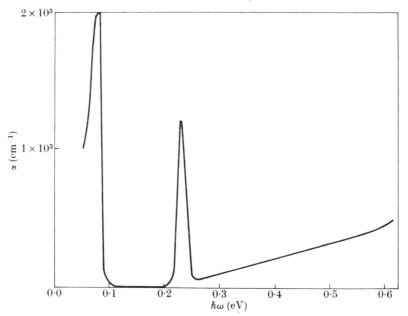

Fɪɢ. 8.21. Infrared absorption spectrum of amorphous germanium prepared by glow-discharge deposition (from Chittick 1970). Film thickness = 4·1 μm.

films. His results are shown in Fig. 8.21. At the time of writing it is not clear why such strong absorption is not seen in the evaporated films of Spicer *et al.* Nor is it clear why Tauc *et al.* and other investigators fail to see a sharp absorption edge in some of their films.

Some preliminary measurements by Piller, Seraphin, Markel, and Fischer (1969) of the electroreflectance spectra of germanium films are of interest. Electromodulation techniques (Cardona 1969) are

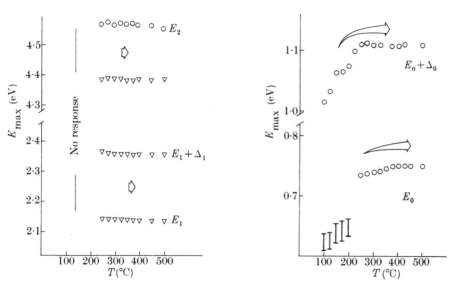

FIG. 8.22. Spectral positions of electroreflectance signals in amorphous germanium as a function of deposition temperature. The signal split by spin–orbit coupling at the edge is shown on the right (E_0, $E_0 + \Delta$). Bars indicate very weak structure (from Piller *et al.* 1969).

used to enhance the sensitivity and resolution of conventional optical transmission and reflectivity measurements. They involve the application of a periodic electric field to the sample and the synchronous detection of induced charges in the optical properties. With such a modulation technique it is possible to resolve easily at room temperature the spin–orbit splitting of the valence-band edge in crystalline germanium. This splitting (not shown in Fig. 7.35) is of the order of 0·35 eV and leads to the first direct $\Gamma_{25'} \to \Gamma_{2'}$ transition being observed as a doublet. Figure 8.22 shows the position of the electroreflective signals in various germanium films deposited on to substrates held at temperatures between 100 and 500°C. According to electron-diffraction patterns obtained from the various films, Piller *et al.* assert that above

200°C the films are polycrystalline. Although the size of the electro-reflectance signals decreases as the deposition temperature is lowered from 500°C to 200°C, they stay sharp and indicate a slight decrease in the energy of the peak at 0·75 eV associated with the uppermost valence band. At deposition temperatures below 200°C the electron diffraction patterns are characteristic of the amorphous phase and the conversion is accompanied by an abrupt decrease in the energy of this peak by 0·1–0·2 eV. Although the signals are weak and there is con-siderable uncertainty in the data, we have to regard the experiments as providing substantiating evidence for a decrease in the optical gap in going from crystalline to amorphous germanium. The signal at 1·1 eV associated with transitions from the deeper-lying valence band is observed to move continuously to lower energies through the transition temperature. According to Piller *et al.*, this observation suggests that the electronic band structure several tenths of an eV below the valence band edge is less affected by the loss of long-range order.

The absorption due to interband transitions above the fundamental edge has been discussed in § 7.6.3 and the plot of ϵ_2 against $\hbar\omega$ for crystalline and amorphous germanium presented in Fig. 7.34. The spectrum for the amorphous film shown was obtained from a Kramers–Kronig analysis of reflectivity data by Tauc *et al.* (1965). Similar spectra have been obtained by Tauc and Abraham (1969), Donovan *et al.* (1970), and Beaglehole and Zavetova (1970).

Interpretation of the spectrum of Fig. 7.34 is of fundamental importance for a full understanding of the electronic properties of amorphous semiconductors. The significant question is whether the spectrum can be calculated from a knowledge of the electronic band structure of crystalline germanium or whether a different approach, such as that introduced by Phillips (1970) and mentioned in § 7.6.3, is necessary.

As shown in Fig. 7.36 a calculation based on the crystal density of states but allowing the k-conservation selection rule to be relaxed (non-direct transitions allowed) yields a smoothed-out ϵ_2 spectrum which peaks at 4·5 eV compared with the experimental curve which peaks at 2·65 eV. Noting that the density of amorphous germanium is generally lower than the density of the crystal, Herman and Van Dyke (1968) suggested that a dilated germanium lattice may be a better starting point; using the calculated band structure for a germanium lattice in which the lattice constant was increased by 11 per cent (Fig. 8.23) they recomputed the ϵ_2 spectrum. The result is shown in Fig.

8.24: the peak in ϵ_2 occurs at 3·1 eV, much closer to the experimental result. However, the shift is still not far enough and in fact a 33 per cent reduction in density is certainly an overestimate. The nearest-neighbour distance in amorphous germanium is at the most ∼5 per cent larger than in the crystal.

An alternative explanation for the low energy at which the maximum for amorphous germanium occurs is suggested by the observation that the dominant peak near 4·5 eV in the reflectivity or ϵ_2 spectrum of crystalline germanium is very sensitive to surface condition. Measurements on polished surfaces, for example, sometimes produce a peak which is smaller than the peak near 2 eV (Lukes 1959). As polished surfaces may be expected to have a structural condition approaching that of amorphous germanium, it is not unreasonable to suppose that the first effect of disorder is to reduce the matrix element associated with the electronic transitions occurring near 4·5 eV. Stuke (1970b) considers that for the crystal, the matrix elements near 4·5 eV are enhanced above the average, and that this enhancement is lost on a non-direct-transition model. (see also Maschke and Thomas 1970).

Using a density of states appropriate to a 'slightly' (∼3 per cent) dilated germanium lattice, Brust (1969) considered the effect of disordering on the matrix elements for optical transitions. In the crystal, the oscillator strengths of transitions near the forbidden gap are strongly Umklapp-enhanced. Disorder smears out the structure but leaves the red end of the spectrum much more intense than the blue. Using this fact and replacing the assumption of non-direct transitions by a disorder scattering term, Brust found a calculated ϵ_2 spectrum in very good agreement with experiment.

Any model proposed to account for the ϵ_2 spectrum is also required to explain the optical density of states as determined by photoemission. Fig. 7.42 showed the results of Donovan and Spicer (1968). According to Herman and Van Dyke's calculation shown in Fig. 8.23, dilation does shift the density of states maximum in the valence band closer to the band edge. Again we mention the excessive dilation required, which would actually make germanium a semi-metal, as seen in Fig. 8.23. According to Brust, the actual density of states is virtually unchanged on disordering and the optical density of states appears too close to the forbidden gap because the electron escape function shifts the photo-emission peaks towards higher energies. Later photo-emission measurements by Spicer and Donovan (1970b), in which caesium was used to lower the photo-emission threshold, convinced these authors

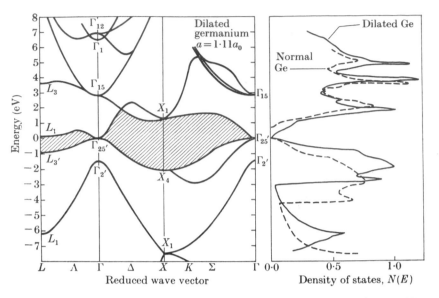

FIG. 8.23. Calculated energy-band structure of dilated germanium ($a/a_0 = 1.11$) and density of states of normal and dilated germanium (from Herman and Van Dyke 1968).

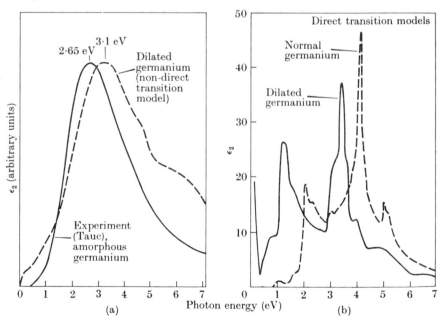

FIG. 8.24. (a) Comparison of experimental ϵ_2 curve for amorphous germanium and theoretical ϵ_2 curve based on the band structure of Fig. 8.23 and the model of non-direct transitions and constant matrix elements. (b) Comparison of theoretical ϵ_2 curves for normal and dilated germanium based on direct transitions (pseudopotential-type matrix elements) (from Herman and Van Dyke 1968).

that Brust's explanation was not tenable and they concluded that there was no evidence to support the suggestion that features of the crystalline band structure are carried over into the amorphous material.

If indeed there is a difference in the density of states between crystalline and amorphous germanium, it could arise from the fact that the structure of the latter may be closer to that of the hexagonal wurtzite lattice than to that of diamond. As described in § 8.1.2, Grigorovici's model for amorphous germanium is based on the assumption that a large proportion of adjacent sets of bonds are in the eclipsed configuration. Optical measurements on the cubic and hexagonal modifications of ZnS (Baars 1967; Drews, Davis, and Leiga 1967) have revealed striking differences in the reflectivity specta. In the cubic modification the equivalent peak to the 4·5 eV peak in crystalline germanium is strong, whereas in the hexagonal modification it is weak.[†] The band structure of a hypothetical hexagonal germanium lattice may possibly be a better starting point for an understanding of the optical properties of the amorphous phase.

8.1.6. Optical properties of amorphous silicon

The optical absorption edge of amorphous silicon is, like that of amorphous germanium, dependent on the conditions of sample preparation. A measurement by Beaglehole and Zavetova (1970) on an evaporated film approximately 1 μm thick is compared with the edge of crystalline silicon (Dash and Newman 1955) in Fig. 8.25. In the crystal the absorption edge at about 1·1 eV corresponds to indirect transitions from $\Gamma_{25'}$ to the minimum in the conduction band along the Δ-axis of the Brillouin zone (Fig. 8.26). Direct transitions to Γ_{15} do not occur until a photon energy of about 3 eV is reached. The high values of α observed for amorphous silicon in the range from 1–3 eV thus provide good evidence for a relaxation of the k-conservation selection rule.

The edge in amorphous silicon has also been measured by Grigorovici and Vancu (1968), by Chittick (1970), and by Brodsky, Title, Weiser, and Pettit (1970). Brodsky et al. studied the effect of film annealing on the position of the edge (Fig. 8.27). As for amorphous germanium, annealing shifts the edge closer to that in the crystal. (In glow-discharge-deposited films Chittick finds that annealing shifts the photoconductivity edge to lower energies: the changes in the electrical

---

† We refer also to the calculations of Klima and McGill (1971) mentioned in Chapter 2. Details in the density of states for amorphous carbon are sensitive to whether neighbouring tetrahedra are eclipsed or staggered.

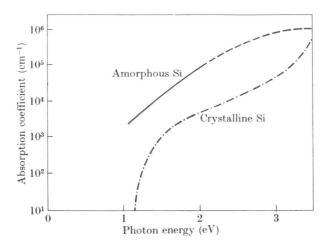

FIG. 8.25. Comparison of room-temperature optical absorption edges in amorphous (Beaglehole and Zavetova 1970) and crystalline (Dash and Newman 1955) silicon (from Stuke 1970*b*).

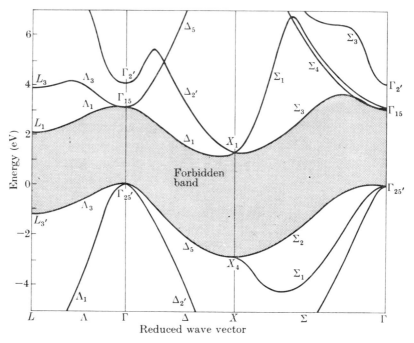

FIG. 8.26. Electronic band structure of silicon (from F. Herman and J. P. Van Dyke, unpublished).

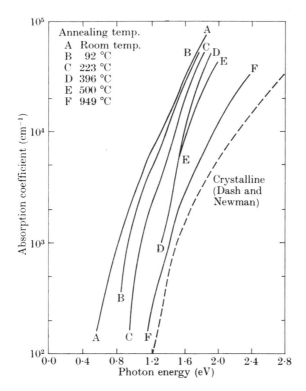

FIG. 8.27. Optical absorption edge in amorphous silicon before and after two-hour anneals at the temperatures shown. The film crystallized during the 500°C anneal (from Brodsky *et al.* 1970).

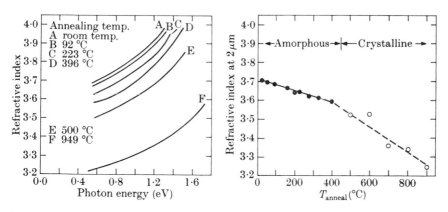

FIG. 8.28. Effect of the same annealing treatments as in Fig. 8.27 on the refractive index of amorphous silicon. In (b) the refractive index is that determined at 2 μm (0·62 eV) (from Brodsky *et al.* 1970).

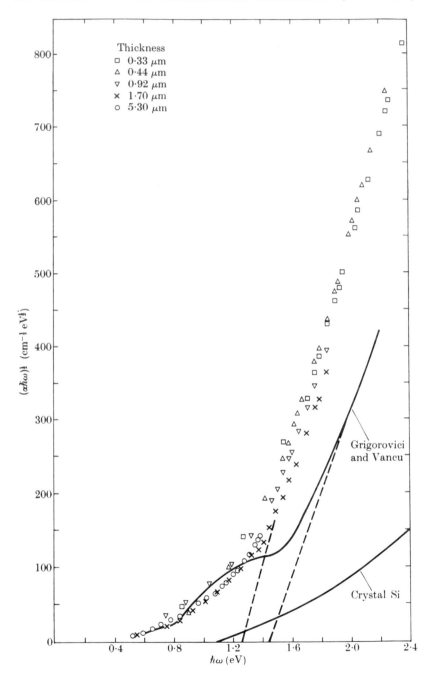

FIG. 8.29. Plot of $(\alpha\hbar\omega)^{\frac{1}{2}}$ against photon energy for several unannealed films of amorphous silicon as determined by Brodsky *et al.* The results are compared to those of Grigorovici and Vancu (1968) and to the single-crystal spectrum reported by Dash and Newman (1955). (From Brodsky *et al.* 1970.)

properties of these films on annealing are also different from those observed in evaporated films.) In contrast to amorphous germanium, however, annealing reduces the refractive index, as shown in Fig. 8.28. The 'knee' in Fig. 8.28(b) corresponds to the X-ray diffraction patterns showing evidence of crystallization.

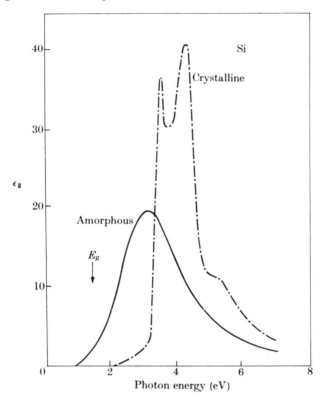

FIG. 8.30. Fundamental absorption bands (ϵ_2 as a function of $\hbar\omega$) in amorphous and crystalline silicon (from Stuke 1970b).

For an unannealed sample Brodsky et al. find from 1·4 to 2·4 eV that a relation of the form $\alpha\hbar\omega \sim (\hbar\omega - E_0)^2$ with $E_0 = 1\cdot26$ eV fits the absorption data. This is shown in Fig. 8.29. Also shown in this figure are the results of Grigorovici and Vancu (probably an annealed film), which yield $E_0 = 1\cdot44$ eV. Note that the structure in the tail reported by Grigorovici and Vancu is not present in the data of Brodsky et al.

The fundamental absorption band above the edge in amorphous silicon is compared with that in the crystal in Fig. 8.30. The strong absorption below the onset of direct transitions in the crystal is very evident in this plot of ϵ_2.

In view of the similarity of the optical properties of amorphous silicon to those of amorphous germanium, we shall not discuss the results further. The observation of a sharp absorption edge in amorphous silicon (Fig. 8.27) has brought the data on the two materials into even closer correspondence.

Data on the optical spectra of amorphous alloys of Ge and Si have been published by Beaglehole and Zavetova (1970).

8.2. InSb and other (III)-(V) compounds

Amorphous films of InSb, GaAs, and GaSb can be prepared by flash evaporation on to cooled substrates (Eckenbach, Fuhs, and Stuke 1971). The electrical and optical properties of these materials as well as their sensitivity to annealing treatments are in many respects similar to those observed in amorphous Ge and Si. In view of this, data obtained on these materials will be presented without much further discussion.

In Chapter 7 the temperature dependences of electrical conductivity and thermoelectric power of the above materials were shown in Fig. 7.21, and the reader is referred to a discussion of the results there. Results for InSb over a wider temperature range are shown in Fig. 8.31. Several of the most important and characteristic features of the electrical properties of amorphous semiconductors can be seen in this figure.

(a) The insensitivity of the electrical conductivity to the presence of impurities. Curves (1) and (2) for crystalline InSb refer to samples heavily doped with Te and Zn respectively.

(b) The observation of a conductivity that obeys the relationship $\sigma = C\exp(-E/kT)$ with $C \sim 10^3\ \Omega^{-1}\,\mathrm{cm}^{-1}$, suggesting conduction in extended states at a mobility shoulder.

(c) The 'knee' in the conductivity curve near 250K, below which conduction occurs predominantly in localized states at the conduction-band edge. The change of slope is $\sim 0\cdot 12$ eV and the intercept on the σ-axis is ~ 1–$10\ \Omega^{-1}\,\mathrm{cm}^{-1}$, i.e. in the range expected for this process.

(d) The maximum in the absolute value of the thermoelectric power at ~ 140K, indicating the possibility of a change of sign at a lower temperature (as observed for amorphous germanium when the conduction mechanism changes to hopping at the Fermi level).

The magnetoresistance of InSb at 25kgauss as measured by Mell and Stuke (1970) was shown in Fig. 7.23 as a function of temperature. These results, together with more recent measurements by

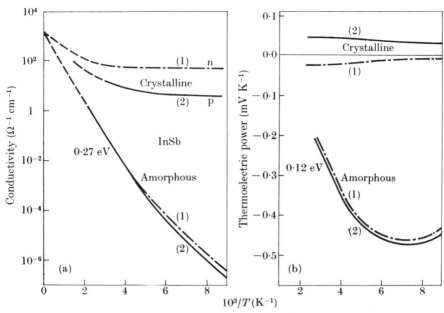

FIG. 8.31. Temperature dependence of electrical conductivity and thermoelectric power in degenerate n-type and p-type crystals and amorphous films of InSb (from Stuke 1970*b*).

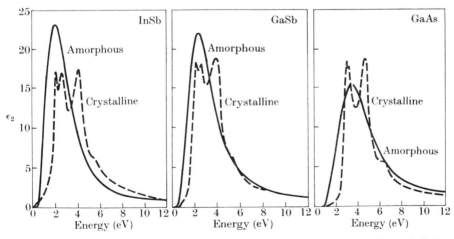

FIG. 8.32. ϵ_2 spectra of amorphous and crystalline films of InSb, GaSb, and GaAs (from Zimmerer 1970).

Mell (private communication) on InP and InAs, which yield a positive magnetoresistance, are not understood at the present time.

Figures 8.32 and 8.33 give the room-temperature optical absorption spectra of InSb, GaAs, and GaSb. The ϵ_2 spectra have the same form as for amorphous Ge and Si (Figs. 8.24 and 8.30). Without detailed knowledge of the electronic band structure for the crystalline form of these materials it is impossible to say at present to what extent

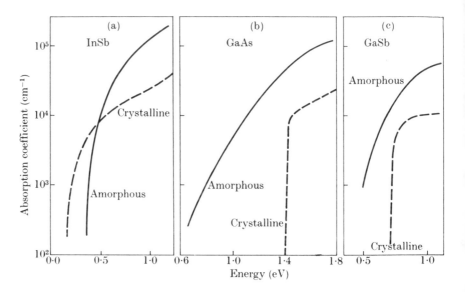

FIG. 8.33. Optical absorption edges in amorphous and crystalline films of InSb, GaSb, and GaAs (from Eckenbach et al. 1971 and unpublished results of J. Niklas).

the featureless peak in ϵ_2 can be accounted for by a relaxation of the k-conservation selection rule. As suggested by Phillips (1970) the position of the peak in ϵ_2 may be determined principally by the strength of the nearest-neighbour bond. The optical absorption edges (Fig. 8.33) include yet another material with a sharp threshold (InSb): an unusual feature here is that it occurs at a higher energy than in the crystal. These results have not been analysed in detail because of the variability of position, sharpness, etc. with conditions of sample preparation.

Measurements of the temperature dependence of piezoresistance in several amorphous (III)–(V) compounds have been reported by Fuhs and Stuke (1970).

8.3. CdGeAs$_2$ and similar ternaries

CdGeAs$_2$, isoelectric with (III)–(V) compounds, crystallizes in the chalcopyrite structure and can be prepared in the amorphous state by rapid cooling from the molten state. It is only one of a non-chalcogenide family of glasses based on CdAs$_2$ or CdP$_2$. The system on which most data is available is CdGe$_x$As$_2$. Cervinka et al. (1970) have reported that ingots obtained by cooling from a melt that has been heated a few hundred degrees above the melting point are brittle, but that internal strains can be removed by annealing at 200–250°C. Differential thermal analysis results show a recrystallization (exothermic) peak at above 400°C and an endothermic peak corresponding to melting at about 650°C. X-ray analysis reveals that between these two temperatures there is a mixture of at least two crystalline phases, CdGeAs$_2$ (tetragonal chalcopyrite) and CdAs$_2$ (tetragonal but not chalcopyrite). However, stoichiometric CdGeAs$_2$ can remain amorphous. Glasses of the type CdX$_x$As$_2$ with the element X being Ge, Si, Tl, In, Al, Sb, Mg, and Ga, and x varying from approximately 0·05 to 1·0, can be prepared in a similar way and show similar D.T.A. results.

An analysis of the radial distribution curve for amorphous CdGe$_x$As$_2$ (Cervinka, Hosemann, and Vogel 1970) shows that the number of nearest neighbours is close to four, and the position of the first maximum is an average of distances between atoms in CdAs$_2$. The latter is a tetragonal lattice ($a = 11·275$ Å, $c/a = 0·122$) composed of tetrahedra formed from one Cd atom and four As atoms. Three interwoven networks can be recognized, which are held together by bonds between As atoms. It is likely that the presence of Ge (and the other elements mentioned above) disrupts these bonds, favouring glass formation. The Ge atom tries to coordinate itself tetrahedrally with 4 As atoms. Magnetic susceptibility measurements, to be described below, indicate the presence of a large number of one-electron centres, suggesting that such coordination is incomplete.

The temperature dependence of the magnetic susceptibility of crystalline CdAs$_2$ and of glasses of the type CdGe$_x$As$_2$ as determined by Cervinka et al. is shown in Fig. 8.34. In contrast with the temperature-independent diamagnetic susceptibility of the crystal, the susceptibility in the glasses can be represented by

$$\chi = \chi_0 + A/T.$$

There is thus a positive contribution to χ that obeys Curie's law. The variation of A, assumed to be proportional to the number of unpaired spins, increases with the percentage of Ge present, with a tendency towards saturation as x approaches unity. From this data, assuming $A = n\mu^2/3\rho k$ (§ 7.7.3), Cervinka *et al.* estimate that the number of paramagnetic centres in $CdGe_xAs_2$ varies between 3×10^{19} and 10^{20} cm^{-3} as x changes from 0·2 to 1·0. Similar measurements have been made

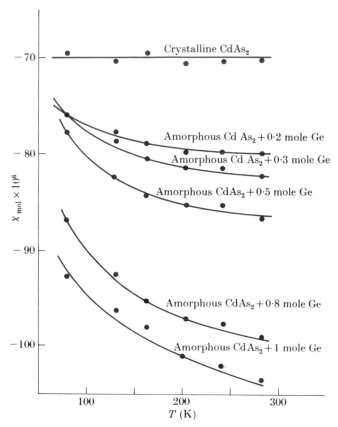

FIG. 8.34. Temperature dependence of magnetic susceptibility in crystalline $CdAs_2$ and in vitreous samples of $CdGe_xAs_2$ (from Cervinka *et al.* 1970).

by Abraham *et al.* (1970) on $CdTl_xAs_2$ and $CdSb_xAs_2$ glasses. With increasing x, A is found to increase only slightly in the glasses containing Tl and it actually decreases in those containing Sb.

8.3.1. *Electrical properties of glasses of the type* $CdGeAs_2$

The temperature variation of the conductivity of $CdGe_xAs_2$ glasses as determined by Cervinka *et al.* (1970) is compared with that in crystalline $CdGeAs_2$ in Fig. 8.35. Below the melting point the slope of the plot of $\ln \sigma$ against $1/T$ for the crystal is 0·4 eV; above the melting point it increases to about 0·6 eV. The conductivity of the corresponding glass ($x = 1$) obeys the relation $\sigma = C\exp\{-(E/kT)\}$ down to about 200K with $E \sim 0\cdot62$ eV and $C \sim 10^4\,\Omega^{-1}\,\text{cm}^{-1}$. Fig. 8.36 shows the variation of E with composition x of the second element in glasses of the kind CdX_xAs_2. Extrapolation of the dependence of E on composition for

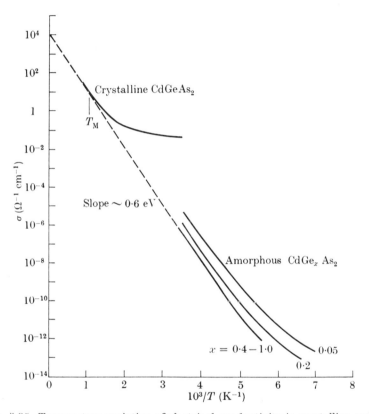

Fig. 8.35. Temperature variation of electrical conductivity in crystalline and vitreous samples of $CdGe_xAs_2$.

these glasses to $x = 0$ leads to a value of approximately 0·55 eV, which when doubled can be compared with the energy gap of crystalline $CdAs_2(\sim 1$ eV$)$.

The ternaries containing thallium provide a useful family of high-conductivity glasses. Fig. 8.37 shows the temperature variation of the conductivity in this system as measured by Cervinka et al.

A series of measurements of conductivity, thermoelectric power, and Hall effect in $CdGe_xAs_2$ glasses have been made by Callaerts, Denayer, Hashmi, and Nagels (1971). The temperature variation of conductivity

shown in Fig. 8.38(a) agrees very well with that found by Cervinka *et al.*
Callaerts *et al.* find $E = 0.55$ eV from the high-temperature slope of
their plots. The thermoelectric power data is of particular interest
(Fig. 8.38(b)). With increasing Ge content the thermoelectric power
changes from strongly p-type to strongly n-type. For $CdGe_{0.3}As_2$ and
$CdGe_{0.1}As_2$ the thermoelectric power changes sign as a function of
temperature near 330K. (Tauc *et al.* (1968) find a similar change of sign

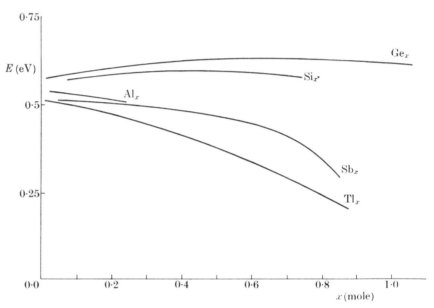

FIG. 8.36. Variation of the electrical activation energy for conduction (slope of plots of
ln σ against $1/T$) in glasses of the type CdX_xAs_2 (from Cervinka *et al.* 1970).

in $CdGeAs_2$ near 220K.) Measurements of the Hall effect (not shown
here) yield a negative sign for all samples except for the stoichiometric
composition $CdGeAs_2$. Thus, particularly for the two samples with the
smallest and highest Ge content, the thermoelectric power and Hall
coefficient have contradictory signs. For all samples the temperature
variation of the Hall coefficient R_H yields approximately the same
activation energy as that determined from the plot of ln σ against $1/T$.
The Hall mobilities ($R\sigma$) are therefore roughly temperature independent
and have values $\sim 10^{-1}$ cm^2 V^{-1} s^{-1} for $CdGe_{0.3}As_2$ and $CdGe_{0.6}As_2$ and
$\sim 2 \times 10^{-2}$ cm^2 V^{-1} s^{-1} for the other samples.

Although the data have not been analysed in detail, the following
model may be able to explain at least qualitatively the behaviour of

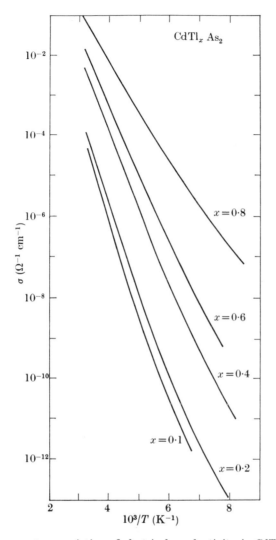

FIG. 8.37. Temperature variation of electrical conductivity in $CdTl_xAs_2$ glasses (from Cervinka *et al.* 1970).

thermoelectric power and conductivity. The slope and intercept (at $1/T = 0$) of the conductivity curves suggest conduction due to electrons in extended states with energies at a mobility shoulder $\sim$0·55 eV away from the Fermi level. Assuming that the Fermi level is approximately in the middle of a gap in the density of states, but that conduction in $CdGe_{0.2}As_2$ is p-type because the range of localized states at the valence-band edge is smaller than at the conduction band edge, we see

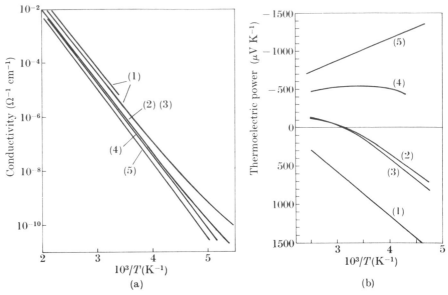

FIG. 8.38. Temperature variation of conductivity and thermoelectric power in CdGe$_x$As$_2$ glasses: (1) $x = 0\cdot2$; (2) $x = 0\cdot3$; (3) $x = 0\cdot4$; (4) $x = 0\cdot6$; (5) $x = 1$ (from Callaerts *et al.* 1971).

that the conversion to n-type conduction with increasing Ge content could result from a decrease in the range of localized states in the conduction band. The activation energy for electrical conductivity would remain constant.

8.3.2. *Optical properties of glasses of the type* CdGeAs$_2$

The over-all forms of the fundamental optical absorption in amorphous and crystalline CdGeAs$_2$ are compared in Fig. 8.39 (from Goryunova *et al.* 1970; see also Tauc *et al.* 1968). As in other amorphous

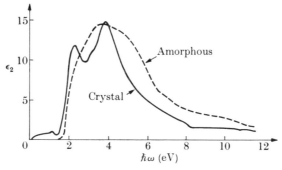

FIG. 8.39. ε_2 spectra of amorphous and crystalline CdGeAs$_2$ (from Goryunova *et al.* 1970).

semiconductors, the ε_2 curve for the glass exhibits far less structure than for the crystal. The integral $\int \omega \varepsilon_2 \, d\omega$ over this main absorption band has essentially the same value as in the crystal. It would appear that a simple non-direct-transition model might account for the curve. However, the electronic band structure of the crystal is not sufficiently well known to enable this to be tested.

The fundamental edge absorption (Fig. 8.40) occurs at higher energies than in crystalline CdGeAs$_2$ but at lower energies than in crystalline CdAs$_2$. The slope of the exponential region of the edge is $\Gamma = 19 \cdot 2 \text{ eV}^{-1}$ at 300K, i.e. of approximately the same magnitude as found in many

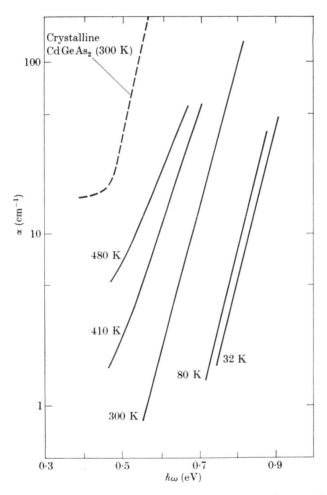

FIG. 8.40. Optical absorption edge as a function of temperature in amorphous CdGeAs$_2$. The edge in the crystal at 300K is also shown (from Cervinka *et al.* 1970).

other amorphous semiconductors (see Table 7.4). Below room temperature there is a parallel shift of the edge to higher energies with decreasing temperature of approximately 5×10^{-4} eV K^{-1} (about twice as large as in crystalline CdGeAs$_2$). Above room temperature the slope decreases in accordance with Urbach's rule.

Above about 0·8 eV ($\alpha \sim 100$ cm^{-1}) the absorption constant follows the relation
$$\alpha \hbar \omega = B(\hbar \omega - E_0)^2,$$

with $B \sim 10^4$ cm^{-1} eV^{-1} and $E_0 = 0·71$ eV at room temperature. This value of E_0 can be compared with twice the activation energy for

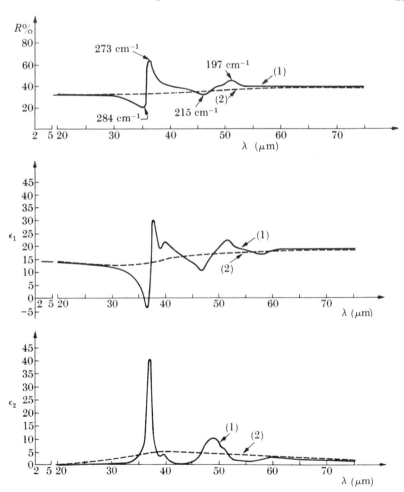

Fig. 8.41. Infrared vibrational spectra of CdGeAs$_2$. In these curves of reflectivity, ε_1 and ε_2, (1) refers to the crystalline spectrum and (2) to the amorphous spectrum (from Goryunova et al. 1970).

electrical conduction, $\sim 1{\cdot}20$ eV, which should give a lower limit to the value of the mobility gap. The large energy range of localized states implied by these figures is difficult to reconcile with the high value of the pre-exponential factor observed in the conductivity (see § 7.4).

Decreasing the Ge content in amorphous $CdGe_xAs_2$ shifts the optical absorption edge to slightly lower energies. The variations of the position of the edge with composition in glasses of the type $CdSi_xAs_2$, $CdSb_xAs_2$, and $CdTl_xAs_2$ can be correlated with the variation of the activation energy for conduction shown in Fig. 8.36 (Cervinka et al. 1970).

The infrared vibrational spectrum of $CdGeAs_2$ has been studied by Goryunova et al. (1970) (see also Zlatkin et al. 1970). Fig. 8.41 shows that the structure in the absorption observed in crystalline $CdGeAs_2$ is almost completely absent in the glass. These results should be compared with those for As_2Se_3 (§ 7.6.6).

THE CHALCOGENIDE GLASSES

9.1. Introduction
9.2. Summary of electrical and optical properties of chalcogenide glasses
9.3. Arsenic trisulphide As_2S_3 and the As–S system
9.4. Arsenic triselenide As_2Se_3 and the As–Se system
9.5. Arsenic tritelluride As_2Te_3

9.6. Mixed binary systems
   9.6.1. As_2Se_3–As_2Te_3
   9.6.2. As_2Se_3–As_2S_3
   9.6.3. As_2S_3–As_2Te_3
   9.6.4. As_2Se_3–Sb_2Se_3
9.7. Germanium telluride GeTe
9.8. Multicomponent glasses

9.1. Introduction

IN this chapter the properties of amorphous semiconductors containing one or more of the chalcogenide elements, S, Se, or Te, are reviewed. Within certain ranges of composition it is possible to form glasses by combination with one or more of the elements As, Ge, Si, Tl, Pb, P, Sb, Bi, among others. Of the binary glasses, As_2S_3 and As_2Se_3 have been most extensively studied and are often regarded as prototypes of the chalcogenide glasses. Mixed systems of binaries such as the As_2Se_3–As_2Te_3 and the As_2Se_3–As_2Te_3–Tl_2Se systems have also been the subjects of detailed investigations. Because of the large variety of such ternary and quaternary systems, classification of these materials becomes difficult. This problem is heightened by the freedom that is allowed in amorphous systems to depart from stoichiometric proportions of the constituents. Multicomponent glasses of (seemingly) arbitrary composition, for instance $As_{30}Te_{48}Si_{12}Ge_{10}$, have been studied in connection with the phenomenon of electrical switching (§ 7.9). However, the properties of amorphous semiconductors formed from a wide variety of elements of differing valency may not necessarily be more complex than those of the binaries, for example. Such compositions may favour a fully connected structure with all bonds satisfied and hence approach an ideal random network of atoms. However in some systems there may be a greater tendency for phase separation than in others.

In many cases there does not seem to be any significant qualitative difference between the properties of amorphous chalcogenide semiconductors of stoichiometric proportions, and those of others (compare

§3.16.2.). However, use of stoichiometric compositions does allow useful comparison with the material in its crystalline phase. For many of the stoichiometric materials discussed in this chapter the crystalline phase has a layer structure.

For any given group of elements it is not normally possible to form glasses for all compositions. The extent of the glass-forming region in several ternary systems was displayed graphically in Fig. 7.2. Table 9.1 (from Owen 1970) indicates the extent of the glass-forming region in some other ternaries (see also Savage and Nielsen 1965a). Well inside a glass-forming boundary, samples can be prepared by cooling from the melt; samples with compositions outside the boundary require deposition by evaporation or a similar technique in order to attain the amorphous phase. Near the boundary, fast quenching of the melt (like splat cooling) is sometimes used to obtain a glass. Even with compositions that readily form glasses it is sometimes useful to prepare specimens by deposition for certain experiments requiring thin films.

Annealing of chalcogenide glasses does not appear to lead to marked changes of properties such as were described in Chapter 8 for amorphous Ge and Si. Results from different laboratories on the same material are generally in good agreement.

There have been several reports of the effect of impurities on the electrical conductivity of chalcogenide glasses. Sometimes these are quite marked: for example the addition of 1 per cent of Ag to As_2S_3 has been reported to raise the room-temperature conductivity by several decades. We do not think that this necessarily violates the suggestion made in earlier chapters, namely that these amorphous semiconductors cannot be doped in the normal sense. Instead it seems likely that impurities in concentrations as high as 1 per cent may play a role in modifying the structure (e.g. by cross-linking). The effect of this may be to increase or decrease the range of localized states at the band edges and hence change the conductivity.

The elements Se and Te, although having some properties similar to those of the general group of chalcogenides, apparently contain structural units with molecular properties, and in view of this are discussed separately in Chapter 10. Chapter 10 also contains experimental results on Se containing small amounts of As and other elements.

In this chapter we shall not attempt to review all the published literature on chalcogenide glasses. A summary of some of the extensive Russian work up to 1964 has been given by Kolomiets (1964). We shall

TABLE 9.1

Extent of glass-forming regions in some ternary chalcogenide systems A–B–C (from Owen 1970): × *very small;* ○ *small;* ⊗ *moderate;* ● *large.*

A	B	Group Ia			Group IIa			Group IIIa				C GroupIVa		Group Va				Group VIa		Group VIIa		
		Cu	Ag	Au	Zn	Cd	Hg	B	Ga	In	Tl	Sn	Pb	P	As	Sb	Bi	Se	Te	Cl	Br	I
As	S	×	×	×	×	×	×		×	×	○	×	×	×	●	⊗	×	●	⊗	×	⊗	●
	Se	○	○	×	○	○	○	○	×	×	⊗	○	×	⊗	●	⊗	×		⊗			⊗
	Te										⊗				⊗						×	⊗
Ge	S				×				×	○		×		●	●				×			
	Se					×				×	○	×	×	⊗	●	⊗	×		×			
	Te													○	⊗							
Si	S														⊗	⊗						
	Se													⊗	⊗	⊗						
	Te																					

concentrate on recent work concerned with electronic properties. Even with this restriction, some selection is necessary.

9.2. Summary of electrical and optical properties of chalcogenide glasses

The d.c. conductivity of most of these glasses near room temperature obeys the relation $\sigma = C\exp(-E/kT)$. Figure 9.1 shows some typical plots of $\ln \sigma$ against $1/T$ for chalcogenides with E varying from about 0.3 eV to more than 1 eV. (Although the values of $2E$ lie close to the

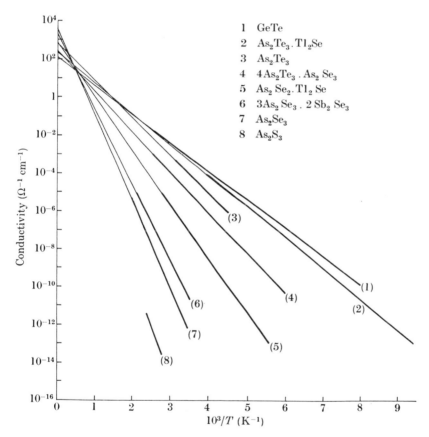

FIG. 9.1. Temperature dependence of electrical conductivity in some amorphous chalcogenide semiconductors, illustrating the relationship $\sigma = C\exp(-E/kT)$. Heavy lines are the experimental results and fine lines are the extrapolation to $1/T = 0$ (note that the actual variation of σ with T is not expected to follow this extrapolation). (1) GeTe (Tsu, Howard, and Esaki 1970) ;(2) As₂Te₃.Tl₂Se (Andriesh and Kolomiets 1965); (3) As₂Te₃ (Weiser and Brodsky 1970); (4) 4As₂Te₃.As₂Se₃ (Uphoff and Healy 1961); (5) As₂Se₂.Tl₂Se (Andriesh and Kolomiets 1965); (6) 3As₂Se₃.2Sb₂Se₃ (Platakis, Sadagopan, and Gatos 1969); (7) As₂Se₃ (Edmond 1968); (8) As₂S₃ (Edmond 1968).

photon energy corresponding to the onset of strong optical absorption, intrinsic conduction cannot be assumed, and therefore we shall not double the values of E observed.) Values of E and C for some chalcogenide glasses were shown in Fig. 7.8. As explained in Chapter 7, we regard values of C in the range 10^3–10^4 Ω^{-1} cm^{-1} as indicating conduction in extended states. Much lower values have been observed in some materials and for these we suggest that conduction is predominantly by carriers hopping between localized states at the band edge.

The variations of C and E in various binary and ternary systems as a function of composition are of interest. Figure 9.2 shows a few of these. We point out here the approximate invariance of C in the Se–Te and As$_2$Se$_3$–As$_2$Te$_3$ systems and the approximate invariance of E in the

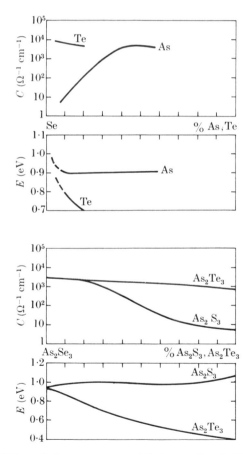

FIG. 9.2. Variation of the pre-exponential factor C and the activation energy for conduction E in the Se–Te, Se–As, As$_2$Se$_3$–As$_2$Te$_3$, and AsSe$_3$–As$_2$S$_3$ systems.

Se–As and As_2Se_3–As_2S_3 systems. Because of the difficulty of measuring the electrical conductivity of selenium over a wide temperature range, it is difficult to determine E and C in this and other high-resistivity materials with any confidence.

The thermoelectric powers of chalcogenide glasses are normally positive, with values consistent with the idea of a Fermi energy near the centre of the gap but nearer to the mobility edge in the valence band. In those materials for which measurements have been made as a function of temperature, activation energies similar to those observed in electrical conductivity are found. Unfortunately most of the data available have been obtained only in the liquid state (where the conductivity is higher and measurements are easier).

Hall effect measurements on chalcogenide glasses are difficult, especially on those with low conductivity, because of the small magnitude of the effect. For materials on which measurements have been made, the Hall effect has been found to be negative (i.e. opposite in sign to the thermoelectric power). When interpreted in terms of the formulae appropriate for crystalline semiconductors it yields an unreasonably high value for the carrier concentration, or alternatively a low value for the Hall mobility. Some results by Male (1967) were shown in Fig. 7.22 and discussed in Chapter 7. (see also § 2.12).

The optical absorption edges of the chalcogenide glasses are all characterized by absorption coefficients α that rise exponentially with increasing photon energy up to a value of α in the range 10^3–10^4 cm^{-1}. This spectral Urbach's rule has been discussed in Chapter 7, and some chalcogenide glasses were included in Fig. 7.31. At higher values of the absorption coefficient, the most frequently reported behaviour is $\alpha\hbar\omega = B(\hbar\omega - E_0)^2$, where B lies in the range 10^5 to 10^6 cm^{-1} eV^{-1} and E_0 can be taken as an optical gap. Examples of glasses obeying this relation were shown in Fig. 7.32. Values of E_0 determined in this way generally correspond to actual values of α (on the Urbach edge) lying between 10^2 and 10^3 cm^{-1}.

Table 9.2 from Edmond (1968) lists for a variety of chalcogenide systems the photon energy corresponding to 15 per cent optical transmission though a specimen 0·178 cm thick. This corresponds, after a correction for the reflectivity, to an absorption coefficient α of about 8 cm^{-1}. Using the assumption that the Urbach tails in all these materials have the same slope (which is not strictly accurate), this table gives the relative positions of the optical absorption edges. Also listed are resistivities at 50°C and 130°C. In Fig. 9.3

we have plotted from this table the resistivities at 130°C against the value of $\hbar\omega$ for which $\alpha = 8$ cm^{-1}, to illustrate the obvious correlation between conductivity and the optical gap. Out of all the materials listed, only As_2S_3 with 1 per cent Ag falls out of line. Some detailed comparisons of optical and electrical gaps will be made later in this chapter. The spectral dependence of photoconductivity in several amorphous chalcogenide films was shown in Fig. 7.24.

TABLE 9.2

Positions of room-temperature optical absorption edges and resistivities in several chalcogenide systems (from Edmond 1968).

Material	Wave number for 15% transmission for specimen 0·178 cm thick (cm^{-1})	Corresponding energy (eV)	Resistivity at 50°C (Ω cm)	130°C (Ω cm)
$As_{34.25}Se_{65.75}$	12 330	1·53		$4·10 \times 10^8$
$As_{37.6}Se_{62.4}$	12 248	1·52		$1·57 \times 10^8$
$As_{38.7}Se_{61.3}$				$1·49 \times 10^8$
$As_{40}Se_{60}$	12 131	1·50		$1·54 \times 10^8$
$As_{42}Se_{58}$	12 049	1·49		$1·82 \times 10^8$
$As_{50}Se_{50}$	12 510	1·55		$18·4 \ \times 10^8$
$As_{35}(Se_2Te)_{65/3}$	7892	0·98	$1·7 \ \times 10^7$	
$As_{40}(Se_2Te)_{60/3}$	8045	1·00	$3·3 \ \times 10^7$	$2·5 \ \times 10^5$
$As_{45}(Se_2Te)_{55/3}$	8260	1·02	$6·9 \ \times 10^8$	
As_2S_3	16 555	2·05		$2·0 \ \times 10^{12}$
As_2S_2Se	14 435	1·79		$9·4 \ \times 10^{10}$
As_2SSe_2	13 069	1·62		$3·1 \ \times 10^9$
As_2Se_3	12 131	1·51	$(2 \ \times 10^{11})$	$1·54 \times 10^8$
$As_2Se_{2.5}Te_{0.5}$	9095	1·13	$8·75 \times 10^8$	$4·05 \times 10^6$
As_2Se_2Te	8045	1·00	$3·3 \ \times 10^7$	$2·5 \ \times 10^5$
As_2SeTe_2	6715	0·83	$1·8 \ \times 10^5$	$3·5 \ \times 10^3$
$(As_4Sb_2)Se_9$	10 461	1·30	$2·2 \ \times 10^9$	$7·4 \ \times 10^6$
$As_{40}S_{60}$	16 555	2·05		$2·0 \ \times 10^{12}$
$As_{40}S_{60}Ag_1$	16 205	2·01		$7·9 \ \times 10^8$
$As_{40}Se_{60}$	12 131	1·51		$1·54 \times 10^8$
$As_{40}Se_{60}Ag_1$	11 445	1·42		$8·1 \ \times 10^7$
$As_{40}Se_{40}Te_{20}$	8045	1·00	$3·3 \ \times 10^7$	$2·5 \ \times 10^5$
$As_{40}Se_{40}Te_{20}Ag_1$	7527	0·93	$5·5 \ \times 10^7$	$4·2 \ \times 10^5$
$As_{34.25}Se_{65.75}Ag_1$	11 702	1·45		$1·17 \times 10^8$
$As_{40}Se_{60}Ag_1$	11 445	1·42		$0·81 \times 10^8$
$As_{50}Se_{50}Ag_1$	(11 480)	(1·42)		$1·48 \times 10^8$
$As_{34}S_{66}Ag_1$				$2·1 \ \times 10^9$
$As_{40}Se_{60}$	12 131	1·51		$1·54 \times 10^8$
$As_{40}Se_{60}Ge_5$	12 525	1·55		$7·5 \ \times 10^8$
$As_{40}Se_{40}Te_{20}$	8045	1·00	$3·3 \ \times 10^7$	$2·5 \ \times 10^5$
$As_{40}Se_{40}Te_{20}Ge_5$	8260	1·03		$5·9 \ \times 10^5$

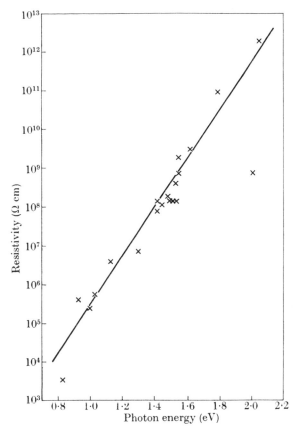

FIG. 9.3. Resistivity at 130°C plotted against the photon energy corresponding to an absorption coefficient of about 8 cm^{-1} (from Table 9.2).

9.3. Arsenic trisulphide As$_2$S$_3$ and the As–S system

Arsenic trisulphide crystallizes in a monoclinic structure (C$_{2h}^5$) with twenty atoms in the unit cell (Fig. 9.4). Each As atom is surrounded by three S atoms and each S atom is shared by two As atoms. It is a layer lattice with weak bonds between layers: the crystals can be cleaved in a plane containing the a-axis and the c-axis. Evans and Young (1967) have reported on the optical properties of naturally occurring crystals (orpiment) near the absorption edge, and Slade and Zallen (private communication) have made an infrared study of the phonon spectrum.

X-ray diffraction studies of As$_2$S$_3$ glass (Vaipolin and Porai-Koshits 1960, 1963) have shown that the nearest-neighbour and next-nearest-neighbour coordinations are the same as in the crystal. Thus one might envisage that the layer structure is conserved to some extent, the sheets being wavy and cross-linked. However it is also possible that the layers may break up into the twelve-membered puckered rings shown in Fig. 9.4 or into smaller units. A less likely possibility is the formation of chains, which can be recognized in the structure of the crystal along the c-axis.

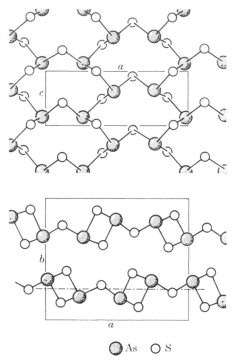

$\bullet$ As $\bigcirc$ S

FIG. 9.4. Structure of crystalline As_2S_3 (Zallen, private communication).

The glass can be prepared in the customary way, by melting the elements in an evacuated quartz ampoule, which is then rotated in a furnace at about 600°C for a day or more and subsequently cooled. Ingots so produced can be sliced and the wafers lapped and polished. For samples less than about 100 μm thick it is more convenient to produce amorphous films by evaporation.

Figure 9.5 compares the optical absorption edges of amorphous and crystalline As_2S_3 at room temperature. The data on the amorphous phase was obtained by Kosek and Tauc (1970) from a combination of measurements on films and glassy samples. Thicknesses (needed to compute α) were obtained from interference fringes, observed at low values of α, using a value for the refractive index $n_0 = 2\cdot55$. Below

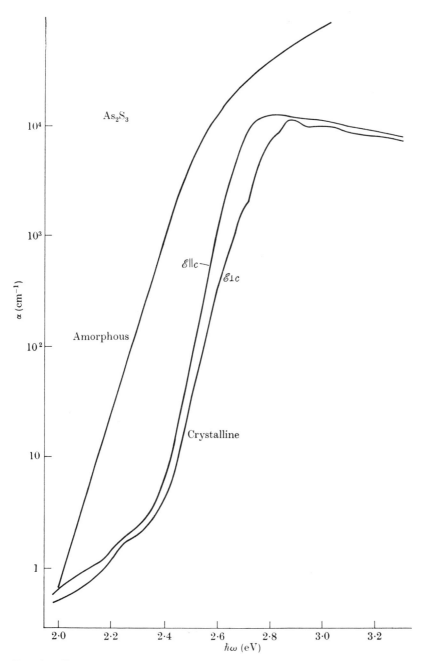

FIG. 9.5. Room-temperature optical absorption edges in amorphous and crystalline As_2S_3 (from Kosek and Tauc 1970).

$\alpha \simeq 10^3$ cm^{-1} the edge accurately obeys the relation

$$\alpha = \alpha_0' \exp(\Gamma \hbar \omega),$$

with $\Gamma = 18 \cdot 6$ eV^{-1}. Similar results have been obtained by Kolomiets *et al.* (1970).

Figure 9.6 compares the edge in amorphous As$_2$S$_3$ at room and liquid-nitrogen temperatures. Figure 9.6(a) shows that the slope of the

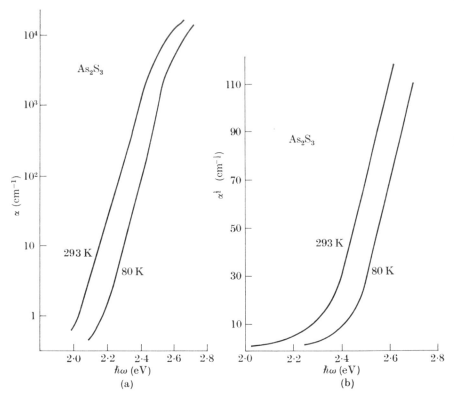

FIG. 9.6. Optical absorption edge in amorphous As$_2$S$_3$ at 293K and 80K plotted as (a) ln α against $\hbar\omega$, (b) $\alpha^{\frac{1}{2}}$ against $\hbar\omega$ (from Kosek and Tauc 1970).

exponential part of the edge is increased by only $\sim$13 per cent for this fall in temperature. According to Urbach's empirical rule $\Gamma \propto 1/T$ and the slope should increase by a factor $\sim$3·7. However, as discussed in Chapter 7, an almost parallel shift of the edge below room temperature is commonly observed in amorphous semiconductors. Figure 9.6(b) shows more clearly the behaviour of the absorption constant at photon energies above the exponential region. Although this is a plot of $\alpha^{\frac{1}{2}}$

against $\hbar\omega$, good straight lines are also obtained on a plot of $(\alpha\hbar\omega)^{\frac{1}{2}}$ against $\hbar\omega$, and an optical gap E_0 of magnitude 2·32 eV at room temperature can be obtained by extrapolation. Kolomiets *et al.* (1970) obtain $E_0 = 2\cdot4$ eV from a plot of $\hbar\omega\varepsilon_2^{\frac{1}{2}}$ against $\hbar\omega$. Fig. 9.6 yields a temperature coefficient of the optical gap in amorphous As_2S_3 of $-5\cdot1\times10^{-4}$ eV K^{-1} in this temperature range. It is worth noting that the value of E_0 at room temperature corresponds roughly with the indirect gap in crystalline As_2S_3, seen as weak structure in Fig. 9.5. Evans and Young give values for the direct gaps in the crystal of 2·74 eV for $\mathscr{E}$ parallel to c and 2.80 eV for $\mathscr{E}$ perpendicular to c (parallel to a), and these have a temperature coefficient equal to $-6\cdot92\times10^{-4}$ eV K^{-1}. Kosek and Tauc interpreted the exponential region of the absorption edge in terms of transitions involving states in band-edge tails. More recently Tauc, Menthe, and Wood (1970) have made a study of the optical absorption in pure samples of As_2S_3 at very low values of α. Their results are shown in Fig. 9.7. A second exponentially varying tail is observed below 1 cm^{-1} which, up to the softening point ($\sim$470K), has a slope $\Gamma' \simeq 3\cdot3$ eV^{-1}. Tauc *et al.* propose that *this* absorption arises from band tails, and suggest that the steeper portion of the edge arises from the effect of internal electric fields on absorption involving extended states (see § 7.6.1).

Kolomiets *et al.* (1970) have observed a shift in the position of the edge in amorphous As_2S_3 with electric field using the modulation technique of electrotransmission. Figure 9.8 shows their results at room temperature. The shift is small and proportional to the electric field raised to the power 1·8–2·0. The results are interpreted in terms of the theory of Franz (1958). In contrast to Dow and Redfield's (1970) theory (§ 7.6.1), Franz predicted a parallel shift of an exponential absorption edge in an electric field F according to the relation

$$\Delta E = e^2h^2\Gamma^2F^2/24m^*,$$

where Γ is the slope of the edge. Kolomiets *et al.* report that $\Delta E/F^2$ is independent of wavelength, as expected on this theory, and compute an effective mass ratio $m^*/m = 7\cdot5\pm0\cdot5$.

The spectral dependence of d.c. photoconductivity in amorphous As_2S_3 films has been measured also by Kolomiets *et al.* Their results are shown in Fig. 9.9. The peak photoresponse at room temperature occurs at 2·40–2·45 eV, in good agreement with their extrapolated value of $E_0 = 2\cdot4$ eV from a plot of $\hbar\omega\varepsilon_2^{\frac{1}{2}}$ against $\hbar\omega$. The subsidiary maximum

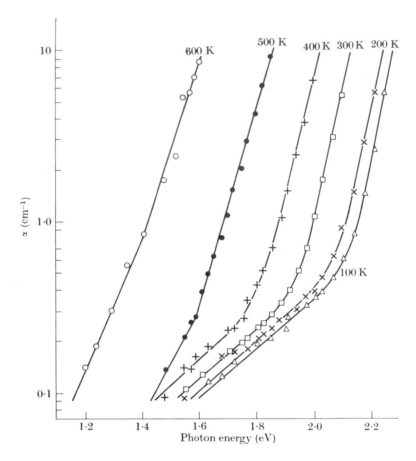

FIG. 9.7. Low-energy tail of the optical absorption edge in amorphous As_2S_3 as a function of temperature (from Tauc, Menthe, and Wood 1970).

near 1·2 eV is correlated with the energy at which Kolomiets *et al.* observe recombination radiation (see below).

Figure 9.10 shows the spectral response of recombination radiation in crystalline and vitreous As_2S_3 as determined at 77K by Kolomiets, Mamontova, and Babaev (1970). Excitation was with short-wavelength light modulated at 40 Hz. The peak emission occurs at 1·13 eV compared with 1·265 eV in the crystal: the half-width of the emission ($\sim$0·45 eV) is similar in both the glass and the crystal but the emission intensity is reported as being about 8 times less in the glass. No band-to-band emission was observed. Davis and Mott (1970) have used this and similar emission experiments by Kolomiets as supporting evidence for a high density of defect centres near the centre of the mobility gap in some amorphous semiconductors.

At photon energies above the fundamental edge, amorphous As_2S_3 shows far less structure due to interband transitions than does crystalline As_2S_3. Figure 9.11 compares the reflectivity spectra out to 14 eV (Drews, private communication). The over-all shape of the curves for the crystal is retained in the amorphous state: however, there is

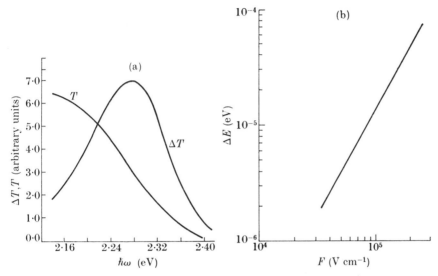

FIG. 9.8. (a) Transmission and electrotransmission spectra of amorphous As_2S_3. (b) Shift of the optical absorption edge as a function of electric field (from Kolomiets *et al.* 1970).

clearly a shift to lower energies of the first group of peaks (occurring at 2–6 eV), even if an average of curves for the two directions of polarization in the crystal is considered. (Data for the case of $\mathscr{E}$ parallel to b in the crystal are not available, because of the difficulty of preparing samples of the desired orientation.) The deep minimum in the reflectivity near 8 eV is interesting; electronic transitions responsible for structure beyond this energy possibly arise from a deeper-lying maximum in the valence-band density of states. The similarity of this minimum in both amorphous and crystalline As_2S_3 suggests that the valence-band density of states is not significantly changed. As_2Se_3 behaves similarly (§ 9.4).

The electrical properties of amorphous As_2S_3 have been investigated by Edmond (1968), Owen (1967), Andreychin, Getov, and Simidchieva

(1966), and Uphoff and Healy (1961). Edmond gives a value for the resistivity at 130°C of $2 \cdot 0 \times 10^{12}$ cm and a slope of the plot of $\ln \sigma$ against $1/T$ equal to $1 \cdot 045$ eV. If the temperature variation of the gap, β, is taken as 7×10^{-4} eV K^{-1} (from the optical data above), this yields a value for the room-temperature activation energy for conduction of $(1 \cdot 045 - \frac{1}{2}\beta \times 300) = 0 \cdot 94$ eV (see § 7.4.2).

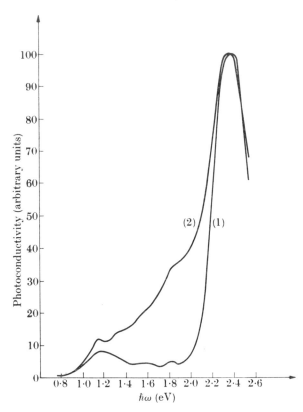

FIG. 9.9. Photoconductivity spectra of amorphous As$_2$S$_3$: (1) without and (2) with supplementary illumination (from Kolomiets *et al.* 1970).

We can use the figures so far obtained to present a preliminary picture of the electron energy-level scheme at room temperature in amorphous As$_2$S$_3$ as shown in Fig. 9.12(a). In accord with the general observation of p-type thermoelectric powers in chalcogenide glasses we assume a (pinned) Fermi energy nearer to E_V than to E_C, and take a value for $(E_F - E_V)$ of order 1 eV. This figure is chosen to fit approximately values obtained from conductivity data (0·94 eV) and the energy of the maximum radiative emission corrected to room temperature

(1·05 eV). Thus for this material $2(E_F - E_V)$ is considerably less than the optical and photoconductivity gap of 2·3–2·4 eV. The photoconductivity peak observed by Kolomiets *et al.* near 1·2 eV could be due to excitation of holes or electrons from the defect levels at E_F to E_V or E_C respectively.

The value of C (or σ_0) for amorphous As_2S_3 is very low (see Fig. 7.8). It is suggested that this arises from a wide range (perhaps about

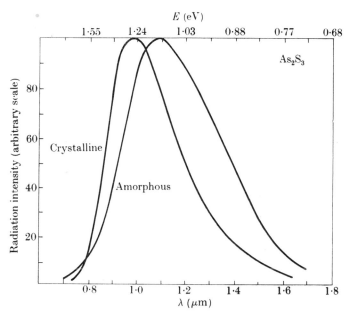

FIG. 9.10. Spectral distribution of recombination radiation in crystalline and amorphous As_2S_3 at 77K (from Kolomiets *et al.* 1970).

0·4 eV) of localized states at the valence-band edge, which causes the current at room temperature to be carried mainly by holes in these localized states. Further evidence for this comes from the lack of well-defined transit times in the drift experiments of Ing and Neyhart described below, and is also obtained by a study of the effect of alloying As_2S_3 with silver and other impurities. The effect of silver on the electrical properties of amorphous As_2S_3 is in fact quite dramatic. Although different workers (Owen 1967; Andreychin, Nikiforova, and Simidchieva 1968; Edmond 1968) are not agreed on the magnitude of the effect, all find an increase in conductivity by several orders of magnitude with increasing concentration of Ag. At the same time, the activation energy for electrical conduction E is decreased by several

23

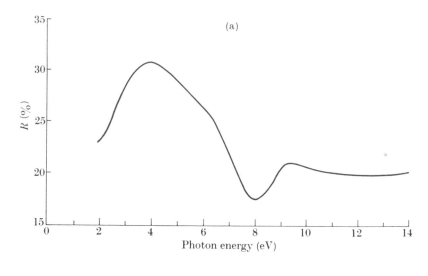

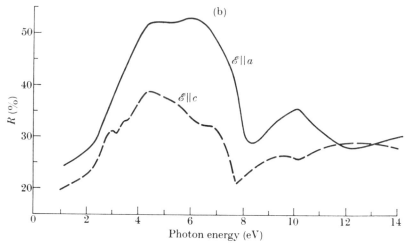

FIG. 9.11. Room-temperature reflectivity spectra of (a) amorphous, (b) crystalline
As$_2$S$_3$ (Drews, private communication).

tenths of an eV. The optical gap E_0 is also decreased but by a smaller
amount. Edmond finds for addition of 1% Ag a decrease in E of
0·24 eV and in E_0 of 0·04 eV. Getov, Simidchieva, Nikiforova, and
Andreychin (1967) and Andreychin (1970) report a decrease in E_0
of 0·1 eV. The value of C increases. We suggest that Fig. 9.12(b)
illustrates the situation in As$_2$S$_3$Ag$_{0.05}$. The Fermi energy is assumed
unchanged with respect to the top of the valence band, but we
make the assumption that the range of localized states is decreased

by silver.† This has the effect of decreasing the activation energy for electrical conduction $(E_F - E_V)$ and causing more of the current extended states at energies below E_V (as suggested by the increase of C). We therefore suppose that the increased conductivity arises, not from the formation of impurity levels, but from structural changes (caused by the presence of Ag) of such a kind as to reduce the disorder. Note that in Fig. 9.12(a) the optical gap E_0 is shown as $(E_C - E_B)$ rather than $(E_A - E_V)$, because the former is the smaller.

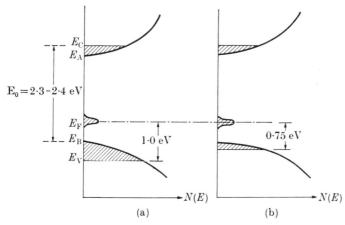

FIG. 9.12. Proposed density of states for amorphous As_2S_3; (a) undoped; (b) doped with Ag.

The effect of other impurities on the conductivity and optical absorption edge of As_2S_3 has been reported by Getov *et al.* (1967), Andreychin *et al.* (1968), and Andreychin (1970). Gold and tin produce effects similar to that of silver. Copper and lead, in concentrations of 0·6%, have the effect of displacing the optical edge to lower energies by ~0·5 eV.

It is interesting that the addition of silver increases the conductivity of amorphous As_2S_3 and also of As_2Se_3, but decreases that of As_2Se_2Te (see § 9.6). The increase in As_2Se_3, however, is only a small fraction of that found in As_2S_3 for the same concentration of Ag. This is perhaps not surprising; conduction in As_2Se_3 at room temperature is due to carriers in extended states $(C \sim 10^3 – 10^4 \ \Omega^{-1} \ cm^{-1})$ and so the mechanism proposed for As_2S_3 cannot operate.

† It is perhaps premature to speculate on how the silver does this; but if the localization is due to any extent to random electric fields round charged point defects, then these might be screened out by silver ions.

As mentioned above, the photoconductivity at room temperature in amorphous As_2S_3 peaks near 2·4 eV (Kolomiets *et al.* 1970; Felty, Lucovsky, and Myers 1967). A more detailed investigation of the processes involved in the generation and transport of photoexcited carriers has been made by Ing and Neyhart (private communication) in a series of experiments similar to those employed on amorphous selenium and described in Chapters 7 and 10. The carriers are generated in a thin layer adjacent to one surface of a film and, by a choice of the correct polarity of an electrode on the opposite surface, either hole or electron transport across the film can be observed. Measurements that do not resolve the transit time, but simply measure the total charge collected as a function of the wavelength of excitation, yield the spectral dependence of quantum efficiency for generation of free carriers. Measurements that do resolve the transit time can be made as a function of electric field and sample thickness, in order to determine the nature of carrier transport. In view of their importance we shall summarize the rather complicated results obtained by Ing and Neyhart on As_2S_3.

Two experimental arrangements were used. In the first (Fig. 9.13(a)) the voltage across R was displayed on an oscilloscope following a short-duration, highly absorbed light pulse. As described in § 7.7, a well-defined transit should lead to a signal which is a ramp function of time. For neither electron nor hole transport was such a transit observed. Instead there was a rapid initial rise in the voltage signal, which tapered off logarithmically with time. Such a pulse shape is interpreted as a spread of arrival times because carriers are trapped and released at a broad spectrum of localized levels. Furthermore, the rate of decay of the voltage pulses was found to be independent of thickness but proportional to $\exp(\beta F^{\frac{1}{2}}/kT)$, and thus in accord with the Poole–Frenkel model for field-assisted emission from traps (§ 7.8). For hole transport the constant β was found to be given correctly by the Poole–Frenkel value of $(4e^3/\kappa)^{\frac{1}{2}}$, using the bulk dielectric constant $\kappa = 6\cdot4$, but for electrons it was half this value.

Figure 9.13(b) illustrates the second arrangement used by Ing and Neyhart. The electric field is applied in either polarity by charging the free surface of the film with ions generated by an air-corona device. After charging, the film is exposed to steady light and the decay of surface potential is monitored by an electrostatic probe. This arrangement permits the use of higher fields without causing breakdown.

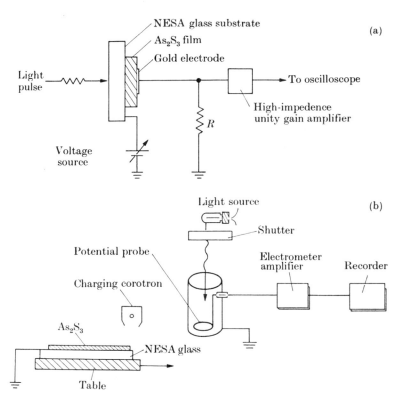

FIG. 9.13. Experimental arrangements for (a) transient photoconductivity measurements, (b) photodischarge measurements (Ing and Neyhart, private communication).

Figure 9.14(a) and (b) shows the field dependence of the transient photocurrents (proportional to the initial rate of decay of the voltage divided by the specimen thickness) for holes and electrons. For holes, the results at low fields confirm the range limitation to the photocurrent found in the pulsed-light experiments, but the independence on thickness observed at high fields suggests a field-dependent photogeneration mechanism. For electrons the transport limitation cannot be overcome even at the highest fields, implying a very short electron range.

The spectral sensitivity of amorphous As_2S_3 for a fixed field is shown in Fig. 9.14(c), along with the absorption coefficient. The photoresponse decreases rapidly with increasing wavelength. It should be emphasized that this is not due to a decreased excitation rate: even though α falls, the number of photons absorbed remains virtually constant for

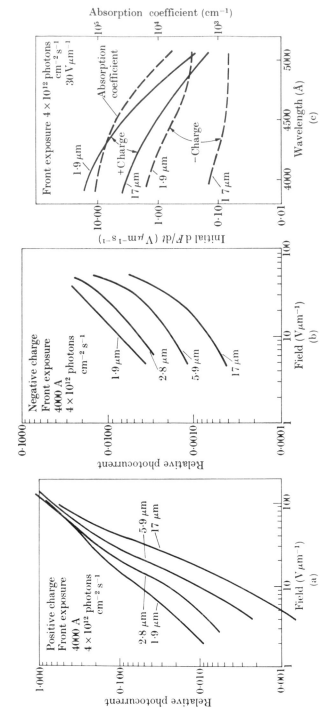

Fig. 9.14. (a) and (b) Electric-field dependence of transient photocurrents in amorphous As₂S₃ due to holes and electrons respectively. (c) Spectral dependence of photodischarge signals and absorption coefficient in amorphous As₂S₃ (from Ing and Neyhart, private communication).

the thicknesses shown. A possible explanation for a quantum efficiency dependent on wavelength was suggested in § 7.5.

Owen and Robertson (1970) have measured the electrical conductivity in As_2S_3 and $As_2S_3 + 0.2$ % Ag as a function of the frequency of the applied electric field. Their results on a silver-doped sample are shown in Fig. 9.15. Below 10^6 Hz the conductivity increases with frequency to a power somewhat less than unity. As discussed in § 7.4.4, this can be interpreted in terms of hopping conduction between states

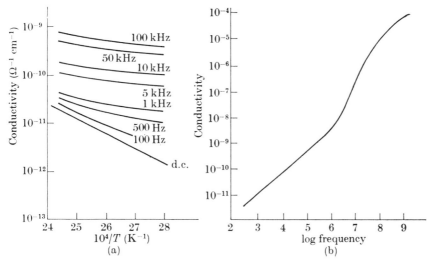

FIG. 9.15. (a) Temperature dependence of conductivity of amorphous As_2S_3 (contaminated with Ag) for d.c. and for frequencies up to 100 kHz. (b) Frequency dependence of conductivity in the same sample at room temperature (from Owen and Robertson 1970).

at the Fermi level. Under the assumptions made in that section and in Fig. 7.16, a density of states $N(E_F) \sim 10^{18}$ cm^{-3} eV^{-1} can be estimated from these results. For pure As_2S_3, a slightly lower value is obtained.

Although there are uncertainties involved in interpreting a.c. conductivity in this way, the estimate for $N(E_F)$ agrees very well with the total concentration of free spins, $\sim 6 \times 10^{17}$ cm^{-3}, obtained by Tauc, Menthe, and Wood (1970) (see also Cimpl et al. 1970) from magnetic-susceptibility measurements. (These authors choose to interpret their figure as an estimate of the density of localized states in a valence-band tail.)

The binary system As–S with compositions away from stoichiometric proportions has not been extensively studied as far as optical and electrical properties are concerned. Indications are that it might be an interesting system. Figure 9.16 shows the glass transition temperatures T_g and the phase diagram of As–S as determined by Myers and Felty (1967). According to these authors the amorphous As_2S_3 network tends to break up into molecular units on either side of stoichiometry: As_4S_4 units or S_8 rings.

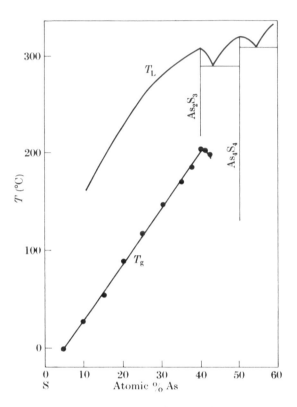

FIG. 9.16. Glass transition temperatures and phase diagram of the S–As system (from Myers and Felty 1967).

Kosek and Tauc (1970) have prepared compositions up to As_2S_5 ($\sim 28 \cdot 6 \%$ As). The optical absorption edge is observed to shift to higher energies as shown in Fig. 9.17. The slope of the exponential portion of the edge decreases slightly to about $17 \cdot 3$ eV^{-1} in As_2S_5. At higher photon energies, the relation $\alpha \hbar \omega \sim (\hbar \omega - E_0)^2$ is obeyed accurately, yielding an optical gap in amorphous As_2S_5 at room temperature of $2 \cdot 48$ eV. The temperature coefficient of the gap, (dE_0/dT), is $\sim -6 \cdot 7 \times 10^{-4}$ eV K^{-1} in the temperature range from 300K to 80K.

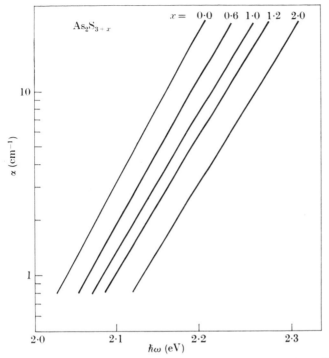

FIG. 9.17. Spectral dependence of optical absorption coefficient in As_2S_{3+x} glasses (from Kosek and Tauc 1970).

Addition of As to As_2S_3 brings one quickly out of the glass-forming region in this system. It is possible to prepare amorphous As_4S_4 by evaporation onto low-temperature substrates (Street, private communication).

9.4. Arsenic triselenide As_2Se_3 and the As–Se system

Like As_2S_3, As_2Se_3 glass has been used as an infrared optical material for many years. It can be prepared in the manner described for As_2S_3. For high-purity glass a distillation process described by Savage and Nielsen (1965b), which is effective in reducing the oxygen content, can be used. The structure of crystalline As_2Se_3 is the same as that of As_2S_3; optical measurements on the crystal have been made by Shaw, Liang, and Yoffe (1970) and by Zallen (private communication).

The fundamental optical absorption edge of amorphous As_2Se_3 has been determined by Vengel and Kolomiets (1957), Edmond (1966), Felty and Myers (private communication), Drews and Zallen (private communication), Rockstad (1970), and Shaw et al. (1970). There is good agreement between different workers concerning the shape and

location of the edge. In Fig. 9.18 we present a composite curve
using the results of several investigators, and compare it with that
found in the crystalline phase. Below $\alpha \sim 10^3$ cm^{-1} the edge in
amorphous As_2Se_3 varies exponentially with photon energy, the
absorption coefficient obeying the relationship $\alpha = \alpha'_0 \exp(\Gamma\hbar\omega)$, with

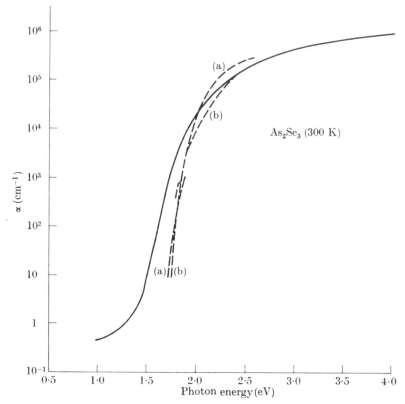

FIG. 9.18. Room-temperature optical absorption edges in amorphous (solid curve) and
crystalline (dotted curves, (a) $\mathscr{E} \parallel a$, (b) $\mathscr{E} \parallel c$) As_2Se_3. Data for amorphous As_2Se_3 from
Felty and Myers (private communication) and Edmond (1966). Data for crystalline
As_2Se_3 from Shaw et al. (1970) and Zallen (private communication).

$\Gamma \sim 20$ eV^{-1}. Above about 2 eV the absorption constant accurately
obeys the relation $\alpha\hbar\omega \sim (\hbar\omega - E_0)^2$ (see Fig. 7.32) yielding an extrapolated optical gap E_0 of 1·76 eV at room temperature. The temperature
coefficient of E_0 is $\sim 5 \times 10^{-4}$ eV K^{-1} near room temperature.

A study of the temperature dependence of the absorption edge up
to 870K, i.e. into the liquid state, has been made by Edmond (1966).
His results were shown in Fig. 7.38. The upper portions of curves

(4)–(7) in this figure appear to represent a broadening of the optical absorption edge in accordance with Urbach's rule. However, the value of the optical absorption coefficient for wave number 4000 cm^{-1} ($\hbar\omega \sim 0\cdot5$ eV) was found for curves (8)–(11) to be proportional to the d.c. conductivity (Fig. 7.39), and the absorption is therefore probably to be attributed to free-carrier absorption as discussed in § 7.6.5. This becomes clearer if we examine Fig. 9.19, in which is plotted the photon energy corresponding to $\alpha = 10^2$ cm^{-1} as a function of temperature.

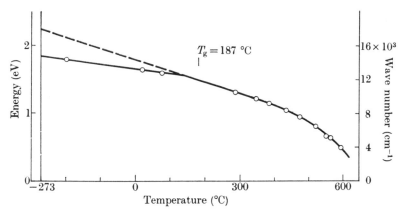

FIG. 9.19. Position of the optical absorption edge (corresponding to $\alpha = 10^2$ cm^{-1}) in amorphous and liquid As$_2$Se$_3$ as a function of temperature (from Edmond 1966). See Fig. 7.38.

The fall-off above about 450°C corresponds to the onset of the free-carrier absorption. The remainder of the curve in Fig. 9.19, however, is taken to represent the temperature variation of the optical gap. Measurements at higher values of α would be needed to confirm this with certainty but, as will be shown below, measurements of thermo-electric power give the same picture. From Fig. 9.19 we can estimate a temperature coefficient of the optical gap of $\sim7 \times 10^{-4}$ eV K^{-1} in the glass and $\sim1\cdot7 \times 10^{-3}$ eV K^{-1} above T_g in the liquid. A higher temperature coefficient of the gap in the liquid state compared with that of the solid is consistent with the temperature variation of conductivity observed in the two states, as will be shown below.

Electrotransmission measurements on crystalline and amorphous As$_2$Se$_3$ have been reported by Kolomiets, Mazets, and Efendiev (1970). For the glass, the results, which are very similar to those found for As$_2$S$_3$ described in the last section, yield when interpreted according to the theory of Franz (1958) an effective mass ratio $m^*/m = 2·9 \pm 0·3$.

Recombination radiation in amorphous As_2Se_3 has been observed by Kolomiets, Mamontova, and Babaev (1970). Figure 9.20 shows that the

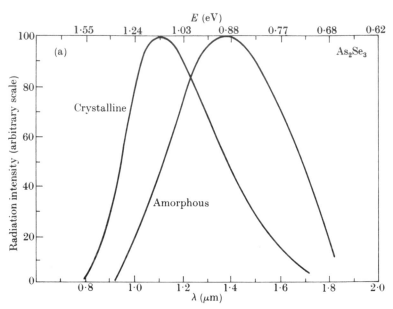

FIG. 9.20. Spectral distribution of recombination radiation in crystalline and amorphous As_2Se_3 at 77K (from Kolomiets *et al.* 1970).

photo-excitation emission observed at 77K peaks at 0·88 eV compared with 1·127 eV in crystalline As_2Se_3. The half-width of the emission ($\sim$0·4 eV) is similar in both, but the intensity of emission is reported as being about 60 times less in the glass. At 120K the maximum of the emission in the glass occurs at 1·14 eV and an additional much smaller peak occurs at 1·71 eV. The former is associated with radiation recombination via defect levels and the latter with band-to-band recombination of free carriers. It was also found that an excess of selenium in the glass increased the emission intensity whereas introduction of oxygen decreased it.

The reflectivity spectrum of amorphous As_2Se_3 out to 14 eV has been compared with that of the crystal by Drews. Figure 9.21 shows that, as for As_2S_3, two main groups of peaks separated by a reflectivity minimum near 7–8 eV are evident in the crystalline spectra. In the

amorphous phase this division appears to be retained and the maximum
of the lower-energy group is shifted to a lower photon energy.

Electrical measurements on amorphous As_2Se_3 have been made by
many workers. Edmond (1968) gives a value for the resistivity at 130°C

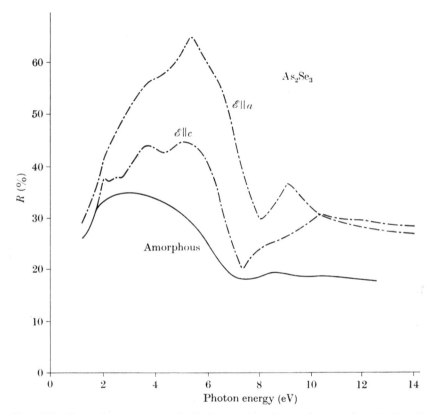

FIG. 9.21. Room-temperature reflectivity spectra of amorphous and crystalline As_2Se_3
(Drews, private communication; see Stuke 1970a).

of $1\cdot54 \times 10^8$ Ω cm and a slope of the plot of ln σ against $1/T$ equal to
$0\cdot91$ eV. Using the temperature coefficient of the optical gap
($\beta \sim 7 \times 10^{-4}$ eV deg^{-1}), one can estimate a room-temperature activation energy for conduction ($E_F - E_V$) of $(0\cdot91 - \tfrac{1}{2}\beta \times 300) = 0\cdot81$ eV.
We remark immediately that an assumption of intrinsic conduction
would yield a mobility gap of $1\cdot62$ eV compared with an optical gap of
$1\cdot76$ eV (p. 348).

Measurements of thermoelectric power in As_2Se_3 glass have been reported by Uphoff and Healy (1961), who find p-type behaviour. However, the magnitude of S found by these workers seems to be surprisingly small when compared with other similar glasses, namely $(As_2Se_3)_x(As_2Te_3)_{1-x}$, and with data in the liquid phase (see Owen and

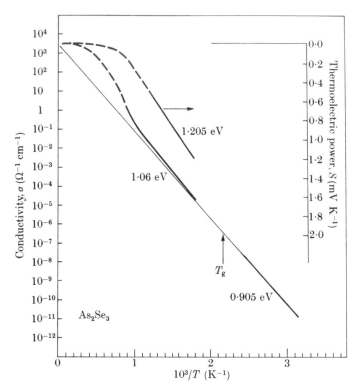

Fig. 9.22. Temperature dependence of conductivity and thermoelectric power in amorphous and liquid As_2Se_3 (data from Edmond 1966).

Robertson 1970). The slope of their curves of $\ln \sigma$ against $1/T$ for As_2Se_3 (0·6 eV) is also much smaller than that found by other workers.

Conductivity and thermoelectric-power data in the liquid phase of As_2Se_3 have been obtained by Edmond (1966). The data are displayed in Fig. 9.22 on which we have also reconstructed the temperature variation of conductivity in the solid. The slope of $\ln \sigma$ against $1/T$ in liquid As_2Se_3 (i.e. the higher-temperature branch of the curve above the glass transition temperature T_g) is 1·06 eV, i.e. ~0·15 eV larger than in the solid. An increased slope suggests an increase in the temperature coefficient of the activation energy (§ 7.4.2). Thus the gap is *decreasing* and we have indicated a possible extrapolation to $(E_F - E_V) = 0$, corresponding to metal-like behaviour with $\sigma \sim 3 \times 10^3 \ \Omega^{-1} \ cm^{-1}$. The thermoelectric power in the liquid exhibits an even higher slope. This is not understood; we speculate that a weak negative temperature dependence of the mobility, and hence of σ_0, could account for the discrepancy. In Fig. 9.22 the scale for S has been chosen so that the activation energies can be compared directly ($k \log_e 10 = 198 \ \mu V \ K^{-1} \equiv 1$ decade in conductivity). It has also been positioned so that $S = 0$

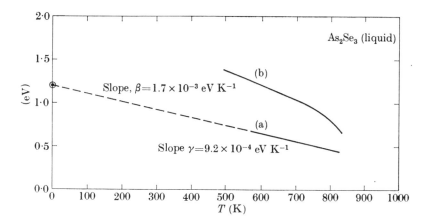

FIG. 9.23. Temperature variation of: (a) the activation energy for conduction $(E_F - E_V)$ in liquid As_2Se_3 as obtained from thermoelectric power data of Edmond (1966); (b) the position of the optical absorption edge ($\alpha = 10^2 \ cm^{-1}$) taken from Fig. 9.19.

corresponds to the 'metallic' conductivity of $3 \times 10^3 \ \Omega^{-1} \ cm^{-1}$. A possible extrapolation to $S = 0$ is indicated.

It should be mentioned that the results on thermoelectric power could be interpreted in terms of ambipolar conductivity. However, no observation of n-type thermoelectric power has been reported in this and many other chalcogenide glasses even at very high temperatures. The one-carrier formula for the thermoelectric power is

$$S(T) = -(k/e)\{E(T)/kT + A\},$$

where A is of the order unity (see § 7.4.5) and $E(T) = (E_F - E_V)$. Thus for $E(T) \gg kT$, the variation of $E(T)$ with T can be obtained from the data. This is shown in curve (a) of Fig. 9.23. The temperature coefficient of $E(T)$ in the liquid state is given by $\gamma \sim 9.2 \times 10^{-4} \ eV \ K^{-1}$. This is expected to be about one-half of the temperature coefficient β of the optical gap. The temperature dependence of the optical gap was shown in Fig. 9.19 and is reproduced as curve (b) in Fig. 9.23. Clearly β is approximately equal to 2γ. These temperature coefficients are about three times larger than found in the solid and account for the increased slope of the plot of ln σ against $1/T$ beyond T_g shown in Fig. 9.22.

The temperature coefficient of an energy gap E can be expressed in terms of a pressure coefficient (see § 7.6.1),

$$\left(\frac{\partial E}{\partial T}\right)_P = \left(\frac{\partial E}{\partial T}\right)_V - \frac{\alpha_V}{K_s}\left(\frac{\partial E}{\partial P}\right)_T.$$

Grant and Ioffe (1970) have determined the pressure coefficients of the optical absorption edge in crystalline and amorphous As_2Se_3. They are given at two different temperatures in Table 9.3. Felty and Myers

TABLE 9.3

	T(K)	Photon energy (eV)	$\partial E/\partial P \times 10^{-6}$ (eV bar^{-1})
As_2Se_3 crystal	274	2·00	−14
	80	2·10	−10
As_2Se_3 film	274	1·98	−7.6
	80	2·10	−11·5

(1967) have determined α_V for As_2Se_3 glass. At room temperature they find 6×10^{-5} K^{-1}. The compressibility K_s is $\sim 10^{-5}$ bar^{-1} (Kolomiets and Raspopova 1970). Thus the second term on the right in the above equation (the contribution to the temperature coefficient due to lattice dilation) is roughly $+5 \times 10^{-5}$ eV K^{-1}. The point we wish to make is that this is of the wrong sign to account for the observed value of

$$(\partial E/\partial T)_P \sim -7 \times 10^{-4} \text{ eV K}^{-1}.$$

The major factor determining the temperature coefficient of the optical gap is therefore $(\partial E/\partial T)_V$. Kolomiets and Raspopova (1970) reach a similar conclusion (although their numbers are different) from measurements of the temperature and pressure coefficients of a photoconductivity peak at the edge. The large value of $(\partial E/\partial T)_V$ is not characteristic only of the amorphous phase but appears to be a property of spiral chain or layer-like lattices. A possible explanation (Mott 1971a) is that the effect of temperature may be to *reduce* the separation between chains or layers i.e. to act in the same direction as pressure. This explanation is open to verification, by X-ray studies for example.

The spectral dependence of photoconductivity in evaporated films of As_2Se_3 has been reported by Shaw et al. (1970) using planar geometry and by Felty, Lucovsky, and Myers (1967) using a sandwich cell. The latter authors find a peak at 1·82 eV when normalized to photocurrent per absorbed photon. No detailed quantum efficiency measurements have been published, but Felty and Myers (private communication) have found a wavelength-dependent and electric-field-dependent generation mechanism similar to that in amorphous As_2S_3 and Se.

Drift mobility studies on amorphous As_2Se_3 have been made by Owen and Robertson (1970), Kolomiets and Lebedev (1967), and by Tabak (1971). In contrast with the well-defined transits observed in amorphous selenium, for example, hole transport is characterized by a statistical spread in arrival times similar to that found in As_2S_3 (and also Se at low temperatures—see Chapter 10). If an 'effective' mobility is determined from the minimum of the spectrum of transit times, it is found to be electric-field dependent (Fig. 9.24). The 'zero-field' hole mobility at room temperature is $\sim 5 \times 10^{-7}$ cm^2 V^{-1} s^{-1} and, as a function of temperature, is observed to have an activation energy of about 0·5 eV. It is not clear how to interpret this. Under well-defined transit conditions an activation energy associated with a drift mobility can be interpreted in terms of the range of localized states at a band edge (§ 7.4.3). However, for a range ~ 0.5 eV, d.c. conduction at room temperature would almost certainly be by hopping and it becomes difficult to reconcile this with the observed value of $C \sim 10^3$–10^4 Ω^{-1} cm^{-1} (Fig. 7.8).

The a.c. conductivity in amorphous As_2Se_3 has been measured as a function of frequency and temperature by Owen and Robertson (1970) and by Ivkin and Kolomiets (1970). The results of the latter authors are shown in Fig. 9.25 (see also Fig. 7.18). Although the temperature dependence is not quite as expected for hopping with energies near E_F (equation (7.15)), it is certainly not sufficiently large to attribute the a.c. conductivity to hopping in localized states at a band edge. An estimate of $N(E_F)$ for As_2Se_3 from these results is ~ 2–3×10^{18} cm^3 eV^{-1}.

The variation of the glass transition temperature in the As–Se system, and the phase diagram have been obtained by Myers and Felty (1967) (Fig. 9.26). These authors suggest that the initial effect of adding As to Se is to branch the selenium chains. Higher concentrations of As lead to a predominance of $AsSe_{3/2}$-linked networks which eventually coalesce into a more or less homogeneous random network at about 40 %–45 % As. It is possible to produce glasses by melt-quenching with as much as 55 % As in Se.

24

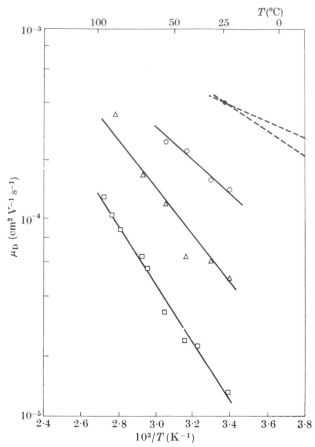

FIG. 9.24. Temperature dependence of hole drift mobility in amorphous As_2Se_3 for different electric fields. □ $9\cdot4 \times 10^4$ V cm^{-1}; △ $18\cdot8 \times 10^4$ V cm^{-1}; ○ $28\cdot2 \times 10^4$ V cm^{-1}; ● 55×10^4 V cm^{-1}. (From Owen and Robertson 1970.)

Hulls and McMillan (private communication) have studied the temperature dependence of d.c. conductivity in the As–Se system. The activation energy for conduction drops from about 1 eV in Se to about $0\cdot9$ eV at $As_{10}Se_{90}$. Further addition of As does not affect this activation energy, which remains at $0\cdot90 \pm 0\cdot04$ eV right through As_2Se_3 up to the limit of glass formation. However, the actual magnitude of the room-temperature conductivity rises by four decades from $As_{10}Se_{90}$ to a maximum at As_2Se_3. Edmond (1968) (see Table 9.2) also finds a maximum conductivity at the stoichiometric composition. These results imply a value of C (Fig. 7.8) for $As_{10}Se_{90}$ of about 10 Ω^{-1} cm^{-1} (as for hopping conduction) and a rapid rise with increasing As concentration to a value $\sim 10^3$–10^4 Ω^{-1} cm^{-1} in As_2Se_3. There may be an

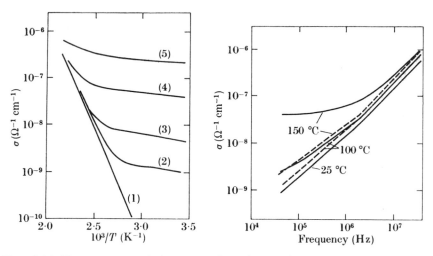

Fig. 9.25. Temperature and frequency dependence of conductivity in amorphous As_2Se_3. (1) d.c.; (2) 5×10^4 Hz; (3) 3×10^5 Hz; (4) 3×10^6 Hz; (5) $1 \cdot 4 \times 10^7$ Hz. The dotted lines in the right-hand figure are obtained after subtraction of the d.c. contribution to the conductivity (from Ivkin and Kolomiets 1970).

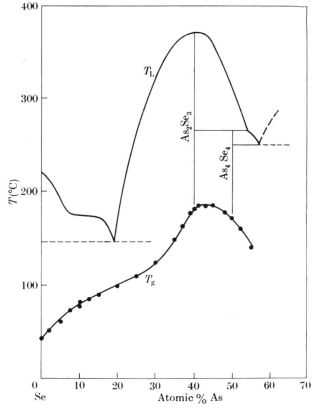

Fig. 9.26. Glass transition temperatures and phase diagram of the Se–As system (from Myers and Felty 1967).

interesting correlation between this behaviour and the structure of the glasses as suggested by the variation of T_g in Fig. 9.26.

Infrared measurements on As_2Se_3 have been made by Felty, Lucovsky, and Myers (1967), Taylor, Bishop, and Mitchell (1970), and Austin and Garbett (1971). The absorption spectrum obtained by Austin and Garbett was shown in Fig. 7.41 and also in Fig. 7.18. Taylor *et al.*, using a slotted-waveguide technique, determined the absorption coefficient in the range $1-6 \times 10^9$ Hz, i.e. between those covered by a.c. conductivity and by far-infrared measurements.

9.5. Arsenic tritelluride As_2Te_3

In contrast with As_2S_3 and As_2Se_3, it is not possible to obtain As_2Te_3 as a glass by cooling the melt except by using extremely fast quenching techniques. The most convenient method of preparation is vacuum evaporation of As_2Te_3 ingots (produced by reacting the constituents in sealed quartz tubes) on to liquid-nitrogen cooled substrates (Weiser and Brodsky 1970). Amorphous films up to 5000 Å thick can be deposited at about 400 Å s^{-1}.

The optical absorption edge in amorphous As_2Te_3 at room temperature as determined by Rockstad (1970) was shown in Fig. 7.24 and also Fig. 7.31. The slope of the exponential region ($\alpha = \alpha_0' e^{\Gamma \hbar \omega}$) is $\Gamma \sim 19$ eV^{-1}. At higher photon energies the absorption coefficient follows the relation (Fig. 7.32) $\alpha \hbar \omega = 5 \cdot 4 \times 10^5 (\hbar \omega - 0 \cdot 82)^2$. Weiser and Brodsky find in their films $\alpha \hbar \omega = 4 \cdot 7 \times 10^5 (\hbar \omega - 0 \cdot 83)^2$, in remarkably good agreement with Rockstad.

Weiser and Brodsky have measured the temperature dependence of the absorption edge for values of $\alpha > 10^4$ cm^{-1}. Their results are shown in Fig. 9.27, plotted as $\ln \alpha$ against $\hbar \omega$ in (a) and as $(\alpha \hbar \omega)^{\frac{1}{2}}$ against $\hbar \omega$ in (b). The temperature coefficient of the optical gap E_0, defined by the intercept on the $\hbar \omega$ axis, is thus found to be -5×10^{-4} eV K^{-1}.

The temperature dependence of the electrical conductivity in amorphous As_2Te_3, as determined by Weiser and Brodsky between 220K and 350K, is given by

$$\sigma = C \exp(-E/kT),$$

with $C = 600 \ \Omega^{-1} \ cm^{-1}$ and $E = 0 \cdot 4 \pm 0 \cdot 02$ eV. Devitrification occurs at about 400K and is accompanied by an abrupt increase in the conductivity of about five decades.

Using the temperature coefficient of the optical gap we can estimate a room-temperature activation energy for conduction given by

$E = (0·4 - \frac{1}{2}\beta \times 300) = 0·325$. Thus, as for As_2S_3 and As_2Se_3, $2E$ is less (by $0·15$ eV in this case) than the optical gap E_0, and the Fermi level is presumably displaced from the centre of the mobility gap towards the valence band.

Croitoru, Vescan, Popescu, and Lazarescu (1970) have also measured the temperature dependence of conductivity in amorphous As_2Te_3

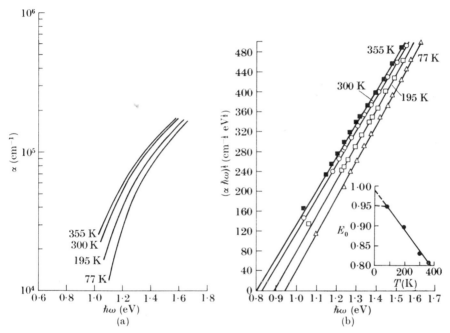

FIG. 9.27. Temperature dependence of the optical absorption edge in amorphous As_2Te_3 plotted as (a) $\ln \alpha$ against $\hbar\omega$; (b) $(\alpha\hbar\omega)^{\frac{1}{2}}$ against $\hbar\omega$. The inset to (b) shows the temperature dependence of the intercept on the $\hbar\omega$-axis (from Weiser and Brodsky 1970).

films. The results for three values of the applied voltage are shown in Fig. 9.28. The activation energy for this film (which was considerably thicker than those used by Weiser and Brodsky) is $0·46$ eV. Below about 220K and above 2×10^4 V cm^{-1} a second activation energy of $0·25$ eV was observed. This could represent a transition to conduction in localized states at the valence-band edge, in which case the results suggest (see § 7.4) that the range of localized states is $0·21$ eV minus any contribution to the $0·25$-eV activation energy due to a hopping energy. Although the data are presented in terms of conductance, the change in the intercept by about a factor of 10^4 is reasonable for this mechanism. In the low-temperature, high-field régime Croitoru et al.

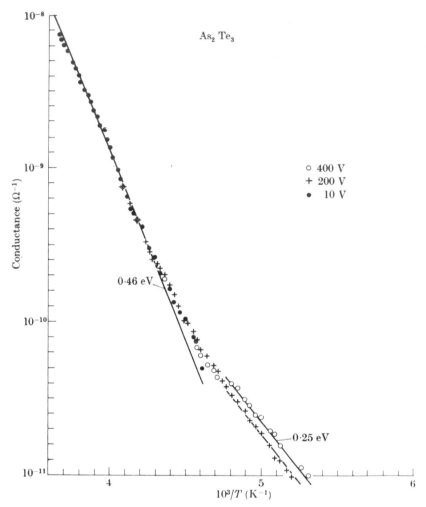

FIG. 9.28. Temperature dependence of electrical conductance in amorphous As₂Te₃ (from Croitoru *et al.* 1970).

find non-linear behaviour of the I–V characteristic; the dependence is $I \propto V^2/d^3$, as expected for space-charge-limited conduction.

The value of the intercept C observed by Weiser and Brodsky together with the optical value of β suggest a value for σ_0 in As₂Te₃ of about $600 \exp(\beta/2k) \sim 33 \ \Omega^{-1} \ \mathrm{cm}^{-1}$. This is rather lower than expected for extended-state conduction but certainly higher than expected for hopping conduction.

Photoconductivity in amorphous As₂Te₃ has been reported by Weiser and Brodsky. They find a change in room-temperature conductance of about 10 per cent for an incident photon energy of 1·08 eV and a flux of $6·5 \times 10^{17}$ photons cm^{-2} s^{-1}. By measuring the lifetime for decay of photoconductivity ($\sim 5 \times 10^{-8}$ s, followed by a much slower decay), these authors place a lower limit on the mobility of 0·3 cm^2 V^{-1} s^{-1}.

Measurements of a.c. conductivity in As_2Te_3 films have been made at room temperature by Rockstad (1970). The results are shown in Fig. 9.29. The behaviour above about 10^6 Hz is $\sigma(\omega) \propto \omega^s$ with $s \sim 0·8$–$0·9$. When interpreted in terms of equation (7.7), a very high density of

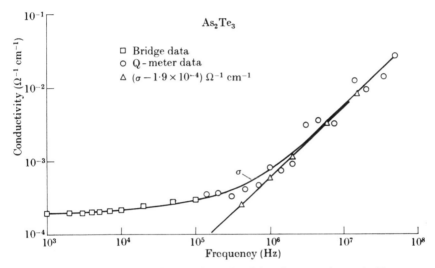

FIG. 9.29. Frequency dependence of conductivity in amorphous As_2Te_3 at room temperature (from Rockstad 1970).

states at the Fermi energy of 3×10^{20} cm^{-3} eV^{-1} is obtained. Pollak (1971b) suggests that multiple hopping may be occurring in this material.

Edmond (1966) has measured the electrical conductivity and thermoelectric power of liquid As_2Te_3 as a function of temperature. His results were shown in Fig. 7.20 and discussed in Chapter 7.

9.6. Mixed binary systems

9.6.1. As_2Se_3–As_2Te_3

This mixed system of binary chalcogenides has been studied by Vengel and Kolomiets (1957), Uphoff and Healy (1961), Edmond (1966, 1968), and Weiser, Fischer, and Brodsky (1970). Bulk samples can be obtained by quenching the melt for concentrations of As_2Te_3 up to 70–80 %.

Across the whole composition range the electrical conductivity obeys the relation $\sigma = C \exp(-E/kT)$ over several decades. Figure 9.30 shows the variation of E and the room-temperature conductivity. There is good agreement between results of many investigators. It would appear that C remains essentially constant for this mixed system, as is seen from the calculated variations of E, when C is assumed to be 10^2, 10^3,

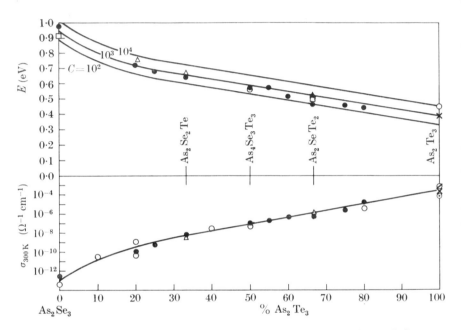

FIG. 9.30. Variation of the activation energy for electrical conduction and the room-temperature conductivity in the As_2Se_3–As_2Te_3 system. Data from: ○ Uphoff and Healy (1961); ● Vengel and Kolomiets (1957); × Weiser and Brodsky (1970); ∅ Rockstad (1970); □ Edmond (1968); △ Male (1970); ⊙ Croitoru et al. (1970).

and $10^4 \, \Omega^{-1} \, cm^{-1}$ (see also Fig. 9.2). It is probable that tellurium replaces selenium isomorphously leading to no significant short-range structural changes. Further evidence for this is obtained from the thermal conductivity (Uphoff and Healy 1961), which remains of the order of $4 \times 10^{-3} \, W \, cm^{-1} \, K^{-1}$ across the whole composition range.

The thermoelectric power has been reported to exhibit some unusual variations with composition in the As_2Se_3–As_2Te_3 system (Uphoff and Healy 1961; Vengel and Kolomiets 1957). However we shall not discuss these results. In the liquid state (Edmond 1966) the thermoelectric powers of As_2SeTe_2 (i.e. $As_2Se_3 . 2As_2Te_3$) and As_2Se_2Te (i.e. $2As_2Se_3 . As_2Te_3$) have temperature coefficients that yield activation energies similar to (but higher than) those exhibited by the electrical conductivity (see Fig. 7.20 and Table 7.2).

The optical absorption edges in As_2SeTe_2 and As_2Se_2Te have been measured by Edmond (1966) and in $As_4Se_3Te_3$ by Rockstad (1970)—see Fig. 7.24. The shift with composition (Vengel and Kolomiets 1957) can be correlated with the change of E shown in Fig. 9.30.

The first reported observation of recombination radiation in an (undoped) amorphous semiconductor was made by Kolomiets, Mamontova, and Negreskul (1968) in $As_2Se_3.As_2Te_3$. Excitation was in the u.v. and the sample was held at liquid-nitrogen temperature. A small emission peak occurs at 1·16 eV close to the mobility gap expected at 77K, and a larger peak occurs at 0·67 eV, probably due to recombination at a high density of levels near the centre of the gap. Similar observations by Kolomiets et al. (1970) in amorphous As_2S_3 and As_2Se_3 have been described earlier in this chapter.

Detailed photoconductivity experiments on films of $As_2Se_3.2As_2Te_3$ have been made by Weiser et al. (1970). These results are discussed in § 7.5.

9.6.2. As_2Se_3–As_2S_3

Baidakov, Borisova, and Ipateva (1962), Felty and Myers (private communication), Felty, Lucovsky, and Myers (1967), and Edmond (1966) have reported electrical and optical measurements on samples of these mixed binaries and also on samples of more general composition in the As–Se–S ternary system. An interesting feature (shown in Fig. 9.2) is that addition of As_2S_3 to As_2Se_3 increases the room-temperature resistivity by more than might be expected from the relatively small change in the activation energy for conduction. This behaviour can be accounted for by a change in the intercept C, as shown in Fig. 9.2. We conjecture that conduction in As_2S_3 near room temperature is by hopping in localized states at the valence-band edge and that the range of localized states decreases with the addition of As_2Se_3.

9.6.3. As_2S_3–As_2Te_3

Detailed electrical measurements in the As–S–Te system have been reported by Minami, Hattori, Nakamachi, and Tanaka (1970). The pre-exponential factor C ($\sigma = C \exp(-E/kT)$) is found to be independent of composition except for the sulphur-rich samples.

9.6.4. As$_2$Se$_3$–Sb$_2$Se$_3$

This amorphous mixed binary system has been studied by Platakis, Sadagopan, and Gatos (1969). These investigators report that glasses with up to 50 % Sb$_2$Se$_3$ can be obtained by rotating the quartz ampoule containing the melt during quenching.

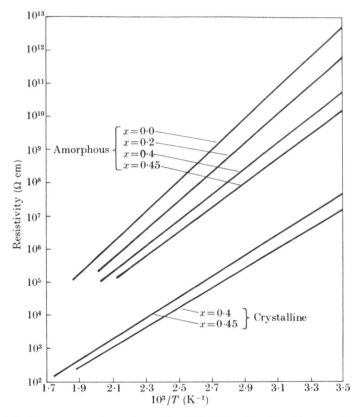

FIG. 9.31. Temperature dependence of resistivity in the $(1-x)$As$_2$Se$_3$.xSb$_2$Se$_3$ system (from Platakis *et al.* 1969).

The temperature dependence of resistivity of several compositions is compared with data on polycrystalline material in Fig. 9.31. The slopes of these curves (E) and the values of the pre-exponential factor (C) are shown in Fig. 9.32. Also in this figure are values obtained by Edmond (1968) on amorphous As$_4$Sb$_2$Se$_9$ (i.e. 2As$_2$Se$_3$.Sb$_2$Se$_3$).

Platakis *et al.* also determined the optical absorption up to $\alpha = 10^2$ cm^{-1} at room temperature and at 77K. The shift of the edge with composition follows that found for E. These authors chose to decompose

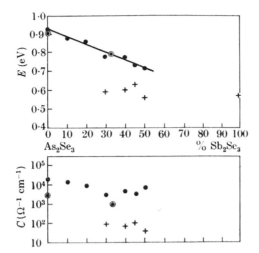

Fɪɢ. 9.32. Variation of E and C ($\sigma = C\exp(-E/kT)$) in the As_2Se_3–$SbSe_3$ system: • amorphous, + polycrystalline (Platakis *et al.* 1969); ⊙ amorphous (Edmond 1968).

the approximately exponential edges into two straight lines obeying the relation $\alpha \propto (\hbar\omega - E_0)^2$ and inferred the presence of phonon-assisted indirect transitions. If, instead, the optical gaps are taken at a photon energy corresponding to $\alpha \sim 10^3$ cm^{-1}, they lie about 0·25 eV towards higher energies than reported by Platakis *et al.* and are slightly larger than the corresponding values of $2E$. The temperature coefficient of the absorption edge is 6–7×10^{-4} eV K^{-1}.

9.7. Germanium telluride GeTe

Films of GeTe deposited by vacuum evaporation or sputtering on to substrates held at temperatures below 50°C are amorphous. At higher temperatures the films are polycrystalline with either rhombohedral or NaCl structure or a continuous mixture of the two phases. To avoid an excess of Te in the films it may be necessary to start with Ge-rich material, although the vapour at 600°C consists predominantly of GeTe species.

Structural studies on amorphous Ge_xTe_{1-x} films have been made by Betts, Bienenstock, and Ovshinsky (1970) who find in the X-ray diffraction radial distribution curve first-nearest-neighbour and second-nearest-neighbour distances of 2·7 Å and 4·2 Å. The absence of a peak at the crystalline GeTe first-neighbour position of 3 Å implies that the local coordinations in the amorphous and crystalline materials are different. This observation, together with n.m.r. studies of Senturia,

Hewes, and Adler (1970), has been discussed by Adler, Cohen, Fagen, and Thompson (1970), who propose a model for the bonding in GeTe in which all valence requirements are satisfied (see Fig. 2.15(c)). Chopra and Bahl (1969) have also made a study of the structure of GeTe (see also Dove, Heritage, Chopra, and Bahl 1970).

Electrical and optical properties of amorphous GeTe have been reported by Bahl and Chopra (1969, 1970), Tsu, Howard, and Esaki (1970), and Howard and Tsu (1970).

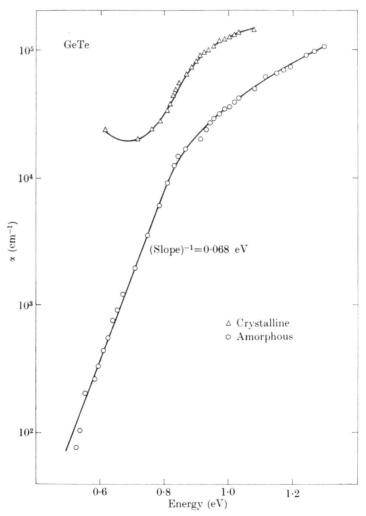

FIG. 9.33. Optical absorption edges in amorphous and crystalline GeTe (fom Bahl and Chopra 1969).

The optical absorption edge at room temperature as reported by Bahl and Chopra (1969) is compared with crystalline GeTe in Fig. 9.33. Although there does not appear to be a large difference in the position of the two edges, crystalline GeTe is in fact a small-band-gap ($\sim$0·3 eV) semiconductor, and the edge is displaced to higher energies on account of a large Burstein shift. The absorption edge in the film is characterized by the commonly observed exponential tail, but the slope,

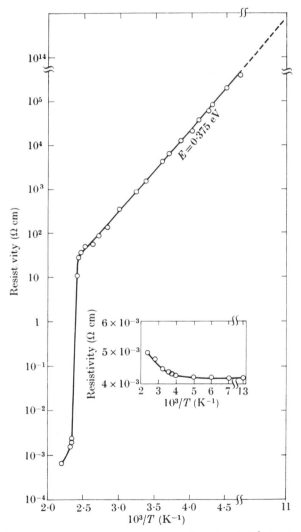

FIG. 9.34. Temperature dependence of resistivity of a 680 Å thick amorphous GeTe film. The inset shows the behaviour of the film after crystallization (from Bahl and Chopra 1970).

$\Gamma \sim 15 \text{ eV}^{-1}$, is lower than found in most materials (see Table 7.4). Tsu *et al.* find an even shallower edge, $\Gamma \sim 13 \text{ eV}^{-1}$. Both groups report that above the exponential edge the absorption coefficient follows the relation $\alpha \hbar \omega = B(\hbar \omega - E_0)^2$. Bahl and Chopra find $B = 6 \times 10^5 \text{ cm}^{-1} \text{ eV}^{-1}$, $E_0 = 0.8 \text{ eV}$, and Tsu *et al.* find $B = 2.1 \times 10^5 \text{ cm}^{-1} \text{eV}^{-1}$, $E_0 = 0.7 \text{ eV}$. The temperature coefficient of E_0 is $3–4 \times 10^{-4} \text{ eV K}^{-1}$.

The electrical conductivity of amorphous GeTe obeys the relation $\sigma = C \exp(-E/kT)$ with $E \sim 0.3\text{--}0.4 \text{ eV}$. A typical result from Bahl and Chopra (1970) is shown in Fig. 9.34. The sharp decrease in resistivity near 400K corresponds to an irreversible transformation to a crystalline phase, the resistivity of which then follows the temperature dependence (shown in the inset) characteristic of a degenerate semiconductor. The pre-exponential factor C for the amorphous film is about $700 \text{ } \Omega^{-1} \text{ cm}^{-1}$. Tsu *et al.* find a much lower value $\sim 100 \text{ } \Omega^{-1} \text{ cm}^{-1}$.

Bahl and Chopra (1970) also report on non-linear voltage–current characteristics, a.c. conductivity, and tunnelling spectroscopy in GeTe films. As the results are similar to those already described on other materials, they will not be discussed here.

Detailed measurements of photoconductivity in amorphous GeTe have been described by Howard and Tsu (1970). Interpretation of the data can be made under the assumption of a range of localized states at the valence-band edge (assuming p-type conduction) of about 0.2 eV. The results and analysis are similar to those described for $As_2Se_3 \cdot 2As_2Te_3$ in § 7.5.

An interesting study of the electric-field dependence of the photoconductivity edge in amorphous GeTe has been made by Stiles, Chang, Esaki and Tsu (1970).

9.8. Multicomponent glasses

In view of the commercial interest in amorphous semiconductors composed of many elements we conclude this chapter with a few results made on such materials. However, because of the difficulty of classification, and the similarity of many of their properties to those of simpler systems, a selection of data will be made. Numerous papers on the properties of materials that exhibit both threshold and memory switching under high-field conditions are collected in the 'Proceedings of the Symposium on Semiconductor Effects in Amorphous Solids'[†] and the 'Proceedings of the International Conference on Amorphous and Liquid Semiconductors'[‡].

† *J. non-cryst. solids* **2** (1970).   ‡ *J. non-cryst. solids* **4** (1970).

Most of the switching materials that have been investigated in detail are based on As_2Te_3 with additions of up to 20 % of one or more of the elements Ge, Si, S, and P. In particular Fagen and Fritzsche (1970a, b) have reported on the optical and electrical properties of $As_{35}Te_{40}Ge_{11}S_{11}P_3$ in both bulk and thin-film form. The electrical conductivity follows the relation $\sigma = C \exp(-E/kT)$ with $E \sim 0.45$ eV, but the low value of C ($\sim 10^2\ \Omega^{-1}\ cm^{-1}$) and a slight

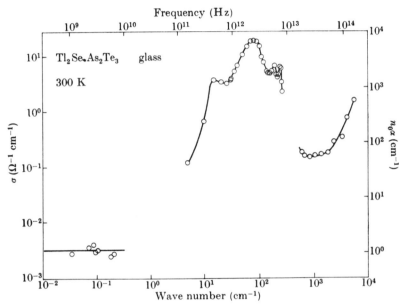

FIG. 9.35. Frequency dependence of conductivity (optical absorption) in $Tl_2Se.As_2Te_3$ glass (from Bishop et al. 1971).

curvature in the plot of ln σ against $1/T$ suggest conduction in localized states. For these alloys, which have compositional as well as structural disorder, it is likely that the ranges of localized states at the band edges are more extensive than in amorphous elements or binary systems. The optical absorption edges for this and similar alloys were shown in Fig. 7.33. Above an exponential tail the absorption coefficient follows the relationship $\alpha\hbar\omega \sim (\hbar\omega - E_0)^s$, with $s = 3$ in contrast to the more normal value $s = 2$. In addition, the value of the absorption coefficient at a photon energy corresponding to twice the activation energy for electrical conduction ($2E$), is lower than in most other amorphous semiconductors. These observations again suggest that the density of states and extent of localization are somewhat different from their values in simpler systems. Many other properties, e.g. photoconductivity, a.c. conductivity, Hall effect, etc. however are very similar to those described for other materials.

Glasses containing Tl also appear to have their own characteristic properties. We mention here the temperature variation of electrical conductivity in the liquid state as determined by Edmond (1966) and shown in Fig. 7.20. The activation energy for conduction decreases as the temperature is raised, a feature exhibited by other materials only on approach to metal-like conductivity at about $10^3\ \Omega^{-1}\ cm^{-1}$.

Fig. 9.35 shows the frequency dependence of conductivity (optical absorption) over a broad range in $Tl_2Se \cdot As_2Te_3$, as determined by Bishop, Taylor, Mitchell, and Slack (1971). No increase in conductivity, such as was described for other materials in § 7.4, is observed up to at least 10^{10} Hz. This may arise because of the high value of the d.c. conductivity, which masks any hopping contribution to the conductivity. Beyond the phonon spectrum but below the fundamental optical absorption edge, another frequency-independent region is observed. From a study of the temperature dependence of the absorption, which has the same activation energy as the d.c. conductivity, Bishop *et al.* ascribe this portion of the spectrum to free-carrier absorption.

10

SELENIUM, TELLURIUM, AND THEIR ALLOYS

10.1. Structure of amorphous selenium and alloys of selenium
    10.1.1. Isoelectronic additives Te and S
    10.1.2. Univalent additives Cl, Br, I, Tl, Na, and K
    10.1.3. Branching additives As, Bi, and Ge
10.2. Electrical properties of amorphous selenium and alloys of selenium

10.2.1. Electrical conductivity
10.2.2. Drift mobilities
10.2.3. Carrier lifetimes and ranges
10.2.4. Space-charge-limited current measurements
10.3. Optical properties of amorphous selenium and tellurium
10.4. Photogeneration in amorphous selenium: xerography

10.1. Structure of amorphous selenium and alloys of selenium

AMORPHOUS selenium is believed to consist predominantly of a mixture of two structural species, long helical chains and eight-membered rings, held to each other by weak forces perhaps of the van der Waal type. Strong covalent bonds exist between the atoms in the chains and rings. The relative proportions of the two species, as well as the length of the chains, is expected to depend on the conditions of preparation, which can be either by melt quenching or by vacuum evaporation.

Evidence for this structure comes in part from X-ray diffraction studies (see Grigorovici 1969; Kaplow, Rowe, and Averbach 1968). Although the shape of the radial distribution curve is sensitive to the manner in which the samples are prepared, the number of nearest neighbours (2) and the radius of the first coordination sphere ($\sim$2·3 Å) are practically the same as those occurring in either of the two crystalline forms (see below). A variety of models have been proposed to explain the shape of particular radial distribution curves beyond the first coordination maximum: however they nearly all invoke Se rings (although not necessarily eight-membered), perhaps bridged by chain-like units.

The techniques of molecular spectroscopy, infrared absorption, and Raman scattering have been especially useful in studies of the structure of amorphous selenium and its alloys (Srb and Vasko 1963; Lucovsky

1969*b*), although not for most amorphous semiconductors, which have complicated network structures. Identification of the vibrational modes that lead to strong absorption in the infrared spectra (Lucovsky, Mooradian, Taylor, Wright, and Keezer 1967) are simplified by the existence of two crystalline forms of selenium, α-monoclinic, a molecular crystal composed of puckered Se_8 rings, and trigonal selenium, built up of long helical chains. Fig. 10.1 shows a portion of the room-temperature infrared transmission spectrum of amorphous selenium compared with that of α-monoclinic selenium. The absorption bands in the crystal have been assigned to internal vibrations of the Se_8 molecule. (The spectrum is very similar to that found in orthorhombic sulphur, with energies scaled by a factor of two.) In amorphous

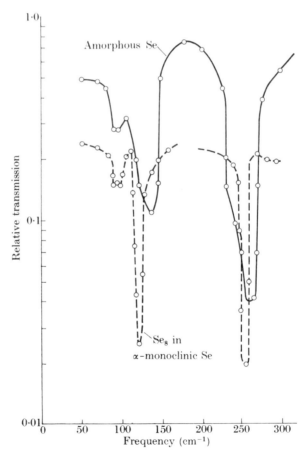

FIG. 10.1. Comparison of the room-temperature transmission spectra of α-monoclinic and amorphous selenium (from Lucovsky 1969*a*).

selenium the bands at 95 cm^{-1} and 254 cm^{-1} and the shoulder near 120 cm^{-1} are close to the 92–97 cm^{-1} doublet, the 254 cm^{-1} singlet, and the 116–122 cm^{-1} doublet observed in the crystal. Other second-order and combination bands, at higher energies than shown here, also appear in both spectra. The strong band at 135 cm^{-1} and the shoulder at 230 cm^{-1} can be correlated with absorption bands observed in the trigonal form of selenium, and hence are attributed to vibrational modes of helical chains. Studies of Raman spectra (Mooradian and Wright 1969) support the above assignments, and furthermore allow estimates to be made of the relative proportions of the two structural species present.

Additional evidence for partial conservation of the chain structure of trigonal selenium in the amorphous and also the liquid phase has been provided by neutron spectroscopy. Figure 10.2 shows the results of

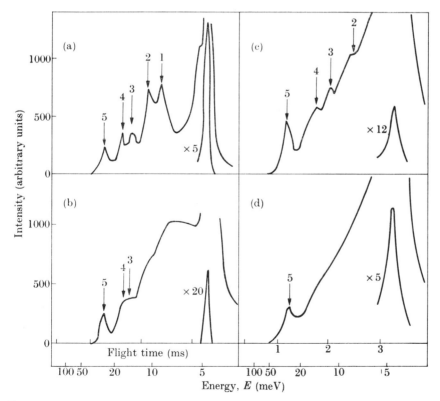

FIG. 10.2. Neutron time-of-flight spectra of selenium: (a) polycrystalline (20°C); (b) amorphous (20°C); (c) liquid (340°C); (d) liquid with 4 atomic % iodine (340°C). (From Axmann *et al.* 1971.)

Axmann, Gissler, Kollmar, and Springer (1971). The peak numbered 5 occurring near 32 meV is assigned to a bond-stretching mode in Se chains, and is retained in the liquid and amorphous phases. Peaks 3 and 4 (probably bond-shearing and torsional modes) are broadened because of changes in inter-chain coupling and, possibly, chain length. The structure at lower energies is assigned to acoustic modes, and it is interesting that here the scattered intensity is greater in the disordered materials. The peak at 4·8 meV is the unscattered radiation.

Electron spin resonance studies in pure amorphous selenium (Abkowitz 1967) suggest that electrons at the ends of Se chains are paired. Large signals reported in earlier work were possibly due to hydrocarbon impurities.

The ring–chain structural model of amorphous selenium provides a basis for consideration of the structure of binary alloys containing selenium. Following Schottmiller, Tabak, Lucovsky, and Ward (1970) we classify the glass-forming alloys of Se into three groups: alloys formed with isoelectronic additives Te and S, those formed with the univalent elements Cl, Br, Tl, Na, and K, and those formed with the so-called branching elements As, Bi, and Ge.

10.1.1. Isoelectronic additives Te and S

If local valence requirements are to be satisfied in the alloys Se–Te and Se–S, then any structural groupings other than rings or chains would appear to be excluded. Raman studies (Fig. 10.3) show very clearly the growth of a peak in the spectrum at 355 cm^{-1} with increasing percentage of sulphur in selenium and at 216 cm^{-1} with increasing percentage of tellurium. These peaks have been associated with the formation of mixed eight-membered rings, possibly Se_3S_5 and Se_6Te_2. These mixed rings increase in concentration at the expense of the Se_8 rings, as shown in Fig. 10.4. Te is much more effective than S in reducing the Se_8-ring concentration. In pure amorphous Se the fraction of atoms in the ring configuration is shown here to be at about 40 per cent, in agreement with estimates obtained from viscosity (Keezer and Bailey 1967) and differential dissolution studies (Briegleb 1929). Although spectroscopic studies yield less information on the chain components, theoretical analysis based on equilibrium in the liquid phase suggests that addition of S reduces the concentration of atoms in chains, whereas Te increases it slightly. However both elements are probably effective in reducing the length of the chains. Neutron spectroscopy (Axmann et al. 1971) in liquid Te suggests an extensive breakdown in

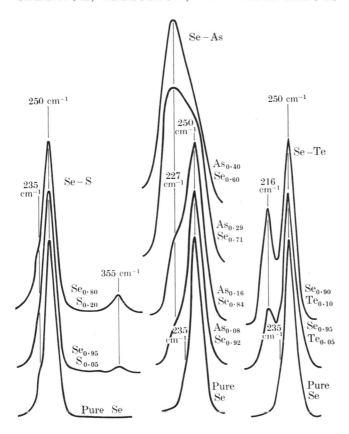

FIG. 10.3. Stokes region Raman spectra for Se–S, Se–As, and Se–Te amorphous alloys (from Schottmiller *et al.* 1970).

the chain structure. Surprisingly the viscosity of Se is increased by the addition of Te (Lanyon 1969): this is probably due to an enhanced interaction between chains.

10.1.2. *Univalent additives* Cl, Br, I, Tl, Na, *and* K

The reduction in the viscosity of liquid Se caused by the addition of the univalent elements mentioned above is interpreted as being due to a significant decrease in the lengths of the chains. As spectroscopic studies indicate little change in the relative fractions of atoms in rings and chains, it is assumed that addition of univalent elements to Se is effective in breaking and terminating the chains. In Cl-doped Se an absorption band at 340 cm^{-1} has been associated with a localized vibrational mode of a chlorine-terminated chain (Lucovsky 1969b). The

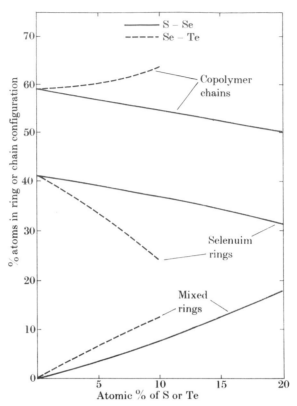

FIG. 10.4. Atomic distributions in Se–S and Se–Te amorphous alloys (from Schottmiller *et al.* 1970).

neutron spectroscopy results shown in Fig. 10.4(d) indicate the presence of short chains in liquid Se with 4 atomic % iodine.

10.1.3. *Branching additives* As, Bi, *and* Ge

Incorporation of As reduces the Se_8-ring population. This is clearly shown in the infrared absorption and the Raman scattering spectra. In the Raman spectrum of Fig. 10.3, the 250 cm^{-1} peak, due to Se_8 rings, is seen to be reduced relative to a peak at 227 cm^{-1} that is characteristic of As_2Se_3. Infrared studies (Lucovsky 1969*a*) suggest that the decrease in the concentration of Se_8 rings is linear with increasing As concentration and approaches zero for 20 % As. In addition, over the 0–40 % range a band appears in the infrared absorption at 650 cm^{-1}, which is also observed in As_2Se_3 glass, and is attributed to a vibrational mode of an $AsSe_{3/2}$ species. An increase in the glass transition temperature with increasing As content has been interpreted by Myers and Felty

(1967) (see § 9.9.4) in terms of a random incorporation of $AsSe_{3/2}$ branching junctions up to 8 % As, followed by a coalescence of these centres. Thus the effect of addition of As is visualized as a breaking of Se_8 rings and the interconnection of chains. This should lead towards a fully branched, three-dimensional network of atoms without any significant concentration of molecular species at a concentration of As approaching that in As_2Se_3. Alloys formed with Bi and Ge are assumed to behave similarly.

Haisty and Krebs (1969*a,b*) report extensively on the electrical properties of melts in the Se–Ge–Sb and Se–Ge–As systems. Their data relate the conductivity (and its temperature dependence) to the proximity of the composition to the glass-forming boundary in these alloys. Figure 10.5(a) and (b) summarizes their results. The dotted line in Fig. 10.5(a) shows the glass-forming region possible with fast quenching. Haisty and Krebs make several comments concerning the structure of Se alloys which support the general ideas presented above concerning the role of various additives. We end this section with a few of their conclusions, which relate structure to the ease with which a given alloy forms a glass.

(a) In Se, each atom needs two neighbours to satisfy the valence requirements. This is achieved either by the formation of small molecules Se_8 or linear polymeric chains Se_n. Selenium can melt without appreciable change within these structural units, the required random arrangement of atoms being obtained by the breaking of the weak bonding between units, and by the increased flexibility of the chains which accompanies this. A rearrangement into a crystal structure on cooling is a difficult step, and a glass is easily formed. Crystallization would appear to require some dissociation of the chains followed by their reformation in an ordered array. Glassy Se does crystallize after moderate heating, presumably because of the thermal dissociation of a few Se bonds.

(b) Addition of Te has a catalytic effect on the crystallization of Se. The presence of Te in Se chains probably favours their thermal dissociation, the Se–Te bond being weaker than the Se–Se bond. This makes crystallization easier, by facilitating the close packing of a few Se chains to form a nucleation centre. An enhanced interaction between chains when Te is incorporated is probably also conducive to crystallization.

(c) The effect of Sb in Se is even greater than that of Te in promoting crystallization (see the reduced glass-forming region in Fig 10.5). At first sight this is surprising, because Sb forms three strong bonds and

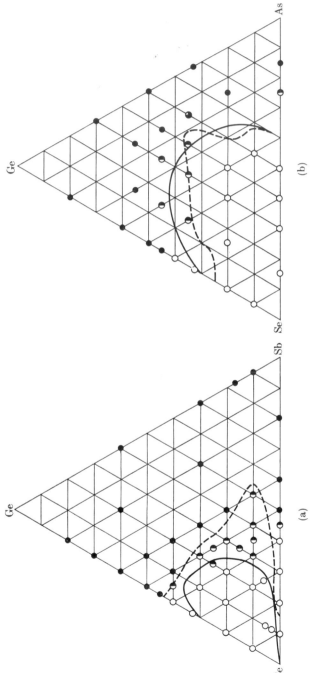

Fig. 10.5. Glass-forming regions and behaviour of conductivity in melts of (a) Se–Ge–Sb and (b) Se–Ge–As. Open dots represent semiconducting behaviour of the melt; solid dots, metallic behaviour. The partly filled dots represent a high conductivity in the melt but with appreciable positive temperature dependence. The glass-forming regions in (a) were determined by air quenching (solid) and water quenching (dotted); in (b) by two different authors (from Haisty and Krebs 1969a,b).

should be effective in cross-linking chains. Haisty and Krebs (1969a) argue that there are weaker bonds that direct themselves towards Se atoms of neighbouring chains. The bonds in these chains are thereby weakened.

(d) Addition of As and Ge inhibits crystallization of Se when these elements are present up to concentrations as high as $\sim$30% and $\sim$60% respectively. Bi has a similar effect. At high concentrations, however, they have the reverse effect, and glasses are not formed by quenching the melts. This is because high-valency elements almost certainly act as branching or cross-linking agents between the chains, leading eventually to the formation of three-dimensional networks. The first effect is thus to prevent an ordering of the chains on cooling the liquid and hence to favour glass formation. However, when the spatial network is strongly developed, as it will be for high concentrations of As or Ge, then, starting from the devitrified solid, melting or softening becomes very difficult. It is possible only by complete disruption of the network rather than thermal dissociation of a relatively few bonds. In Chapter 7 the difference in the structures of crystalline and liquid Ge was cited as the reason for the failure to obtain amorphous Ge by quenching from the melt. The directed sp_3 hybrid bonds in the crystal do not favour atomic displacements: however, a small amount of energy allows conversion to a $p\sigma$ bonding system, which allows greater mobility of atoms, and thus melting. In the case of Ge this results in closer packing and consequently metallic conductivity. Alloys of Ge and As with Se exhibit a similar behaviour. Outside the glass-forming region the melts are metallic; the bonding is such that the atoms are mobile and rearrangement to a crystalline state on cooling is favoured. Near the borderline of the glass-forming region, the melts have a high conductivity but the temperature dependence is that of a semiconductor. Thus the bonding is more localized and rearrangement to a crystalline state is impeded. Glass samples in this range, however, can be crystallized by mild heating.

An increase in the thermal conductivity and also in the velocity of longitudinal acoustic waves on alloying Ge with Se has been observed by Stourac, Vasko, Srb, Musil, and Strba (1968). These authors also report on the growth of an absorption band at 560 cm^{-1}, which they associate with a GeSe$_2$ bond. These observations support the hypothesis that germanium enters a selenium chain substitutionally and acts as a cross-linking element. Thus the weak van der Waals force between the chains is replaced by a strong covalent bond.

10.2. Electrical properties of amorphous selenium and alloys of selenium

10.2.1. Electrical conductivity

Although amorphous selenium can be obtained by quenching the liquid, most electrical measurements have been made on evaporated films. This is because of the commercial applications of selenium in

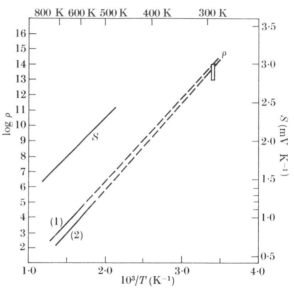

FIG. 10.6. Temperature dependence of resistivity ((1) Henkels and Maczuk 1953; (2) Lizell 1952)) and thermoelectric power (Henkels and Maczuk 1953) in liquid selenium (from Owen 1970) (see also Fig. 3.19).

thin-film form to rectifiers, photocells, the vidicon, and xerography. There is, however, no evidence to suggest significant differences between the properties of films and of bulk samples.

When pure, the conductivity of amorphous selenium is very low ($\sim 10^{-16}\ \Omega^{-1}\,\mathrm{cm}^{-1}$, Hartke 1962) at room temperature. This is not, however, out of line with many other amorphous semiconductors of comparable band gaps (>2 eV), and, as shown in Fig. 7.8, the value of C, if we assume $\sigma = C \exp(-E/kT)$, is estimated to be of order $10^4\ \Omega^{-1}\,\mathrm{cm}^{-1}$. Unfortunately the temperature range over which conductivity measurements can be made is severely limited by the high resistivity at low temperatures, and the low crystallization temperature. Measurements in the liquid state (Fig. 10.6) yield $E = 1\cdot13$ eV and extrapolate to approximately the value of the conductivity commonly found in the glass at room temperature. Thermoelectric-power data (also shown in Fig. 10.6) yield $E = 1\cdot15$ eV if unipolar conduction is assumed.

Differences between reported values for the d.c. conductivity of amorphous selenium can be attributed in part to its sensitivity to the presence of impurities, particularly oxygen. Results of LaCourse,

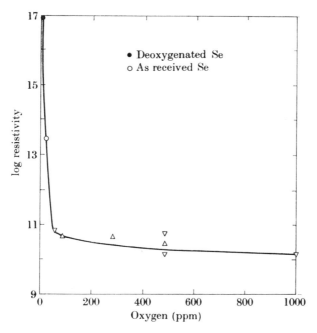

FIG. 10.7. Effects of oxygen on the electrical resistivity of glassy selenium (from LaCourse *et al.* 1970).

Twaddell, and Mackenzie (1970) are shown in Fig. 10.7. The room-temperature resistivity of pure deoxygenated selenium (<2 ppm O_2) according to these authors is about 10^{17} Ω cm and this drops by more than six orders of magnitude with the presence of approximately 50 ppm O_2. Further addition of oxygen (in the form of SeO_2) has little effect. A deoxygenating effect is observed with Si and also with Hg, Ag, Bi, and K. It should be mentioned that the effects of these impurities on the resistivity is probably best attributed to structural modifications rather than to doping in the conventional sense. In Chapter 3 the effect of oxygen on the resistivity of liquid selenium was reported to be just the opposite to that described here for the glass.

In spite of the difficulty of obtaining accurate information on the temperature dependence of the d.c. conductivity, there is a large quantity of useful data available on the transport properties of amorphous selenium. This situation arises mainly from the successful use of the transient drift mobility technique as developed and used on this material by Spear (1957, 1960), Hartke (1962), Tabak (1970), and others. Both hole and electron drift mobilities in thin films have been measured as a function of temperature, pressure, electric field, and sample variables, such as deposition temperature and concentration of additives.

10.2.2. Drift mobilities

The technique for measurement of drift mobilities has been described in Chapter 7 and by Spear (1969). Basically it involves measurement of the time required for a thin sheet of charge carriers, produced by photon or electron irradiation at one surface, to drift across the biased sample. Fig. 10.8 shows the drift mobilities of electrons and of holes in amorphous selenium as a function of temperature (from Hartke 1962). Table 10.1 lists the room-temperature drift mobilities μ_D and activation energies E_D taken from Fig. 10.8 and as determined by other workers. In view of the differences in starting materials and conditions of deposition the consistency of the data is quite remarkable. The spread in the data of Grunwald and Blakney (1968) corresponds to a range in substrate temperatures of 25°–58°C (the activation energies showed an almost linear rise with increase in substrate temperature). The substrates in Tabak's experiments were held at 55°C.

There are at least two plausible explanations for activated drift mobilities. One is that they are trap limited by shallow traps, so that the carriers, during transit through the crystal, are continually trapped in, and thermally released from, localized states lying close to the valence (conduction) band. In this model the transit time observed is larger than it would be in the absence of trapping by the total time a carrier spends in the traps. This is, of course, a function of temperature. In Chapter 7 the relations between the drift mobility μ_D and the conductivity mobility μ_0 in the band of delocalized states were given for a variety of trap distributions. A second possible explanation is that the mobilities determined are conductivity mobilities which are activated because the transport occurs by a hopping process.

In amorphous selenium it is not certain which of these explanations is correct, although the weight of present evidence seems to be in favour

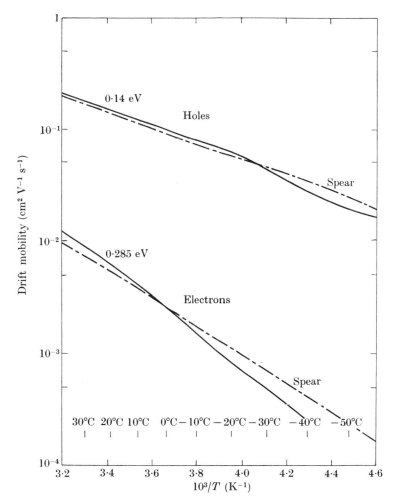

FIG. 10.8. Electron and hole drift mobilities as a function of temperature in amorphous selenium (from Hartke 1962).

of the drift mobility being trap controlled. In any event it is clear that there are basic differences between hole and electron transport. Some observations and deductions concerning the transport processes in amorphous selenium are as follows.

(a) At room temperature, except at low values of the electric field (<100 volts cm^{-1}), no appreciable loss of carriers during transit through the films is found. However, as will be shown below, much higher fields are necessary to ensure that a large proportion of the carriers leave the generation region. Furthermore, the pulse shapes (ramp-like for voltage, rectangular for current) are not rounded, yielding well-defined transit times for both holes and electrons. These observations indicate virtually no spreading of the thin sheet of charge, such as would be obtained if there was a broad spectrum of release times for carriers trapped during transit. They do not, however, rule out a spectrum of trapping levels with release times much less than the transit time.

(b) The drift mobilities are independent of the magnitude of the applied electric field except at low temperatures (<200K).

TABLE 10.1

Drift parameters in amorphous selenium: μ_D is the drift velocity in $cm^2 V^{-1} s^{-1}$, E_D the activation energy in eV.

Electrons		Holes		
μ_D	E_D	μ_D	E_D	Reference
$5\cdot2 \times 10^{-3}$	$0\cdot25$	$0\cdot135$	$0\cdot14$	Spear (1957, 1960)
$7\cdot8 \times 10^{-3}$	$0\cdot285$	$0\cdot165$	$0\cdot14$	Hartke (1962)
$4\cdot5 \times 10^{-3}$	$0\cdot25$	$0\cdot11$	$0\cdot20$	Grunwald and Blakney (1968)
$5\cdot8 \times 10^{-3}$	$0\cdot33$	$0\cdot12$	$0\cdot25$	
$6\cdot0 \times 10^{-3}$		$0\cdot13$		
	$0\cdot33$		$0\cdot16$	Schottmiller, Tabak,
$8\cdot3 \times 10^{-3}$		$0\cdot16$		Lucovsky, and Ward (1970)
		$0\cdot13$		
			$0\cdot23$	Tabak (1970)
		$0\cdot17$		

(c) There is no detectable change in the mobilities or activation energies when a hydrostatic pressure of $4\cdot2$ kbar is applied (Dolezalek and Spear 1970). This is considered to be strong evidence against hopping transport for injected carriers, at least over the temperature range 230K–300K. In other materials such as sulphur and anthracene, where hopping seems probable, a strong pressure effect is observed.

(d) For hole transport neither the magnitude nor activation energy of the drift mobility is affected by alloying with up to 2 % of As (Hartke 1962) or with S. Alloying with Te reduces the room-temperature drift mobility and increases the activation energy.

(e) For electron transport the activation energy associated with the drift mobility is essentially unchanged by light alloying with As, S, or Te. However, the magnitude of the electron drift mobility falls on light alloying with As and Te but not with S.

The alloying effects are shown in Figs. 10.9 and 10.10. In view of the suggested differences between electron and hole transport they will be discussed separately.

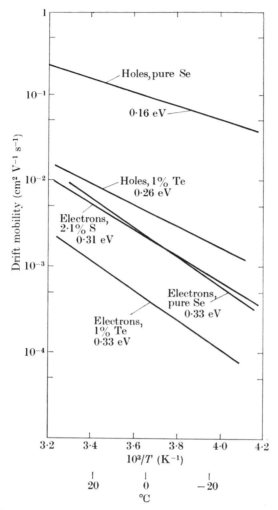

Fɪɢ. 10.9. Temperature dependence of drift mobilities in Se, Se–Te, and Se–S alloys (from Schottmiller *et al.* 1970).

Electron transport. There appears to be some correlation between the presence of Se_8 rings and electron transport. The decrease in the proportion of Se_8 rings on alloying was discussed in § 10.1. Sulphur is less effective than As or Te in decreasing the ring population, and correspondingly the drop in room-temperature drift mobility (Fig. 10.10) is slower (at 12 % S, not shown here, a decrease by a factor of about three occurs). It is not clear whether electron states derived from the Se_8 rings are directly involved in the transport, as suggested by

Schottmiller *et al.* (1970), or whether the effect of their disruption is to increase the disorder elsewhere, for example by distorting Se–Se bonds in chains.

The constancy of E_D, however, suggests that the range of localized states at the conduction-band edge remains unchanged by alloying with the elements shown. Interpretation of the electron drift mobility

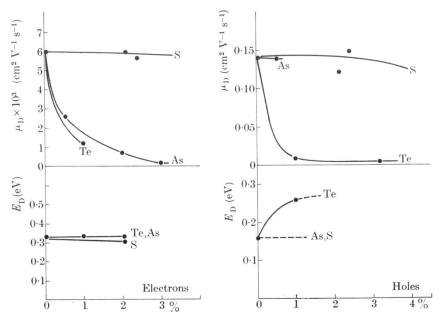

FIG. 10.10. Room-temperature drift mobilities μ_D and activation energies E_D associated with these mobilities in amorphous selenium alloys.

data in terms of epn. (7.11), namely

$$\mu_D = \mu_0(N_c/N_t)\exp\{-(E_D/kT)\},$$

leads, for $\mu_0 = 10$ cm^2 V^{-1} s^{-1} and N_c, the effective density of states at the mobility edge, equal to 10^{20} cm^{-3}, to a value for the density N_t of discrete trapping centres of about 10^{18} cm^{-3} in pure Se. The decrease of μ_D on alloying is then associated with an increase in N_t. On this model, the increase in N_t on alloying with As is found to be approximately equal to the number of As atoms introduced.

Hole transport. It is assumed that the hole drift mobility is, like that of the electrons, shallow-trap limited. However, a calculation of the trap density according to the above equation yields, for pure Se, $N_t \sim 2 \times 10^{19}$ cm^{-3}. In view of the high value of this density, it seems preferable to associate the traps in this case with the range of localized states expected at the top of the valence band. The chain structure in selenium probably gives considerable one-dimensional character to the transport and suggests a very steep rise in the density of states with energy at the band edge (Davis and Mott 1970). Thus the energy range of localized states is expected to be quite small in amorphous selenium. If the activation energy observed for the hole drift mobility ($\sim$0·15 eV for room-temperature substrates) is assumed to be equal to this range, then equation (7.13) yields a value for μ_0 of about 10–20 cm² V⁻¹ s⁻¹. Alloying with 1 % Te reduces the room-temperature drift mobility by more than an order of magnitude to $\sim$9 × 10⁻³ cm² V⁻¹ s⁻¹ (see Fig. 10.10). At the same time the activation energy increases to $\sim$0·26 eV. If this is associated with an increase in the range of localized states produced by disorder, the calculated value of μ_0 for this alloy is about 30 cm² V⁻¹ s⁻¹.

Alloying with S and As might be expected to yield similar behaviour at high concentrations. Unfortunately the hole lifetime decreases so rapidly with these additives (see below) that unambiguous transit-time measurements cannot be made on these alloys.

At low temperatures it becomes improbable for holes once trapped to become re-excited into extended states. The drift mobility should then reflect a transit by hopping between localized states. Tabak (1970) reports that in amorphous Se below 200K the hole transit times become ill-defined and at 178K, for example, approximately 40 % of the total injected charge flows after the first carriers reach the opposite electrode. Furthermore, values of the mobilities determined from such transients become electric-field dependent. Using the smallest transit time to determine mobilities and extrapolating the data to zero electric fields, Tabak finds that the same activation energy E_D is found below 200K as is found above 200K, and concludes that the electric-field dependence of the transit times arises from a field dependence of the trap release times. In contrast, Owen (private communication), using a similar procedure, finds a decreasing gradient of a plot of ln μ_D against $1/T$ as the temperature is lowered, suggesting that a different transport mechanism is occurring. In any case it appears that at low temperatures the majority of carriers cross the sample by hopping, in which case strong electric-field effects are to be expected (§ 7.8).

10.2.3. Carrier lifetimes and ranges

The *range* for carriers injected into a semiconductor is the distance travelled per unit field before loss by trapping into deep levels or by recombination. It is equal to the product of the drift mobility and the carrier lifetime τ. Use of low electric fields in the drift mobility experiments described above can lead to transit times of the order of or less than τ. In this case, the transit pulses become exponential, and it is possible to obtain values of τ from their shape. Using this method Tabak and Warter (1968) determine the following room-temperature

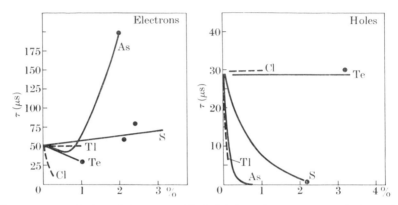

FIG. 10.11. Variation of electron and hole lifetimes in amorphous selenium with light alloying. Data from transient photoconductivity experiments.

values for hole and electron lifetimes in amorphous selenium:

$$\tau_p = 10\text{--}45 \ \mu s, \qquad \tau_n = 40\text{--}50 \ \mu s.$$

These values give room-temperature ranges of

$$1{\cdot}3\text{--}6{\cdot}3 \times 10^{-6} \ cm^2 \ V^{-1} \qquad \text{for holes;}$$

and $\qquad 2{\cdot}4\text{--}3{\cdot}1 \times 10^{-7} \ cm^2 \ V^{-1} \qquad \text{for electrons.}$

It should be noted that the hole lifetime and range as determined by this method are 20–100 times larger than previous estimates by Hartke (1962), who used a probably inappropriate Hecht-type analysis of pulse height against electric field.

The effect of light alloying on the carrier lifetimes is interesting. It should perhaps be stressed that the lifetimes are controlled by deep levels and presumably are not correlated with the shallow-trap-controlled drift mobilities. Figure 10.11 shows that the addition of As, even in small quantities, dramatically reduces the hole lifetime but increases the electron lifetime. The hole lifetime is similarly reduced by alloying with S and Tl, whereas it is essentially unchanged with Te and Cl. The electron lifetime is reduced by alloying with Cl and perhaps Te but is largely unaffected by addition of Tl or S.

A short carrier lifetime makes the measurement of drift mobilities difficult, because of the loss of a significant fraction of the injected charge into deep traps. In the As–Se system for example, no hole transits can be observed in alloys containing from about 2 % to 6 % As. Above 6 % As a transport signal reappears. However, the signals are now of a different character (Schottmiller *et al.* 1970). They are not exponential (which would indicate a lifetime-limited response) nor are they ramp functions (which would indicate transport of a thin sheet of charge). After an initial fast transient their shape is logarithmic, suggesting an effective carrier transit time about five orders of magnitude greater than those observed in amorphous selenium. They are in fact the kind of transits observed in Se at low temperatures and in amorphous As_2S_3 and As_2Se_3 (see Chapter 9).

10.2.4. *Space-charge-limited current measurements*

Information on the density and distribution of trapping levels near the thermal equilibrium Fermi level in amorphous selenium has been obtained by Lanyon and Spear (1961) and Hartke (1962) from measurements of J–V characteristics under space-charge-limited conditions.

Hartke's experimental results on three samples ($\sim 2~\mu$m thick) at room temperature are shown in Fig. 10.12. One electrode (NESA glass) was blocking for electrons, the other (Te or Au) was hole injecting. Above about 1 V, the number of injected holes becomes greater than the normal thermal equilibrium density and the current exceeds that expected for ohmic behaviour.

The J–V characteristics expected under one-carrier space-charge-limited current conditions for various trap distributions near the Fermi level have been outlined by Hartke (1962). The theoretical curve in Fig. 10.12 has been fitted to Hartke's results by Lanyon (1963), assuming an exponential distribution of hole trapping levels, $N(E) = N(0)e^{-E/\Delta}$, where E is measured from the valence-band edge. Such a rate of fall-off in density with energy is expected, under space-charge-limited current conditions, to yield

$$J = \sigma_{\text{th}}(1 + V/V_A)^{\Delta/kT} V/L,$$

where σ_{th} is the thermal equilibrium conductivity, V_A is a constant (proportional to the number of trapped holes when $V = 0$) and L the specimen thickness. Thus an ohmic region ($J \propto V$) is followed by a power law of the form $J \propto V^{(\Delta + kT)/kT}$. Lanyon finds for amorphous selenium $J \propto V^{3 \cdot 8}$; thus $\Delta = 2 \cdot 8kT$. It should be noted that on this interpretation the experimental data probe the trap distribution to only a few tenths of an eV below the thermal equilibrium Fermi level, and it cannot be assumed that the same distribution continues to the mobility edge. If it does, and the density there is $\sim 10^{20}$ cm^{-3} eV^{-1}, then Lanyon's fit suggests that the density of states at the Fermi level ($E \sim 1$ eV) when $V = 0$ is $\sim 10^{20}$ e$^{14\cdot 3}$, i.e. $< 10^{14}$ cm^{-3} eV^{-1}.

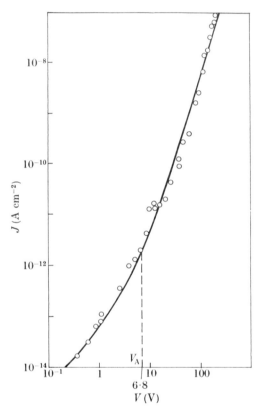

FIG. 10.12. Space-charge-limited conduction in amorphous selenium. Experimental data (○) from Hartke (1962). Theoretical curve (—) from Lanyon (1963).

Other trap distributions can explain the data equally well. Hartke himself proposes that at voltages above about 10 V, the relation $J \propto V\exp(\text{const. } V)$ provides the best fit. This is the relation expected under space-charge-limited current conditions for a uniform distribution in energy of trapping levels. With this interpretation, Hartke estimates a total density of traps $\sim 1\cdot 5$–9×10^{14} cm^{-3} distributed over at least $0\cdot 15$ eV. Müller and Müller (1970) find $\log j \propto F^{\frac{1}{2}}$.

10.3. Optical properties of amorphous selenium and tellurium

The room-temperature optical absorption edges of amorphous selenium and tellurium are compared with those of the crystalline modifications in Fig. 10.13. The exponential portion of the edge in

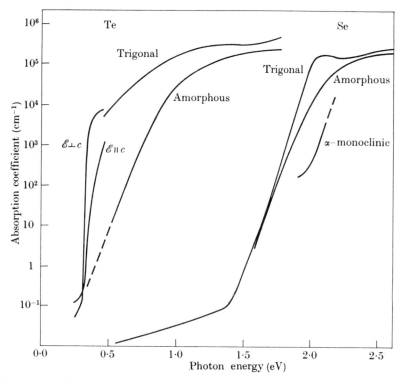

FIG. 10.13. Room-temperature optical absorption edges in amorphous and crystalline tellurium and silicon (from Stuke 1970a).

amorphous selenium is, according to Hartke and Regensburger (1965; see also Fig. 7.27), described by

$$\alpha = 7{\cdot}35 \times 10^{-12}\exp(\hbar\omega/0{\cdot}058 \text{ eV}) \text{ cm}^{-1},$$

although other workers find slightly different parameters. Its position lies between that of the two crystalline modifications of selenium (Prosser 1961; Roberts, Tutihasi, and Keezer 1968). The edge in amorphous tellurium has a similar slope (Keller and Stuke 1965) but its position is considerably displaced towards higher energies relative to the steeper edge in trigonal tellurium (Tutihasi, Roberts, Keezer, and Drews 1969; Grosse 1969). No monoclinic form of Te is known. The larger displacement of the edge in tellurium may be related to the greater interaction between chains in this material.

The temperature dependence of the edge in amorphous and liquid selenium is shown in Fig. 10.14. In the liquid state (above 400K) the slope of the edge is in accord with Urbach's rule (7.6.1). Below room temperature the shift is almost parallel (Knights, private communication) with a temperature coefficient of about -7×10^{-4} eV K^{-1}. In trigonal selenium (Roberts *et al.* 1968) Urbach's rule is observed

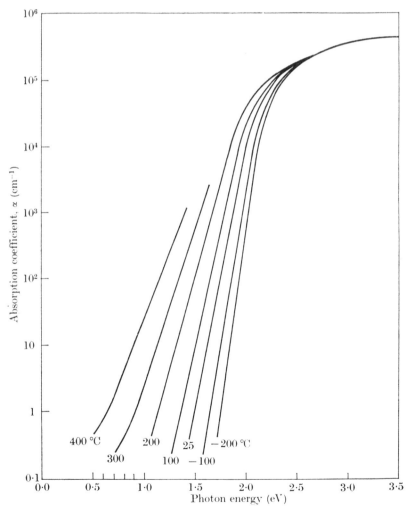

FIG. 10.14. Temperature dependence of the optical absorption edge in amorphous and liquid selenium (from Siemsen and Fenton 1967).

for $\mathscr{E} \perp c$ down to 77K, but a similar value for the indirect edge, observed for $\mathscr{E} \parallel c$, has been inferred (c.f. Weiser and Stuke 1969).

Above the exponential edge, the form of the absorption coefficient in amorphous selenium obeys the relation

$$\alpha\hbar\omega \sim \varepsilon_2(\hbar\omega)^2 \propto (\hbar\omega - E_0),$$

with $E_0 = 2 \cdot 05$ eV at room temperature (Fig. 10.15). This relationship, as opposed to the more common variation with $(\hbar\omega - E_0)^2$, is believed

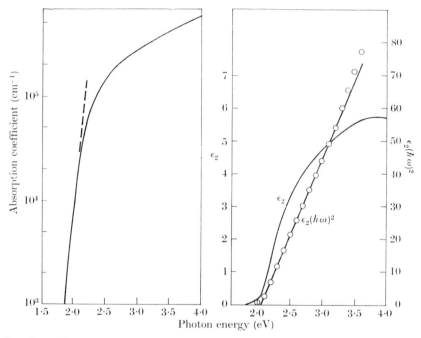

FIG. 10.15. Room-temperature absorption edge in amorphous selenium plotted as α, ϵ_2, and $\epsilon_2(\hbar\omega)^2$ against $\hbar\omega$ (from Davis 1970).

to arise from a sharp rise in the density of states at the band edges (Davis 1970; Davis and Mott 1970), a possibility suggested by the one-dimensional nature of the chain-like structure.

Results of electro-modulated reflectivity experiments at the edge of amorphous and crystalline Se are shown in Fig. 10.16. The sharp electroreflectance signals found for the crystal are absent in amorphous Se. The single broad signal observed near the edge is of opposite sign to that observed near 2 eV in the crystal and furthermore is found to have an opposite temperature dependence. Weiser and Stuke (1969) associate the signal with a Frenkel exciton created on Se_8

rings. Another possibility is that the effect of the electric field ($\sim 2 \times 10^5$ V cm^{-1}) is simply a broadening of the edge in the manner described by Dow and Redfield (1970) (see § 7.6.1). Electroabsorption experiments indicate, however, a parallel shift of the edge (Stuke and Weiser 1966; Drews 1966), as also found in amorphous As_2S_3 by Kolomiets *et al.* (1970) (§ 9.3), and interpreted by these authors in terms of a Franz–Keldysh effect.

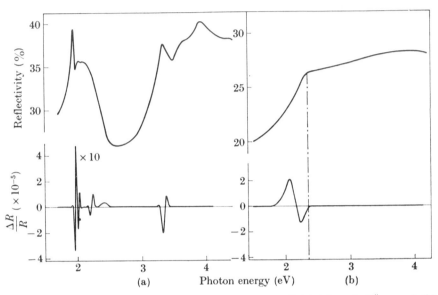

FIG. 10.16. Reflectivity and electroreflectance spectra of (a) trigonal, $\mathscr{E} \parallel c$, and (b) amorphous selenium (from Weiser and Stuke 1969).

The form of the absorption in selenium and tellurium above the fundamental edges is shown in Fig. 10.17. Main features of the spectra for the crystals (trigonal in both cases) can be understood on the basis of the calculated band structures (Treusch and Sandrock 1966; Sandrock 1968) shown in Fig. 10.18. The grouping of the bands into three sets of triplets (originating from atomic p states) divides the absorption spectrum into two parts. This is evident particularly in the case of Se, the ε_2-spectrum of which exhibits a deep minimum near 6 eV for both of the principal directions of polarization with respect to the c-axis (see Fig. 10.19(a)). Monoclinic Se, which has a ring structure but with similar nearest-neighbour distances and bond angles, also displays a minimum near this energy (Leiga 1968). This feature is retained in the amorphous form on account of the preservation of short-range

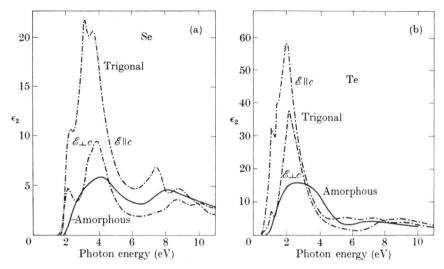

FIG. 10.17. ϵ_2 spectra of amorphous and crystalline (a) selenium, (b) tellurium (from Stuke 1970a).

order in the form of chains and rings. It is worth mentioning that the electronic band structure in the Δ direction ($\Gamma - Z$) of the Brillouin zone (Fig. 10.19(b)) can also be determined by a tight-binding calculation for a single chain, giving similar results (Olechna and Knox 1965). However, the smallest gap occurs in the neighbourhood of the H-point, that is in a direction from Γ corresponding to a crystallographic axis which is neither parallel nor perpendicular to c. The band structure in the direction $H\text{--}K$ is determined to a large extent by interaction between chains. Differences in this interaction between the crystalline and amorphous states probably contribute to the loss of the strong 2 eV peak shown for the crystal in Figs. 10.13 and 10.17.

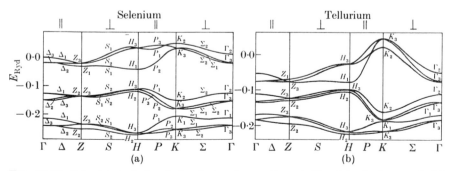

FIG. 10.18. Calculated electronic band structures of crystalline (a) selenium, and (b) tellurium (from Treusch and Sandrock 1966).

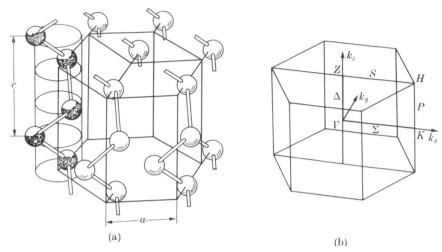

FⅠG. 10.19. (a) Crystal structure of trigonal selenium and tellurium; (b) Brillouin zone.

Apart from this change at the edge, the spectrum for amorphous selenium has been very successfully explained by Kramer, Maschke, Thomas, and Treusch (1970) (see also Maschke and Thomas 1970; Kramer 1970), on the non-direct-transition model discussed in § 7.6. Using the convoluted density of states appropriate to trigonal crystalline Se (Fig. 10.20(a)) and relaxing the k-conservation selection rule for interband transitions, these authors have calculated a

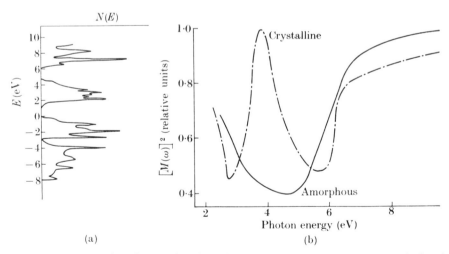

FⅠG. 10.20. (a) Density of states in trigonal selenium, determined from the calculated band structure, part of which was shown in Fig. 10.18. (b) Energy dependence of matrix elements in trigonal and amorphous selenium as calculated by Maschke and Thomas (1970).

spectrum that is in excellent agreement with the experimental curve. With the assumption of a constant value for the matrix elements, the required loss of fine structure is obtained; but to reproduce the relative heights of the two broad maxima seen in Fig. 10.17 it is necessary to use averaged crystalline matrix elements that are functions of energy as shown in Fig. 10.20(b). It should be noted that the crystalline matrix elements before averaging show a pronounced maximum near 4 eV, due to Umklapp enhancement. This is the reason why the absorption

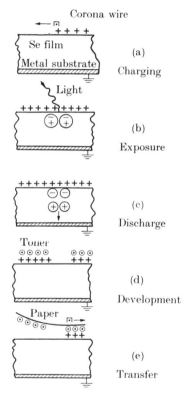

FIG. 10.21. The xerographic process. (a) The photoconducting film is charged positively by a corona discharge induced from a wire, held at a high potential, which is moved parallel to the top surface. (b) The document to be copied is imaged on to the film. Electron–hole pairs are created in the film by strongly absorbed photons reflected from light areas on the document. (c) Under the action of the electric field, the holes drift towards the metal substrate; the electrons move in the opposite direction to neutralize the positive surface charge. (d) Negatively charged 'toner' particles (carbon black dispersed in a low-melting plastic) are cascaded on to the surface, adhering to those areas of the film that have not been discharged. (e) The toner is transferred to paper with the aid of a second corona discharge. The paper is removed and the image made permanent by heating. (For further details of the process see *Xerography and Related Processes* by J. H. Dessauer and H. E. Clark, The Focal Press, New York, 1965.)

in the crystal is so high for these energies. The reduction of this peak in the matrix elements on averaging occurs because only a small region of the Brillouin zone (the top plane H–M–Z) is involved in these particular transitions.

Justification (other than the success of the above calculations) for taking the crystalline density of states to be essentially unchanged in the amorphous phase is provided by electron energy-loss measurements (Robins 1962) and also by synchroton radiation experiments described in Chapter 7 (see Fig. 7.37).

The optical constants of amorphous selenium from the X-ray to the infrared region of the spectrum have been determined by Vasko (1970).

10.4. Photogeneration in amorphous selenium: xerography

The discharge of a selenium (or selenium alloy) film in the electrostatic copying process known as xerography (Fig. 10.21) involves the creation of electron–hole pairs by optical absorption in a thin layer at the surface, and their subsequent separation under the action of an electric field. Transient photoconductivity experiments (Tabak and

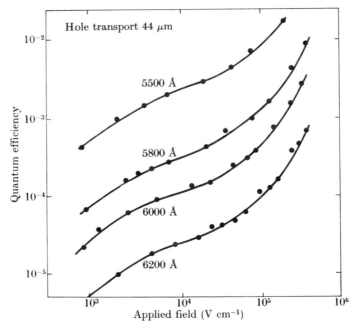

FIG. 10.22. Electric-field dependence of hole quantum efficiency in amorphous selenium at room temperature and four different wavelengths (from Tabak and Warter 1968).

Warter 1968; Pai and Ing 1968) on amorphous selenium have shown that, even for fields sufficiently high that bulk trapping events during transit are negligible, the quantum efficiency of the process is still significantly less than unity. The quantum efficiency, defined as the number of free electron–hole pairs created per absorbed photon, is found to be an increasing function of electric field, temperature, and photon energy. It approaches unity for high values of these parameters.

The dependence of quantum efficiency on photon energy at room temperature and for high values of the electric field has been shown

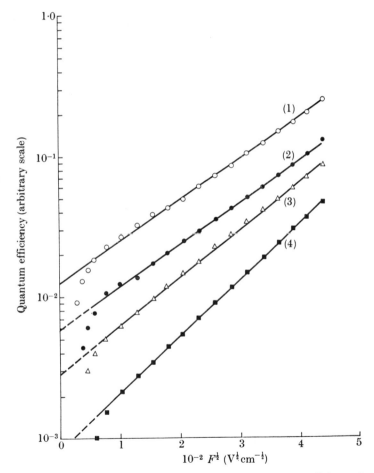

FIG. 10.23. Electric field dependence of relative quantum efficiency in amorphous selenium at $\lambda = 5600$ Å and four different temperatures (from Pai and Ing 1968). Film thickness $d = 15$ μm; $I_{\text{total}} = 7 \cdot 5 \times 10^{14}$ photons m^{-2}; (1) $T = 295$ K, $\beta = 2 \cdot 82 \times 10^{-24}$; (2) $T = 279 \cdot 5$ K, $\beta = 2 \cdot 85 \times 10^{-24}$; (3) $T = 257$ K, $\beta = 2 \cdot 83 \times 10^{-24}$; (4) $T = 224$ K, $\beta = 2 \cdot 85 \times 10^{-24}$.

in Chapter 7, Fig. 7.27. The displacement of this quantum efficiency edge from the optical absorption edge has been discussed in § 7.5.

The electric-field dependence of the quantum efficiency at different photon energies and at room temperature is shown in Fig. 10.22. An approximately linear dependence at low fields becomes exponential above about 10^4 V cm^{-1}. At higher photon energies than those shown here (see Tabak and Warter 1968), the exponential region is absent, and the quantum efficiency shows a tendency to saturate at a value close to unity. The exponential dependence of the quantum efficiency on electric field is shown for one value of the photon energy in Fig. 10.23, which also includes data over a limited temperature range. The quantum efficiency η is thus found to vary according to the relation

$$\eta \propto \exp\{-(E_1 - \beta F^{\frac{1}{2}})/kT\}.$$

Although not strictly independent of T, the coefficient β is within a factor of two of that expected for the Poole–Frenkel mechanism (§ 7.8). However, in the situation normally described by the Poole–Frenkel effect, E_1 is associated with the ground-state energy of a donor (or acceptor) level, whereas E_1 here is found to be a function of photon energy. Following Pai and Ing (1968) we associate E_1 in this situation with the binding energy of the electron–hole pair that exists after thermalization. Its dependence on photon energy, giving rise to the wavelength-dependent quantum efficiency, has been discussed in § 7.5.

Modification to this Poole–Frenkel treatment to include the linear dependence of quantum efficiency on electric field found below $\sim 10^4$ V cm^{-1} has been given by Davis (1970). An alternative description in terms of the Franz–Keldysh effect has been proposed by Lucovsky (1970).

APPENDIX

TABLE A.1

σ, α, R_{H}, and μ_{H} are the electrical conductivity, thermoelectric power, Hall coefficient, and Hall mobility. These data refer to the lowest temperatures in the liquid phase at which measurements were available. In most cases, the temperatures are within a few degrees of the melting points. $R_{\mathrm{HO}} = 1/n_{\mathrm{v}}e$, where $n_{\mathrm{v}} =$ the total density of valence electrons in the liquid. For a given liquid, the data on separate lines refer to different results that do not agree with one another. The symbols separated by commas in the $\mathrm{d}\sigma/\mathrm{d}T$, $\mathrm{d}\,|\alpha|/\mathrm{d}T$, and $\mathrm{d}\,|R_{\mathrm{H}}|/\mathrm{d}T$ columns indicate the signs found in going from the lowest to the highest temperatures. A checkmark in the $\sigma_{\min}$ column indicates the occurrence of a sharp minimum in σ at the given composition as a function of composition. (The authors are grateful to Dr. R. S. Allgaier for preparing this table.)

TABLE A.1

Liquid	σ ($\Omega^{-1}\,\mathrm{cm}^{-1}$)	Sign of $d\sigma/dT$	σ_{min}	α ($\mu\mathrm{V\,K}^{-1}$)	Sign of $d\lvert\alpha\rvert/dT$	R_H ($\mathrm{cm}^3\mathrm{C}^{-1}$)	$\dfrac{R_H}{\lvert R_{HO}\rvert}$	Sign of $d\lvert R_H\rvert/dT$	μ_H ($\mathrm{cm}^2\mathrm{V}^{-1}\mathrm{s}^{-1}$)	References
Na	104 000	−		−7.9	+	-2.5×10^{-4}	−0.98	0	26	B1, C1, G2, K2
K	77 100	−		−14.0	+					C1, K2
GeSi	63 000	−								A2
Ag	58 000	−		+8.5		-1.22×10^{-4}	−1.02	0	7.1	B2, C1, E4
Cu	50 000	−		+16.7		-8.25×10^{-5}	−1.00	0	4.1	B2, C1
Rb	45 500	−		−7.1 / −6.3	+	-4.2×10^{-5}	−0.7		1.9	C1, K2, S2
Li	41 700	−		+21.7	+	-3.9×10^{-5}	−1.00	0	2.0	C1, K2
Al	41 300 / 50 000	−		−2.0	+					B2, C1, M1
Ga	38 800	−		−0.3 / +1.0 / +1.5	+	-3.83×10^{-5}	−0.97	0	1.5	B1, C1, D5 / G2, M1 / C1, E4
Mg	36 500	∼0		+4.5						B2, C1, E4
Au	32 000	−		−1.5		-1.18×10^{-4}	−1.00	0	3.8	B2, C1, D5, / E1, E4, M1
In	30 200	−		−1.0	+	-5.65×10^{-5}	−1.00	0	1.6	B1, C1, E4, / G2, M1
Cd	29 700	0, −		+0.8 / +0.5 / +6.4	+	-7.2×10^{-5}	−0.99	0	2.1	C1, K2, S2
Cs	27 800	−			+ / −					B1, C1, E1 / G2, M1
Zn	26 700	+, −		+0.2	+	-5.2×10^{-5}	−1.01	−, 0 / 0	1.4	C1
Mn	25 000	−								C1, E4, G2, M1
Sn	20 800	−		−0.5	+	-4.4×10^{-5}	−1.00	0	0.92	C1, E2, E4, / G2, M1
Tl	13 700	−		−0.7 / −0.5	+	-4.8×10^{-5}	−0.76	0	0.66	S1
Tl$_4$As	12 800	−		−16	+					C1, G1
Si	12 000 / 16 700	−								

Compound										References
Tl₃Sb	11 900	−		−15	+					S1
Ni	11 800	−		~0	~0					C1
Ge	{ 11 800 / 14 000 / 16 000 }	{ −, ~0 }			+	-3.6×10^{-5}	−1·06	0	0·50	B1, C1, G1 / G2
Hg	11 000	−		−3·5	+	-7.6×10^{-5}	−0·99	0	0·84	B1, C1, G2, M1
Mg₂Sn	10 600	+								G1
GaSb	10 600	−	>	−60	−, +	-3.7×10^{-5}	−0·72	0	0·39	G1
Pb	10 500	−		−3·6	−, −					B1, C1, E4, / G2, M1
InSb	10 000	−	>	{ −20 / +0·4 / −60 }	−, −, −	-5×10^{-5}	−1·0	0	0·5	B2, E2, G1
AlSb	9900	0, +			−					G1
Co	9800	+	>							C1
Mg₂Si	9800	+			+					C1
Fe	9090	−								C1
Sb	8810	−		{ +4·6 / 0 }	+	-4.4×10^{-5}	−1·14	0	0·39	B1, C1, D6, / E4, G2
Mg₂Pb	8600	+								G1
Tl₇Sb₂	8500	+		−22	+					S1
Mg₂Ge	8400	0								G1
GaAs	7900	−			+					B1, C1, E4, / G2, M1
Bi	7810	−		{ −1·2 / −0·7 }	+	-3.0×10^{-5}	−0·69	0	0·23	C1
Ba	7460	−		−19	~0					S1
Tl₃Bi₅	7200	−								G1
InAs	6800	−	>		+					I1
CoTe₂	6000	−	>							D1, D3
Ni₃S₂	5200	+		+20						D4
NiS	5100	+								B2, E2, M3
CdSb	{ 5040 / 5200 }	−, +		~0	−	-8.3×10^{-5}	−1·5	+, 0	0·42	B2, E2, M3
ZnSb	{ 4200 / 5280 / 5400 }	−, +		+3	−	-5.3×10^{-5}	−1·2	0	0·28	B2, E2. I1
Co₄S₃	4100		>							D1

TABLE A.1 CONT.

Liquid	σ (Ω^{-1} cm^{-1})	Sign of $\dfrac{d\sigma}{dT}$	σ_{min}	α (μVK^{-1})	Sign of $\dfrac{d\|\alpha\|}{dT}$	R_H (cm^{3}C^{-1})	$\dfrac{R_H}{\|R_{H0}\|}$	Sign of $\dfrac{d\|R_H\|}{dT}$	μ_H (cm^{2}V^{-1}s^{-1})	References
$AuTe_2$	3440	+				-8.0×10^{-5}	-2.1	0	0.28	E3
Bi_2S_3	3370	−								D4
$CdSnAs_2$	3200	+++								N1
GeTe	2600	++		+21	−	-1.4×10^{-4}	-3.6		0.36	A3, G1
Bi_2Te_3	{2580, 3360}	+		{−3, +4}	{0, +}	-8.7×10^{-5}	-2.2	+, 0	0.29	E2, G1, Z2
$BiTe_2$	2000	++	>							G1
CuTe	{1920, 2200}	++		+60	0	-1.6×10^{-4}	-4.0	0	0.31	D2, E3
Sb_2Te_3	1850	+	>	{+11, +14}	{−, 0; −}	-1.4×10^{-4}	-3.9	0	0.26	E2, G1
Te	1800	{+, 0; +, −}	>	+20	−	-1.26×10^{-4}	-3.3	−	0.23	B1, B2, C2, E2, G1, P2, T1
$NiTe_2$	1400	−								I1
SnTe	{1400, 1800}	+		{+28, +10}	−	{-1.2×10^{-4}, -1.0×10^{-4}}	{−2.7, −2.3}	+, −	0.22	A3, D2, E2, G1
PbTe	{1100, 1520}	+	>	−10	+	-1.0×10^{-4}	-2.1		0.15	A3, G1, I1
$Te_{92}Sb_8$	1050	+++		−35	−	-2.2×10^{-4}	-6	0	0.23	A3, B1
Bi_2Se_3	900	++	>	+80	−					G1
$AgSbTe_2$	850	++								M5
Mg_3Bi_2	800	+++	>							I3
Te_9Se	800	++		+50	−					C2, P2
GaTe	700	+++	>							G1
HgTe	630	+								I1
AgTe	{600, 720}	+		+130	−	-1.3×10^{-3}	-18	−	0.9	D2, E3, E5

BiI	590	+		+10	—,	$-1{\cdot}0\times10^{-3}$	-17	—	0·55	R1, G3
Tl$_{68}$Te$_{32}$	{550 / 700	0, +		-90	0, —					(C4, C5, E2, E3, E5
FeTe$_2$	400	+++								I1
PbSe	{400 / 450			-60	—					G1, G4
FeS	{400 / 1500	—	>							A4, P1
TlTe	350	+	>	+110	—	$-1{\cdot}2\times10^{-3}$	-23	—	0·42	E5, S1
Ag$_2$Se	300	—								G5
Tl$_3$Te$_2$	250	+++	>>	+130	—	$-1{\cdot}8\times10^{-3}$	-33	—	0·45	C4, D7, E5, S1
SnSe$_2$	225			+110	—					G4
Cu$_2$Te	{200 / 500									I1, D2
Cu$_2$Se	200	~0	>	+160	—					I1, G1
Ag$_2$S	200	+, 0								D1
FeO	184	+, 0	>							I2
SnSe	175	+	>	+50	—					G4
Ag$_2$Te	{150 / 250 / 300	+	>	+20 / -200	+, 0 / —	-5×10^{-2}		—	15	D2, D8, G5
PbS	{110 / 220	+								B3, G1
Te$_4$Se	100	++	>	+120	—					P2
Tl$_2$Te	{70 / 156	++		-150	—	$-1{\cdot}6\times10^{-3}$	-28		0·25	C3, C4, E5
Tl$_{53}$Se$_{47}$	50	++	>	+350	—					N2
Cu$_2$S	{45 / 50 / 60			+325						B4, D1, Y1
CdTe	40	++++	>>							G1
ZnTe	40									G1
Bi$_2$I$_3$	39			+85	—					G3, R1
HgSe	32									I1

TABLE A.1 CONT.

Liquid	σ (Ω^{-1}cm^{-1})	Sign of $\dfrac{d\sigma}{dT}$	$\sigma_{\min}$	α (μVK^{-1})	Sign of $\dfrac{d\lvert\alpha\rvert}{dT}$	R_H (cm^{3}C^{-1})	$\dfrac{R_H}{\lvert R_{HO}\rvert}$	Sign of $\dfrac{d\lvert R_H\rvert}{dT}$	μ_H (cm^{2}V^{-1}s^{-1})	References
In$_2$Te$_3$	$\left\{\begin{array}{l}30\\60\end{array}\right.$	$\left\{\begin{array}{l}+,0\\+\end{array}\right.$	$\vee$	$\left\{\begin{array}{l}+30\\+20\end{array}\right.$	$\left\{\begin{array}{l}-,0\\+\end{array}\right.$					G1, Z1
As$_2$Te$_3$	25	+		+200	−					E7
SnS	$\left\{\begin{array}{l}24\\69\end{array}\right.$	+								B5, D4
Ga$_2$Te$_3$	$\left\{\begin{array}{l}10\\30\end{array}\right.$	$\left\{\begin{array}{l}+,0\\+\end{array}\right.$	$\vee$	−100	−					G1, Z1
Te$_7$Se$_3$	8·5	+		+250	−					P2
Tl$_2$Se	$\left\{\begin{array}{l}3·0\\11·7\end{array}\right.$	+	$\vee$	$\left\{\begin{array}{l}+1540\\+100\end{array}\right.$	$\left\{\begin{array}{l}-\\+\end{array}\right.$					N2, S1
Nb$_2$O$_5$	2·5	+	$\vee$							M2
Sb$_2$Se$_3$	2	+		+2	−					K1
Tl$_2$Se$_3$	1·6	+		+360	−					S1
GeS	1·35	+								H2
MoO$_3$	1·2	+		+310	−					A6
TlSe	1·1	+								S1
TeO$_2$	1·1	+								A6
PbO	1·1	+								A6
Te$_3$Se$_2$	0·85	+		+410	−					P2

	ρ							References
CuO	0·4	+						E6
InSe	0·3	+	−100	—				T2
BiI₃	0·28	+						G3
As₂SeTe₂	0·15	+	+500	—	−0.6	—	0·1	E7, M4
TeSe	0·12	+	+690	—				P2
TlS	0·1	+	+580	—				S1
Tl₂S₃	1·7×10⁻²	+	+250	—				S1
As₂Tl₂-Se₃Te	1·5×10⁻²	+	+700	—	−0·5	—	0·1	E7, M4
Tl₄S₃	6·5×10⁻³	+	+1140	—				S1
AsTlSe₂	1×10⁻³	+			−10²	—	0·1	E7, M4
V₂O₅	2×10⁻⁴, 4·6×10⁻², 1·5×10⁻¹	+	+					A6, Y2, Z3
Tl₂S	1×10⁻⁴	+						I1
As₂Se₂Te	5×10⁻⁵	+	+850	—	−1·3×10³	—	0·1	E7, M4
Bi₂O₃	5×10⁻⁵	+	+					I1
Sb₂S₃	2×10⁻⁵, 1·5×10⁻², 2×10⁻¹	+						D4, I1, Y2
Sb₂O₃	1·3×10⁻⁵	+	−100 to +100, +1900	+	−3×10⁵	~0	0·03	A6
Cr₂O₃	6×10⁻⁶	+		—				A6
Se	4×10⁻⁹, 10⁻⁷	+	+					A1, A5, G1, H1, I1
S	<10⁻¹²	+	+					F1

REFERENCES FOR TABLE A1.

A1 ABDULLAEV, G. B., ALIEV, G. M., BARKINKHOEV, KH. G., ASKEROV, CH. M., and LARIONKINA, L. S., *Fizika tverd. Tela* **6**, 1018 (1964). Trans. *Soviet Phys. solid St.* **6**, 786 (1964). (Se.)

A2 ABLOVA, M. S., ELPAT'EVSKAYA, O. D., and REGEL, A. R., *Zh. tekh. Fiz.* **26**, 1366 (1956). Trans. *Soviet Phys. tech. Phys.* **1**, 1337 (1957). (GeSi.)

A3 ANDREEV, A. A. and REGEL', A. R. *Fizika tekh. Poluprov.* **1**, 1832 (1967). Trans. *Soviet Phys. Semicond.* **1**, 1513 (1968). (GeTe, SnTe, PbTe, Te$_{92}$Sb$_8$.)

A4 ARGYRIADES, D., DERGE, G., and POUND, G. M. *Am. Inst. Min. metall. Engrs Trans.* **215**, 909 (1959). (FeS.)

A5 ALIEV, G. M., ABDINOV, D. SH., and MEKHTIEVA, S. I. *Dokl. Akad. Nauk SSSR* **167**, 782 (1966). Trans. *Soviet Phys. Dokl.* **11**, 305 (1966). (Se.)

A6 VAN ARKLE, A., FLOOD, E. A., and BRIGHT, N. *Can. J. Chem.* **31**, 1009 (1953). (MoO$_3$, TeO$_2$, PbO, V$_2$O$_5$, Sb$_2$O$_3$, Cr$_2$O$_3$.)

B1 BUSCH, G. and TIÈCHE, Y. *Phys. kondens. Materie* **1**, 78 (1963). (Liquid metals and semiconductors.)

B2 BUSCH, G. and GÜNTHERODT, H.-J. *Phys. kondens. Materie* **6**, 325 (1967). (Liquid metals and alloys.)

B3 BELL, M. C. and FLENGAS, S. N. *J. electrochem. Soc.* **113**, 31 (1966). (PbS.)

B4 BOURGON, M., DERGE, G., and POUND, G. M. *Am. Inst. Min. metall. Engrs Trans.* **209**, 1454 (1957). (Cu$_2$S.)

B5 BOUTIN, D. and BOURGON, M. *Can. J. Chem.* **39**, 915 (1961). (SnS.)

C1 CUSACK, N. E. *Rep. Prog. Phys.* **26**, 361 (1963). (Liquid metals.)

C2 CUTLER, M. and MALLON, C. E. *J. chem. Phys.* **37**, 2677 (1962). (Te-Se.)

C3 CUTLER, M. and MALLON C. E. *J. appl. Phys.* **36**, 201 (1965). (Tl–Te.)

C4 CUTLER, M. and MALLON, C. E. *Phys. Rev.* **144**, 642 (1966). (Tl–Te.)

C5 CUTLER, M. and FIELD, M. B. *Phys. Rev.* **169**, 632 (1968). (Tl–Te.)

D1 DANCY, E. A. and DERGE, G. J. *Am. Inst. Min. metall. Engrs Trans.* **227**, 1034 (1963). (Co$_4$S$_3$, Ni$_3$S$_2$, Cu$_2$S.)

D2 DANCY, E. A. *Am. Inst. Min. metall. Engrs* **233**, 270 (1965). (Cu–Te, Ag–Te, Sn–Te.)

D3 DANCY, E. A., PASTOREK, R. L., and DERGE, G. J. *Am. Inst. Min. metall. Engrs Trans.* **233**, 1645 (1965). (Ni$_3$S$_2$.)

D4 DELIMARSKI, YU. K. and VELIKANOV, A. A. *Zh. neorg. Khim.* **3**, 1075 (1958). (SnS, Sb$_2$S$_3$, Bi$_2$S$_3$, NiS.)

D5 DUTCHAK, YA. I. and PROKHORENKO, V. YA. *Ukr. fiz. Zh.* **12**, 2057 (1967). Trans. *Ukr. phys. J.* **12**, 1957 (1969). (Ga, In.)

D6 DUTCHAK, YA. I. and STETS'KIV, O. P. *Fizika Metall.* **22**, 123 (1966). Trans. *Physics Metals Metallogr., N.Y.* **22**, 126 (1967). (Sb.)

D7 DONALLY, J. M. and CUTLER, M. *Phys. Rev.* **176**, 1003 (1968). (Tl–Te.)

D8 DONG, N. V. and TUNG, P. N. *Phys. Stat. Solidi* **30**, 557 (1968). (Ag$_2$Te.)

E1 ENDERBY, J. E. *Proc. phys. Soc.* **81**, 772 (1963). (Liquid metals.)

E2 ENDERBY, J. E. and WALSH, L. *Phil. Mag.* **14**, 991 (1966). (CdSb, ZnSb, Bi$_2$Te$_3$, Sb$_2$Te$_3$, Te, Tl$_2$Te, SnTe.)

E3 ENDERBY, J. E., HASAN, S. B., and SIMMONS, C. J. *Adv. Phys.* **16**, 667 (1967). (AuTe$_2$, AgTe, CuTe.)

E4 ENDERBY, J. E., VAN ZYTVELD, J. B., HOWE, R. A., and MIAN, A. J. *Phys. Lett.* **A28**, 144 (1968). (Metals.)

E5 ENDERBY, J. E. and SIMMONS, C. J. *Phil. Mag.* **20**, 125 (1969). (Tl–Te, AgTe.)

E6 ESIN, O. A. and ZYAZEV, V. L. *Zh. neorg. Khim.* **2**, 1998 (1957). (CuO.)

E7 EDMOND, J. T. *Br. J. appl. Phys.* **17**, 979 (1966). (As$_2$Te$_3$.)

F1 FEHER, F. and LUTZ, H. D. *Z. anorg. allg. Chem.* **333**, 216 (1964). (S.)

G1 GLAZOV, V. M., CHIZHEVSKAYA, S. N., and GLAGOLEVA, N. N. *Liquid Semiconductors*. Nauka Press, Moscow (1967). English translation, revised edition, Plenum Press, New York (1969).

G2 GREENFIELD, A. J. *Phys. Rev.* A **135**, 1589 (1964). (Metals.)

G3 GRANTHAM, L. F. and YOSIM, S. J. *J. chem. Phys.* **38**, 1671 (1963). (Bi–I.)

G4 GLAZOV, V. M. and SITULINA, O. V. *Dokl. Akad. Nauk SSSR* **187**, 799 (1969). (Pb–Se, Sn–Se.)

G5 GLAZOV, V. M., MAKHMUDOVA, N. M., and KRESTOVNIKOV, A. N. *Neorg. Mater.* **5**, 1185 (1969). (Ag_2Se.)

H1 HENKELS, H. W. and MACZUK, J. *J. appl. Phys.* **24**, 1056 (1953). (Se.)

H2 HANDFIELD, G., D'AMBOISE, M., and BOURGON, M. *Can. J. Chem.* **44**, 853 (1966). (GeS.)

I1 IOFFE, A. F. and REGEL, A. R. *Prog. Semicond.* **4**, 239 (1960).

I2 INOUYE, H., CHIPMAN, J., and TOMLINSON, J. W. *Trans. Faraday Soc.* **49**, 796 (1953). (FeO.)

I3 ILSCHNER, B. R. and WAGNER, C. *Acta Metall.* **6**, 712 (1958). (Mg_3Bi_2.)

K1 KAZANDZHAM, B. I. *Fizika tekh. Poluprov.* **2**, 400 (1968). Trans. *Soviet Phys. Semicond.* **2**, 329 (1968). (Sb_2Se_3.)

K2 KENDALL, P. W. *Phys. Chem. Liquids* **1**, 33 (1968). (Metals.)

M1 MARWAHA, A. S. *Adv. Phys.* **16**, 617 (1967). (Metals.)

M2 MANAKOV, A. I., ESIN, O. A., and LEPINSKIKH, B. M. *Zh. neorg. Khim.* **7**, 2220 (1962). Trans. *Russ. J. inorg. Chem.* **7**, 1149 (1962). (Nb_2O_5.)

M3 MILLER, E., PACES, J., and KOMAREK, K. L. *Am. Inst. Min. metall. Engrs Trans.* **230**, 1557 (1964). (CdSb.)

M4 MALE, J. C. *Br. J. appl. Phys.* **18**, 1543 (1967). (As_2Se_2Te, As_2SeTe_2, $AsTlSe_2$, $As_2Tl_2Se_3Te$.)

M5 MAL'SAGOV, A. U. *Neorg. Mater.* **4**, 1593 (1968). Trans. *Inorg. Mater.* **4**, 1389 (1968). ($AgSbTe_2$.)

N1 NIKOL'SKAYA, G. F., BERGER, L. I., EVFIMOVSKII, I. V., KAGIROVA, G. N., SHCHUKINA, I. K., and KOVALEVA, I. S. *Neorg. Mater.* **2**, 1876 (1966). Trans. *Inorg. Mater.* **2**, 1622 (1966). ($CdSnAs_2$.)

N2 NAKAMURA, Y. and SHIMOJI, M. *Trans. Faraday Soc.* **65**, 1509 (1969). (Tl–Se.)

P1 POUND, G. M., DERGE, G., and OSUCH, G. *Am. Inst. Min. metall. Engrs Trans.* **203**, 481 (1955). (FeS.)

P2 PERRON, J. C. *Adv. Phys.* **16**, 657 (1967). (Te–Se.)

R1 RALEIGH, D. O. *J. chem. Phys.* **41**, 3179 (1964). (Bi–T.)

S1 STONEBURNER, D. F. *Am. Inst. Min. metall. Engrs Trans.* **233**, 153 (1965). (Metals and semiconductors.)

S2 SUNDSTRÖM, L. J. *Phil. Mag.* **11**, 657 (1965). (Metals.)

T1 TIÈCHE, Y. and ZAREBA, A. *Phys. kondens. Materie* **1**, 402 (1963). (Te.)

T2 TIÈCHE, Y. and ZAREBA, A. *Phys. Stat. Solidi* **14**, K139 (1966). (InSe.)

Y1 YANG, L., POUND, G. M., and DERGE, G. *Am. Inst. Min. metall. Engrs Trans.* **206**, 783 (1956). (Cu_2S.)

Y2 YURKOV, V. A. *Zh. éksp. teor. Fiz.* **22**, 223 (1952). (V_2O_5, Sb_2S_3.)

Z1 ZHUZE, V. P. and SHELYKH, A. I. *Fizika tverd. Tela* **7**, 1175 (1965). Trans. *Soviet Phys. solid St.* **7**, 942 (1965). (In_2Te_3, Ga_2Te_3.)

Z2 ZHUZE, A. P. and REGEL', A. R. *Proceedings of the International Conference on Semiconductor Physics*, p. 929. Publishing House of the Czechoslovak Academy of Sciences, Prague (1961). (Bi_2Te_3.)

Z3 ZYAZEV, V. L. and ESIN O. A. *Zh. tekh. Fiz.* **28**, 18 (1958). Trans. *Soviet Phys. tech Phys.* **3**, 15 (1958). (V_2O_5.)

REFERENCES

ABKOWITZ, M. (1967). *J. chem. Phys.* **46**, 4537.

ABRAHÁM, A., GREGORA, I., HRUBÝ, A., MATYÁŠ, M., ŠTOURAČ, L., TAUC, J., VORLÍČEK, V., and ZÁVĚTOVÁ, M. (1970). *Proceedings of the 10th international conference on the physics of semiconductors, Cambridge, Massachusetts* (ed. S. P. Keller, J. C. Hensel, and F. Stern), p. 784. United States Atomic Energy Commission.

ACRIVOS, J. V. and MOTT, N. F. (1971). *Phil. Mag.* in press.

ADAMS, P. D. and KRAVITZ, S. (1961). Unpublished, *internal report*, Department of Metallurgy, Imperial College, London.

ADKINS, C. J., FREAKE, S. M., and HAMILTON, E. M. (1970). *Phil. Mag.* **22**, 183.

ADLER, D. (1968). *Solid St. Phys.* **21**, 1.

—— COHEN, M. H., FAGEN, E. A., and THOMPSON, J. C. (1970). *J. non-cryst. Solids* **3**, 402.

AFROMOWITZ, M. A. and REDFIELD, D. (1968). *Proceedings of the 9th international conference on the physics of semiconductors, Moscow*, p. 98. Nauka, Leningrad.

ALDEA, A. (1971). *Z. Phys.* in press.

ALEXANDER, M. N. and HOLCOMB, D. F. (1968). *Rev. mod. Phys.* **40**, 815.

ALLCOCK, G. R. (1956). *Adv. Phys.* **5**, 412.

ALLGAIER, R. S. (1969). *Phys. Rev.* **185**, 227.

—— (1970). *Phys. Rev.* B **2**, 2257.

—— and HOUSTON, B. B. (1962). *Proceedings of the international conference on the physics of semiconductors, Exeter*, p. 172. The Institute of Physics and The Physical Society, London.

—— and SCANLON, W. W. (1958). *Phys. Rev.* **111**, 1029.

AMITAY, M. and POLLAK, M. (1966). *Proceedings of the international conference on the physics of semiconductors, Kyoto. J. phys. Soc. Japan* (Suppl.) **21**, 549.

AMRHEIN, E. M. and MUELLER, F. H. (1968). *Trans. Faraday Soc.* **64**, 666.

ANDERSON, P. W. (1958). *Phys. Rev.* **109**, 1492.

—— (1970). *Comments Solid St. Phys.* **2**, 193.

ANDREWS, P. V., WEST, M. B., and ROBESON, C. R. (1969). *Phil. Mag.* **19**, 887.

ANDREYCHIN, R. (1970). *J. non-cryst. Solids* **4**, 73.

—— GETOV, G. K., and SIMIDCHIEVA, P. A. (1966). *Soviet Phys. solid St.* **8**, 1546.

—— NIKIFOROVA, M., and SIMIDCHIEVA, P. (1968). *C. r. Acad. bulg. Sci.* **21**, 753.

ANDRIESH, A. M. and KOLOMIETS, B. T. (1965). *Soviet Phys. solid St.* **6**, 2652.

ANIMALU, A. O. E. and HEINE, V. (1965). *Phil. Mag.* **12**, 1249.

ANTONOV, V. N., KOPAEV, YU. V., PASHINTSEV, YU. I., and RAKOV, A. V. (1969). *Soviet Phys. solid St.* **11**, 1160.

APPEL, J. (1968). *Solid St. Phys.* **21**, 193.

ASHCROFT, N. W. (1966). *Phys. Lett.* **23**, 529.

ASHCROFT, N. W. and LEKNER, J. (1966). *Phys. Rev.* **145**, 83.
AUSTIN, I. G. (1962). *Phil. Mag.* **7**, 961.
—— and GARBETT, E. S. (1971). *Phil. Mag.* **23**, 17.
—— and MOTT, N. F. (1969). *Adv. Phys.* **18**, 41.
AXMANN, A., GISSLER, W., KOLLMAR, A., and SPRINGER, T. (1971). *Discuss. Faraday Soc.* No. 50. In press.
BAARS, J. W. (1967). *II–VI semiconducting compounds* (ed. D. G. Thomas), p. 631. Benjamin, New York.
BABER, W. G. (1937). *Proc. R. Soc.* A **158**, 383.
BAHL, S. K. and CHOPRA, K. L. (1969). *J. appl. Phys.* **40**, 4940.
—— —— (1970). *J. appl. Phys.* **41**, 2196.
BAIDAKOV, L. A., BORISOVA, Z. U., and IPATEVA, V. V. (1962). *Vest. leningr. gos. Univ. Ser. Fiz I Khim* **4**, no. 22, 90.
BALLENTINE, L. E. (1965). Ph.D. thesis, Cambridge.
—— (1966). *Can. J. Phys.* **44**, 2533.
BANUS, M. D. and REED, T. B. (1970). *The chemistry of extended defects in non-metallic solids* (ed. LeRoy Eyring and M. O'Keefe), p. 488. North-Holland, Amsterdam.
BANYAI, L. (1964). *Physique des semiconducteurs* (ed. M. Hulin), p. 417. Dunod, Paris.
—— and ALDEA, A. (1966). *Phys. Rev.* **143**, 652.
BARDASIS, A. and HONE, D. (1967). *Phys. Rev.* **153**, 849.
BARDEEN, J. and SHOCKLEY, W. (1950). *Phys. Rev.* **80**, 72.
BEAGLEHOLE, D. and ZAVETOVA, M. (1970). *J. non-cryst. Solids* **4**, 272.
BECKMAN, O., HANAMURA, E., and NEURINGER, L. J. (1967). *Phys. Rev. Lett.* **18**, 773.
BEEBY, J. L. (1964). *Proc. R. Soc.* A **279**, 82.
BELL, R. J., BIRD, N. F., and DEAN, P. (1968). *J. Phys. C: Solid St. Phys.* **1**, 299.
—— and DEAN, P. (1971). *Discuss. Faraday Soc.* No. 50. In press.
BERGLUND, C. N. and SPICER, W. E. (1964). *Phys. Rev.* **136**, A1044.
BETTS, F., BIENENSTOCK, A., and OVSHINSKY, S. R. (1970). *J. non-cryst. Solids* **4**, 554.
BHATIA, A. B. and KRISHNAN, K. S. (1948). *Proc. R. Soc.* A **194**, 185.
BISHOP, S. G., TAYLOR, P. C., MITCHELL, D. L., and SLACK, L. H. (1971). *J. non-cryst. Solids* **5**, 351.
BLAKEMORE, J. S. (1962). *Semiconductor statistics*. Pergamon Press, London.
BLINOWSKI, J. and MYCIELSKI, J. (1964). *Phys. Rev.* A **136**, 266.
BÖER, K. W. (1970). *J. non-cryst. Solids* **4**, 583.
—— and HAISLIP, R. (1970a). *Phys. Rev. Lett.* **24**, 230.
BOGOMOLOV, V. N., KUDINOV, E. K., and FIRSOV, YU. A. (1968). *Soviet Phys. solid St.* **9**, 2502.
BONCH-BRUEVICH, V. L. (1970a). *J. non-cryst. Solids* **4**, 410.
—— (1970b). *Phys. Stat. Solidi* **42**, 35.
BORLAND, R. E. (1963). *Proc. R. Soc.* A **274**, 529.
BOSMAN, A. J. and CREVECOEUR, C. (1966). *Phys. Rev.* **144**, 763.
—— and VAN DAAL, H. J. (1970). *Adv. Phys.* **19**, 1.

BRADLEY, C. C., FABER, T. E., WILSON, E. G., and ZIMAN, J. M. (1962). *Phil. Mag.* **7**, 865.

BRIEGLEB, G. (1929). *Z. phys. Chem.* A **144**, 321.

BRINKMAN, W. F. and RICE, T. M. (1970a). *Phys. Rev.* B **2**, 1324.

—— —— (1970b). *Phys. Rev.* B **2**, 4302.

BRINSON, M. E. and DUNSTAN, W. (1970). *J. Phys. C: Solid St. Phys.* **3**, 483.

BRODSKY, M. H. and TITLE, R. S. (1969). *Phys. Rev. Lett.* **23**, 581.

—— —— WEISER, K., and PETTIT, G. D. (1970). *Phys. Rev.* B **1**, 2632.

BRUST, D. (1969). *Phys. Rev. Lett.* **23**, 1232.

BUNKER, D. L. (1964). *J. chem. Phys.* **40**, 1946.

BUSCH, G., GÜNTHERODT, H. J., KÜNZI, H. U., and SCHWEIGER, A. (1970). *Phys. Lett.* A **33**, 64.

CABANE, B. and FRIEDEL, J. (1971). *J. Phys., Paris* **32**, 73.

—— and FROIDEVAUX, C. (1969). *Phys. Lett.* **29A**, 512.

CALLAERTS, R., DENAYER, M., HASHMI, F. H., and NAGELS, P. (1971). *Discuss. Faraday Soc.* No. 50. In press.

CARDONA, M. (1969). Modulation spectroscopy. *Solid St. Phys. Suppl. 11.* Academic Press, New York.

—— GUDAT, W., SONNTAG, B., and YU, P. Y. (1970). *Proceedings of the 10th international conference on the physics of semiconductors, Cambridge, Massachusetts* (ed. S. P. Keller, J. C. Hensel, and F. Stern), p. 209. United States Atomic Energy Commission.

CARON, L. G. and PRATT, G. W. (1968). *Rev. mod. Phys.* **40**, 802.

CASTELLAN, G. W. and SEITZ, F. (1951). *Semi-conducting materials (Proceedings of a conference at the University of Reading)* (ed. H. K. Henisch), p. 8. Butterworths Scientific Publications, London.

CATTERALL, J. A. and TROTTER, J. (1963). *Phil. Mag.* **8**, 897.

CATTERALL, R. (1970). *Phil. Mag.* **22**, 779.

—— and MOTT, N. F. (1969). *Adv. Phys.* **18**, 665.

ČERVINKA, L., HOSEMANN, R., and VOGEL, W. (1970). *J. non-cryst. Solids* **3**, 294.

—— HRUBÝ, A., MATYÁŠ, M., ŠIMEČEK, T., ŠKÁCHA, J., ŠTOURAČ, L., TAUC, J., VORLÍČEK, V., and HÖSCHL, P. (1970). *J. non-cryst. Solids* **4**, 258.

CHEN, H. S. and WANG, T. T. (1970). *Phys. Stat. Solidi (a)* **2**, 79.

CHEN, I. (1970). *Phys. Rev.* B **2**, 1053, 1060.

CHITTICK, R. C. (1970). *J. non-cryst. Solids* **3**, 255.

—— ALEXANDER, J. H., and STERLING, H. F. (1969). *J. electrochem. Soc.* **116**, 77.

CHO, S. J. (1967). *Phys. Rev.* **157**, 632.

—— (1970). *Phys. Rev.* B **1**, 4589.

CHOPRA, K. L. (1969). *Thin film phenomena.* McGraw-Hill, New York.

—— and BAHL, S. K. (1969). *J. appl. Phys.* **40**, 4171.

—— —— (1970). *Phys. Rev.* B **1**, 2545.

CHROBOCZEK, J. A., PROHOFSKY, E. W., and SLADEK, R. J. (1968). *Phys. Rev.* **169**, 593.

—— and TRYLSKI, J. (1970). *J. non-cryst. Solids* **4**, 200.

CIMPL, Z., KOSEK, F., and MATYÁS, M. (1970). *Phys. Stat. Solidi* **41**, 535.
CLARK, A. H. (1967). *Phys. Rev.* **154**, 750.
COHEN, M. H. (1970). *J. non-cryst. Solids* **2**, 432 and **4**, 391.
—— FRITZSCHE, H., and OVSHINSKY, S. R. (1969). *Phys. Rev. Lett.* **22**, 1065.
—— and THOMPSON, J. C. (1968). *Adv. Phys.* **17**, 857.
COLEMAN, M. V. and THOMAS, D. J. D. (1968). *Phys. Stat. Solidi* **25**, 241.
COLLINGS, E. W. (1969). *Phys. kondens. Materie* **8**, 284.
CONWELL, E. M. (1956). *Phys. Rev.* **103**, 51.
COOK, B. E. and SPEAR, W. E. (1969). *J. Phys. Chem. Solids* **30**, 1125.
CREVECOEUR, C. and DE WIT, H. J. (1968). *Solid St. Commun.* **6**, 295.
CROITORU, N. and VESCAN, L. (1969). *Thin Solid Films* **3**, 269.
—— —— POPESCU, C., and LĂZĂRESCU, M. (1970). *J. non-cryst. Solids*
   4, 493.
CUMMING, J. B., KATCOFF, S., PORILE, N. T., TANAKA, S., and WYTTENBACH,
   A. (1964). *Phys. Rev.* **134**, B1262.
CUSACK, N. E. (1963). *Rep. Prog. Phys.* **26**, 361.
CUTLER, M. (1971). *Phil. Mag.* To be published.
—— and FIELD, M. B. (1968). *Phys. Rev.* **169**, 632.
—— and LEAVY, J. F. (1964). *Phys. Rev.* **133**, A1153.
—— and MALLON, C. E. (1965). *J. appl. Phys.* **36**, 201.
—— and MOTT, N. F. (1969). *Phys. Rev.* **181**, 1336.
D'ALTROY, F. A. and FAN, H. Y. (1956). *Phys. Rev.* **103**, 1671.
DARBY, J. K. and MARCH, N. H. (1964). *Proc. phys. Soc.* **84**, 591.
DASH, W. C. and NEWMAN, R. (1955). *Phys. Rev.* **99**, 1151.
DAVIS, E. A. (1970). *J. non-cryst. Solids* **4**, 107.
—— and COMPTON, W. D. (1965). *Phys. Rev.* **140**, A2183.
—— and MOTT, N. F. (1970). *Phil. Mag.* **22**, 903.
—— and SHAW, R. F. (1970). *J. non-cryst. Solids* **2**, 406.
DE BOER, J. H. and VERWEY, E. J. W. (1937). *Proc. phys. Soc.* A **49**, 59.
DE GENNES, P. G. (1960). *Phys. Rev.* **118**, 141.
—— and FRIEDEL, J. (1958). *J. Phys. Chem. Solids* **4**, 71.
DES CLOIZEAUX, J. (1965). *J. Phys. Chem. Solids* **26**, 259.
DÉVÉNYI, A., BELU, A., and KORONY, G. (1970). *J. non-cryst. Solids* **4**, 380.
DEXTER, D. L. (1967). *Phys. Rev. Lett.* **19**, 1383.
—— and KNOX, R. S. (1965). *Excitons.* Interscience, New York.
DOLEZALEK, F. K. and SPEAR, W. E. (1970). *J. non-cryst. Solids* **4**, 97.
DOMB, C. (1970). *J. Phys. C: Solid St. Phys.* **3**, 256.
DONIACH, S. (1969). *Adv. Phys.* **18**, 819.
DONOVAN, T. M., ASHLEY, E. J., and SPICER, W. E. (1970). *Phys. Lett.* A **32**,
   85.
—— and SPICER, W. E. (1968). *Phys. Rev. Lett.* **21**, 1572.
—— —— and BENNETT, J. M. (1969). *Phys. Rev. Lett.* **22**, 1058.
—— —— —— and ASHLEY, E. J. (1970). *Phys. Rev.* B **2**, 397.
DOVE, D. B., HERITAGE, M. B., CHOPRA, K. L., and BAHL, S. K. (1970). *Appl.
   Phys. Lett.* **16**, 138.
DOW, J. D. and REDFIELD, D. (1970). *Phys. Rev.* B **1**, 3358.
DRAKE, C. F. and SCANLAN, I. F. (1970). *J. non-cryst. Solids* **4**, 234.

DREWS, R. E. (1966). *Appl. Phys. Lett.* **9**, 347.

—— DAVIS, E. A., and LEIGA, A. G. (1967). *Phys. Rev. Lett.* **18**, 1194.

DRICKAMER, H. G., LYNCH, R. W., CLENDENEN, R. L., and PEREZ-ALBUERNE, E. A. (1966). *Solid St. Phys.* **19**, 135.

DURKAN, J., ELLIOTT, R. J., and MARCH, N. H. (1968). *Rev. mod. Phys.* **40**, 812.

DUSSEL, G. A. and BÖER, K. W. (1970). *Phys. Stat. Solidi* **39**, 375.

ECKENBACH, W., FUHS, W., and STURKE, J. (1971). *J. non-cryst. Solids* **5**, 264.

ECONOMOU, E. N. and COHEN, M. H. (1970). *Phys. Rev. Lett.* **24**, 218.

EDMOND, J. T. (1966). *Br. J. appl. Phys.* **17**, 979.

—— (1968). *J. non-cryst. Solids* **1**, 39.

EDWARDS, S. F. (1958). *Phil. Mag.* **3**, 1020.

—— (1961). *Phil. Mag.* **6**, 617.

—— (1962). *Proc. R. Soc.* A **267**, 518.

—— (1970). *J. non-cryst. Solids* **4**, 417.

EMIN, D. and HOLSTEIN, T. (1969). *Ann. Phys.* **53**, 439.

ENDERBY, J. E. and COLLINGS, E. W. (1970). *J. non-cryst. Solids* **4**, 161.

—— and HOWE, R. A. (1968). *Phil. Mag.* **18**, 923.

—— NORTH, D. M., and EGELSTAFF, P. A. (1966). *Phil. Mag.* **14**, 961.

—— and SIMMONS, C. J. (1970). *Phil. Mag.* **20**, 125.

EVANS, B. L. and YOUNG, P. A. (1967). *Proc. R. Soc.* A **297**, 230.

EVANS, R. (1970). *J. Phys. C: Solid St. Phys.* **3**, S137.

FABER, T. E. (1966). *Adv. Phys.* **15**, 547.

—— (1967). *Adv. Phys.* **16**, 637.

—— (1971). *An introduction to the theory of liquid metals.* Cambridge University Press. In preparation.

—— and ZIMAN, J. M. (1965). *Phil. Mag.* **11**, 153.

FAGEN, E. A. and FRITZSCHE, H. (1970*a*). *J. non-cryst. Solids* **2**, 170, 180.

—— —— (1970*b*). *J. non-cryst. Solids* **4**, 480.

—— HOLMBERG, S. H., SEGUIN, R. W., THOMPSON, J. C., and FRITZSCHE, H. (1970). *Proceedings of the 10th international conference on the physics of semiconductors, Cambridge, Massachusetts* (ed. S. P. Keller, J. C. Hensel, and F. Stern), p. 672. United States Atomic Energy Commission.

FAN, H. Y. (1951). *Phys. Rev.* **82**, 900.

FELTY, E. J., LUCOVSKY, G., and MYERS, M. B. (1967). *Solid St. Commun.* **5**, 555.

—— and MYERS, M. B. (1967). *J. Am. Ceram. Soc.* **50**, 335.

FERRIER, R. P. and HERRELL, D. J. (1969). *Phil. Mag.* **19**, 853.

FEYNMAN, R. P., HELLWARTH, R. W., IDDINGS, C. K., and PLATZMAN, P. M. (1962). *Phys. Rev.* **127**, 1004.

FIRSOV, YU A. (1964). *Soviet Phys. solid St.* **5**, 1566.

FISTUL, V. I. (1969). *Heavily doped semiconductors.* Plenum Press, New York.

FLASCHEN, S. S., PEARSON, A. D., and NORTHOVER, W. R. (1959). *J. Am. Ceram. Soc.* **42**, 450.

FRANZ, W. (1958). *Z. Naturf.* **13a**, 484.

FREISER, M. J., HOLTZBERG, F., METHFESSEL, S., PETTIT, G. D., SHAFER, M. W., and SUITS, J. C. (1968). *Helv. phys. Acta* **41**, 832.

FRENKEL, J. (1938). *Phys. Rev.* **54,** 647.

FRIEDEL, J. (1954). *Adv. Phys.* **3,** 446.

FRIEDMAN, L. (1971). *J. non-cryst. Solids.* To be published.

—— and HOLSTEIN, T. (1963). *Annln Phys.* **21,** 494.

FRISCH, H. L. and LLOYD, S. P. (1960). *Phys. Rev.* **120,** 1175.

FRITZSCHE, H. (1958). *J. Phys. Chem. Solids* **6,** 69.

—— (1959). *Phys. Rev.* **115,** 336.

—— (1960). *Phys. Rev.* **119,** 1899.

—— (1969). *IBM Jl Res. Dev.* **13,** 515.

—— and CUEVAS, M. (1960). *Phys. Rev.* **119,** 1238.

—— and LARK-HOROVITZ, K. (1959). *Phys. Rev.* **113,** 999.

—— and OVSHINSKY, S. R. (1970). *J. non-cryst. Solids* **2,** 148.

FRÖHLICH, H. (1947). *Proc. R. Soc.* **188A,** 521.

—— (1954). *Adv. Phys.* **3,** 325.

—— (1958). *Theory of dielectrics.* 2dn edn, Clarendon Press, Oxford.

FUHS, W. and STUKE, J. (1970). *Mater. Res. Bull.* **5,** 611.

FULENWIDER, J. E. and HERSKOWITZ, G. J. (1970). *Phys. Rev. Lett.* **25,** 292.

GEBALLE, T. H. and HULL, G. W. (1955). *Phys. Rev.* **98,** 940.

GETOV, G., SIMIDCHIEVA, P., NIKIFOROVA, M., and ANDREYCHIN, R. (1967). *Phys. Stat. Solidi* **21,** K87.

GHOSH, P. K. and SPEAR, W. E. (1968). *J. Phys. C: Solid St. Phys.* **1,** 1347.

GIBBONS, D. J. and PAPADAKIS, A. C. (1968). *J. Phys. Chem. Solids* **29,** 115.

GLAZOV, V. M., CHIZHEVSKAYA, S. N., and GLAGOLEVA, N. N. (1969). *Liquid semiconductors.* Plenum Press, New York.

GOLIN, S. (1963). *Phys. Rev.* **132,** 178.

GORYUNOVA, N. A., GROSS, E. F., ZLATKIN, L. B., and IVANOV, E. K. (1970). *J. non-cryst. Solids* **4,** 57.

GRANT, A. J. and YOFFE, A. D. (1970). *Solid St. Comm.* **8,** 1919.

GREENE, M. P. and KOHN, W. (1965). *Phys. Rev.* **137,** 513.

GREENFIELD, A. J. (1966). *Phys. Rev. Lett.* **16,** 6.

GREENWOOD, D. A. (1958). *Proc. phys. Soc.* **71,** 585.

GRIGOROVICI, R. (1969). *J. non-cryst. Solids* **1,** 303.

—— CROITORU, N, and DÉVÉNYI, A. (1966). *Phys. Stat. Solidi* **16,** K143.

—— —— —— (1967a). *Phys. Stat. Solidi* **23,** 621.

—— —— —— (1967b). *Phys. Stat. Solidi* **23,** 627.

—— —— —— and TELEMAN, E. (1964). *Proceedings of the international conference on physics of semiconductors, Paris,* p. 423. Dunod, Paris.

—— and DÉVÉNYI, A. (1968). *Proceedings of the 9th international conference on the physics of semiconductors, Moscow,* p. 1267. Nauka, Leningrad.

—— and MĂNĂILĂ, R. (1968). *Thin Solid Films* **1,** 343.

—— and VANCU, A. (1968). *Thin Solid Films* **2,** 105.

GROSSE, P. (1969). *Die Festkörpereigenschaften von Tellur* (Springer Tracts in Modern Physics, vol. 48). Springer, Berlin.

GRUNWALD, H. P. and BLAKNEY, R. M. (1968). *Phys. Rev.* **165,** 1006.

GUBANOV, A. I. (1963). *Quantum electron theory of amorphous conductors.* Consultants Bureau, New York, 1965.

GUTZWILLER, M. C. (1963). *Phys. Rev. Lett.* **10,** 159.

GUTZWILLER, M. C. (1964). *Phys. Rev.* **134**, A923.

HAISTY, R. W. and KREBS, H. (1969a). *J. non-cryst. Solids* **1**, 399.

—— —— (1969b). *J. non-cryst. Solids* **1**, 427.

HALBO, L. and SLADEK, R. J. (1970). *J. non-cryst. Solids* **4**, 192.

HALPERIN, B. I. (1967). *Adv. chem. Phys.* **13**, 123.

—— and LAX, M. (1966). *Phys. Rev.* **148**, 722.

—— and RICE, T. M. (1968). *Rev. mod. Phys.* **40**, 755.

HALPERN, B., LEKNER, J., RICE, S. A., and GOMER, R. (1967). *Phys. Rev.* **156**, 351.

HAM, F. S. (1962). *Phys. Rev.* **128**, 82, 2524.

HANEMAN, D. (1968). *Phys. Rev.* **170**, 705.

HARRISON, W. A. (1966). *Pseudopotentials in the theory of metals*. Benjamin, New York.

HARTKE, J. L. (1962). *Phys. Rev.* **125**, 1177.

—— (1968). *J. appl. Phys.* **39**, 4871.

—— and REGENSBURGER, P. J. (1965). *Phys. Rev.* **139**, A970.

HARTMAN, R. (1969). *Phys. Rev.* **181**, 1070.

HASEGAWA, A. (1964). *J. phys. Soc. Japan* **19**, 504.

HEIKES, R. R. and URE, R. W. (1961). *Thermoelectricity*, p. 81. Interscience, New York.

HEINE, V. (1970). *Solid St. Phys.* **24**, 1.

—— (1971). *Phys. Rev. Lett.* In press.

HENKELS, H. W. and MACZUK, J. (1953). *J. appl. Phys.* **24**, 1056.

HENSEL, F. and FRANCK, E. U. (1968). *Rev. mod. Phys.* **40**, 697.

HERMAN, F., KORTUM, R. L., KUGLIN, C. C., and SHAY, J. L. (1967). *II–VI semiconducting compounds* (ed. D. G. Thomas), p. 503. Benjamin, New York.

—— and VAN DYKE, J. P. (1968). *Phys. Rev. Lett.* **21**, 1575.

HERRING, C. (1966). *Magnetism* (ed. G. T. Rado and H. Suhl), vol. 4. Academic Press, New York.

HILL, R. M. (1971). *Phil. Mag.* **23**, 59.

HILTON, A. R. (1970). *J. non-cryst. Solids* **2**, 28.

—— and BRAU, M. (1963). *Infrared Phys.* **3**, 69.

HINDLEY, N. K. (1970). *J. non-cryst. Solids* **5**, 17, 31.

HODGSON, J. N. (1963). *Phil. Mag.* **8**, 735.

HOLLAND, L. (1963). *Vacuum deposition of thin films*. Chapman and Hall, London.

HOLSTEIN, R. and FRIEDMAN, L. (1968). *Phys. Rev.* **165**, 1019.

HOLSTEIN T. (1959). *Ann. Phys.* **8**, 343.

—— (1961). *Phys. Rev.* **124**, 1329.

HOPFIELD, J. J. (1968). *Comments Solid St. Phys.* **1**, 16.

HOWARD, W. E. and TSU, R. (1970). *Proceedings of the 10th international conference on the physics of semiconductors, Cambridge, Massachusetts* (ed. S. P. Keller, J. C. Hensel, and F. Stern), p. 789. United States Atomic Energy Commission.

HUBBARD, J. (1964). *Proc. R. Soc. A* **277**, 237.

HULTHÉN, L. and LAURIKAINEN, K. V. (1951). *Rev. mod. Phys.* **23**, 1.

HUNG, C. S. and GLEISSMAN, J. R. (1950). *Phys. Rev.* **79**, 726.

ILSCHNER, B. R. and WAGNER, C. (1958). *Acta metall.* **6**, 712.

IOFFE, A. F. and REGEL, A. R. (1960). *Prog. Semicond.* **4**, 237.

IVKIN, E. V. and KOLOMIETS, B. T. (1970). *J. non-cryst. Solids* **3**, 41.

JAMES, H. M. and GINZBARG, A. S. (1953). *J. phys. Chem.* **57**, 840.

JAYARAMAN, A., McWHAN, D. B., REMEIKA, J. P., and DERNIER, P. D. (1970). *Phys. Rev.* B **2**, 3751.

—— NARAYANAMURTI, V., BUCHER, E., and MAINES, R. G. (1970). *Phys. Rev. Lett.* **25**, 368.

JONSCHER, A. K. (1967). *Thin Solid Films* **1**, 213.

JORTNER, J. (1959). *J. chem. Phys.* **30**, 839.

JULLIEN, R. and JEROME, D. (1971). *J. Phys. Chem. Solids* **32**, 257.

KAGAN, YU. and ZHERNOV, A. P. (1966). *Soviet Phys. JETP* **23**, 737.

KANAMORI, J. (1963). *Prog. theor. Phys.* **30**, 275.

KAPLOW, R., ROWE, T. A., and AVERBACH, B. L. (1968). *Phys. Rev.* **168**, 1068.

KASEN, M. B. (1970). *Phil. Mag.* **21**, 599.

KASUYA, T. and YANASE, A. (1968). *Rev. mod. Phys.* **40**, 684.

—— —— and TAKEDA, T. (1970). *Solid State Commun.* **8**, 1551.

KATZ, M. J. (1965). *Phys. Rev.* **140**, A1323.

—— KOENIG, S. H., and LOPEZ, A. A. (1965). *Phys. Rev. Lett.* **15**, 828.

KEEZER, R. C. and BAILEY, M. W. (1967). *Mater. Res. Bull.* **2**, 185.

KEIL, T. H., (1966). *Phys. Rev.* **144**, 582.

KELDYSH, L. V. and KOPAEV, YU. V. (1965). *Soviet Phys. solid St.* **6**, 2219.

KELLER, H. and STUKE, J. (1965). *Phys. Stat. Solidi* **8**, 831.

KEMENY, G. and CARON, L. G. (1967). *Phys. Rev.* **159**, 768.

KEYES, R. W. and SLADEK, R. J. (1956). *J. Phys. Chem. Solids* **1**, 143.

KLIMA, J. and McGILL, T. C. (1971). *Discuss. Faraday Soc.* No. 50. In press.

KNOX, R. S. (1963). Theory of excitons. *Solid St. Phys. Suppl.* 5. Academic Press.

KOBE, A. and HANDRICH, K. (1970). *Phys. Stat. Solidi* **42**, K69.

KOHN, W. (1964). *Phys. Rev.* **133**, A171.

—— (1967). *Phys. Rev. Lett.* **19**, 439.

KOLOMIETS, B. T. (1964). *Phys. Stat. Solidi* **7**, 359, 713.

—— and LEBEDEV, E. A. (1967). *Soviet Phys. Semicond.* **1**, 244.

—— and LYUBIN, V. M. (1960). *Soviet Phys. solid St.* **2**, 46.

——MAMONTOVA, T. N., and BABAEV, A. A. (1970). *J. non-cryst. Solids* **4**, 289.

—— —— and NEGRESKUL, V. V. (1968). *Phys. Stat. Solidi* **27**, K15.

—— and MAZETS, T. F. (1970). *J. non-cryst. Solids* **3**, 46.

—— —— and EFENDIEV, SH. M. (1970). *Soviet Phys. Semicond.* **4**, 934.

—— —— —— and ANDRIESH, A. M. (1970). *J. non-cryst. Solids* **4**, 45.

—— and RASPOPOVA, E. M. (1970). *Soviet Phys. Semicond.* **4**, 124.

KOSEK, F. and TAUC, J. (1970). *Czech. J. Phys.* B **20**, 94.

KRAMER, B. (1970). *Phys. Stat. Solidi* **41**, 725.

—— MASCHKE, K., THOMAS, P., and TREUSCH, J. (1970). *Phys. Rev. Lett.* **25**, 1020.

KREBS, H. (1951). *Semiconducting materials* (ed. H. K. Henisch), p. 246. Butterworths, London.

Krebs, H. (1969). *J. non-cryst. Solids* **1**, 455.

—— and Fischer, P. (1971). *Discuss. Faraday Soc.* No. 50. In press.

Krieger, J. B. and Strauss, S. (1968). *Phys. Rev.* **169**, 674.

Krishnan, K. S. and Bhatia, A. B. (1945). *Nature, Lond.* **156**, 503.

Kubo, R. (1952). *Phys. Rev.* **86**, 929.

LaCourse, W. A., Twaddell, V. A., and Mackenzie, J. D. (1970). *J. non-cryst. Solids* **3**, 234.

Landau, L. D. (1937). *On the theory of phase transitions.* In *Collected papers of L. D. Landau* (ed. D. Ter Haar), p. 193. Pergamon Press, Oxford, 1965.

Landauer, R. (1970). *Phil. Mag.* **21**, 863.

—— and Helland, J. C. (1954). *J. chem. Phys.* **22**, 1655.

Langreth, D. C. (1967). *Phys. Rev.* **159**, 717.

Lanyon, H. P. D. (1963). *Phys. Rev.* **130**, 134.

—— (1969). *The physics of selenium and tellurium* (ed. W. C. Cooper), p. 205. Pergamon Press.

—— and Spear, W. E. (1961). *Proc. phys. Soc.* **77**, 1157.

Lax, M. (1951). *Rev. mod. Phys.* **23**, 287.

—— (1952). *Phys. Rev.* **85**, 621.

—— and Phillips, J. C. (1958). *Phys. Rev.* **110**, 41.

Le Comber, P. G. and Spear, W. E. (1970). *Phys. Rev. Lett.* **25**, 509.

Leiga, A. G. (1968). *J. opt. Soc. Am.* **58**, 1441.

Lekner, J. (1967). *Phys. Rev.* **158**, 130.

—— (1968). *Phys. Lett.* A **27**, 341.

Lieb, E. H. and Wu, F. Y. (1968). *Phys. Rev. Lett.* **20**, 1445.

Lien, S. Y. and Sivertsen, J. M. (1969). *Phil. Mag.* **20**, 759.

Lifshitz, I. M. (1964). *Adv. Phys.* **13**, 483.

—— and Kaganov, M. I. (1963). *Soviet Phys. Usp.* **5**, 878.

Lizell, B. (1952). *J. chem. Phys.* **20**, 672.

Lucovsky, G. (1969a). *Mater. Res. Bull.* **4**, 505.

—— (1969b). *The physics of selenium and tellurium* (ed. W. C. Cooper), p. 255. Pergamon Press.

—— (1970). *Proceedings of the 10th international conference on the physics of semiconductors, Cambridge, Massachusetts* (ed. S. P. Keller, J. C. Hensel, and F. Stern), p. 799. United States Atomic Energy Commission.

—— Mooradian, A., Taylor, W., Wright, G. B., and Keezer, R. C. (1967). *Solid St. Commun.* **5**, 113.

Lueder, H. and Spenke, E. (1935). *Z. techn. Phys.* **16**, 11.

Lukes, F. (1959). *Czech. J. Phys.* **9**, 118.

Lukes, T. and Somaratna, K. T. S. (1970). *J. non-cryst. Solids* **4**, 452.

Luttinger, J. M. (1960). *Phys. Rev.* **119**, 1153.

Mackenzie, R. C. (1970). *Differential thermal analysis* (ed. R. C. Mackenzie). Academic Press, London.

Mackintosh, A. R. (1963). *J. chem. Phys.* **38**, 1991.

McGill, T. C. and Klima, J. (1970). *J. Phys. C: Solid St. Phys.* **3**, L163.

—— and Rice, T. M. (1969). *Phys. Rev. Lett.* **22**, 887.

—— —— and Remeika, J. P. (1969). *Phys. Rev. Lett.* **23**, 1384.

—— —— and Schmidt, P. H. (1969). *Phys. Rev.* **177**, 1063.

MADER, S. (1965). *J. Vac. Sci. Tech.* **2**, 35.
—— WIDMER, H., D'HEURLE, F. M., and NOWICK, A. S. (1963). *Appl. Phys. Lett.* **3**, 201.
MAHAN, G. D. (1966). *Phys. Rev.* **145**, 602.
MAHR, H. (1963). *Phys. Rev.* **132**, 1880.
MAKINSON, R. E. B. and ROBERTS, A. P. (1962). *Proc. phys. Soc.* **79**, 222.
MALE, J. C. (1967). *Br. J. appl. Phys.* **18**, 1543.
—— (1970). *Electronics Lett.* **6**, 91.
MANY, A. and RAKAVY, G. (1962). *Phys. Rev.* **126**, 1980.
MARK, P. and HARTMAN, T. E. (1968). *J. appl. Phys.* **39**, 2163.
MASCHKE, K. and THOMAS, P. (1970). *Phys. Stat. Solidi* **41**, 743.
MATTHEISS, L. F. (1964). *Phys. Rev.* **133**, A1399.
MEEKS, T. and KRIEGER, J. B. (1969). *Phys. Rev.* **185**, 1068.
MELL, H. and STUKE, J. (1970). *J. non-cryst. Solids* **4**, 304.
METHFESSEL, S. and MATTIS, D. C. (1968). *Handb. Phys.* **18**, 387.
MILLER, A. and ABRAHAMS, E. (1960). *Phys. Rev.* **120**, 745.
—— —— (1961). *Proceedings of the international conference on semiconductor physics. Prague*, p. 218. Czechoslovak Academy of Sciences, Prague.
MILLER, L. S., HOWE, S., and SPEAR, W. E. (1968). *Phys. Rev.* **166**, 871.
MILWARD, R. C. and NEURINGER, L. J. (1965). *Phys. Rev. Lett.* **15**, 664.
MINAMI, T., HATTORI, M., NAKAMACHI, F., and TANAKA, M. (1970). *J. non-cryst. Solids* **3**, 327.
MOON, R. M. (1970). *Phys. Rev. Lett.* **25**, 527.
MOORADIAN, A. and WRIGHT, G. B. (1969). *The physics of selenium and tellurium* (ed. W. C. Cooper), p. 269. Pergamon Press.
MOORJANI, K. and FELDMAN, C. (1970). *J. non-cryst. Solids* **4**, 248.
MOSS, S. C. and GRACZYK, J. F. (1969). *Phys. Rev. Lett.* **23**, 1167.
—— —— (1970). *Proceedings of the 10th international conference on the physics of semiconductors, Cambridge, Massachusetts* (ed. S. P. Keller, J. C. Hensel, and F. Stern), p. 658. United States Atomic Energy Commission.
MOTT, N. F. (1949). *Proc. phys. Soc. A* **62**, 416.
—— (1956). *Can. J. Phys.* **34**, 1356.
—— (1961). *Phil. Mag.* **6**, 287.
—— (1964). *Adv. Phys.* **13**, 325.
—— (1966). *Phil. Mag.* **13**, 989.
—— (1967). *Adv. Phys.* **16**, 49.
—— (1968a). *J. non-cryst. Solids* **1**, 1.
—— (1968b). *Rev. mod. Phys.* **40**, 677.
—— (1969a). *Phil. Mag.* **19**, 835.
—— (1969b). *Phil. Mag.* **20**, 1.
—— (1969c). *Festkörperprobleme* **9**, 22.
—— (1970). *Phil. Mag.* **22**, 7.
—— (1971a). *Phil. Mag.* Paper VI. **24**. 1.
—— (1971b). *Phil. Mag.* Paper VII. **24**. In press.
—— (1971c). *Phil. Mag.* Paper VIII. **24**. In press.
—— (1971d). *Phil. Mag.* Paper IX. **24**. In press.

MOTT, N. F. and ALLGAIER, R. S. (1967). *Phys. Stat. Solidi* **21**, 343.

—— and DAVIS, E. A. (1968). *Phil. Mag.* **17**, 1269.

—— and GURNEY, R. W. (1940). *Electronic processes in ionic crystals.* Clarendon Press, Oxford.

—— and JONES, H. (1936). *The theory of the properties of metals and alloys.* Clarendon Press, Oxford.

—— and MASSEY, H. S. W. (1965). *The theory of atomic collisions.* 3rd edn, p. 86. Clarendon Press, Oxford.

—— and TWOSE, W. D. (1961). *Adv. Phys.* **10**, 107.

—— and ZINAMON, Z. (1970). *Rep. Prog. Phys.* **33**, 881.

MÜLLER, L. and MÜLLER, M. (1970). *J. non-cryst. Solids* **4**, 504.

MYERS, M. B. and FELTY, E. J. (1967). *Mater. Res. Bull.* **2**, 535.

NAGAOKA, Y. (1966). *Phys. Rev.* **147**, 392.

NEUSTADTER, H. E. and COOPERSMITH, M. H. (1969). *Phys. Rev. Lett.* **23**, 585.

NISHIMURA, H. (1965). *Phys. Rev.* **138**, A815.

NORDHEIM, L. (1931). *Annln Phys.* **9**, 641.

NORTH, D. M., ENDERBY, J. E., and EGELSTAFF, P. A. (1968). *J. Phys. C: Solid St. Phys.* **1**, 1075.

NORWOOD, T. E. and FRY, J. L. (1970). *Phys. Rev.* B **2**, 472.

NWACHUKU, A. and KUHN, M. (1968). *Appl. Phys. Lett.* **12**, 163.

OLECHNA, D. J. and KNOX, R. S. (1965). *Phys. Rev.* **140**, A986.

OSMUN, J. W. and FRITZSCHE, H. (1970). *Appl. Phys. Lett.* **16**, 87.

OVERHAUSER, A. W. (1962). *Phys. Rev.* **128**, 1437.

OVSHINSKY, S. R. (1968). *Phys. Rev. Lett.* **21**, 1450.

OWEN, A. E. (1967). *Glass Ind.* **48**, 637, 695.

—— (1970). *Contemp. Phys.* **11**, 227, 257.

—— and ROBERTSON, J. M. (1970). *J. non-cryst. Solids* **2**, 40.

PAI, D. M. and ING, S. W. JR. (1968). *Phys. Rev.* **173**, 729.

PANOVA, G. KH., ZHERNOV, A. P., and KUTAĬTSEV, V. I. (1968). *Soviet Phys. JETP* **26**, 283.

PAPADAKIS, A. C. (1967). *J. Phys. Chem. Solids* **28**, 641.

PAUL, W. (1970). *Mater. Res. Bull.* **5**, 691.

PEARSON, A. D. (1970). *J. non-cryst. Solids* **2**, 1.

—— DEWALD, J. F., NORTHOVER, W. R., and PECK, W. F. (1962). *Advances in Glass Technology*, part I, p. 357. Plenum Press, New York.

PEIERLS, R. E. (1937). *Proc. phys. Soc.* **49**, 3.

PENN, D. R. (1962). *Phys. Rev.* **128**, 2093.

—— and COHEN, M. H. (1967). *Phys. Rev.* **155**, 468.

PENNEY, T. (1969). *Solid St. Commun.* **7**, 3.

PERRON, J. C. (1967). *Adv. Phys.* **16**, 657.

PHARISEAU, P. and ZIMAN, J. M. (1963). *Phil. Mag.* **8**, 1487.

PHILLIPS, J. C. (1966). *Solid St. Phys.* **18**, 56.

—— (1970). *Proceedings of the 10th international conference on the physics of semiconductors, Cambridge, Massachusetts* (ed. S. P. Keller, J. C. Hensel, and F. Stern), p. 22. United States Atomic Energy Commission.

PILLER, H., SERAPHIN, B. O., MARKEL, K., and FISCHER, J. E. (1969). *Phys. Rev. Lett.* **23**, 775.

PIPPARD, A. B. (1965). *The dynamics of conduction electrons*, p. 90. Gordon and Breach, New York.

PLATAKIS, N. S., SADAGOPAN, V., and GATOS, H. C. (1969). *J. electrochem. Soc.* **116**, 1436.

POLK, D. E. (1971). *J. non-cryst. Solids* **5**, 365.

POLLAK, M. (1964). *Phys. Rev.* **133**, A564.

—— (1965). *Phys. Rev.* **138**, A1822.

—— (1971a). *Discuss. Faraday Soc.* No. 50. In press.

—— (1971b). *Phil. Mag.* **23**, 519.

—— and GEBALLE, T. H. (1961). *Phys. Rev.* **122**, 1742.

POOLE, H. H. (1916). *Phil. Mag.* **32**, 112.

—— (1917). *Phil. Mag.* **34**, 195.

POSTILL, D. R., ROSS, R. G., and CUSACK, N. E. (1967). *Adv. Phys.* **16**, 493.

PROSSER, V. (1961). *Proceedings of the international conference on semiconductor physics, Prague*, p. 993. Czechoslovak Academy of Sciences, Prague.

RAWSON, H. (1967). *Inorganic glass-forming systems*. Academic Press, London and New York.

RAZ, B. and JORTNER, J. (1970). *Proc. R. Soc.* A **317**, 113.

REDFIELD, D. (1963). *Phys. Rev.* **130**, 916.

REGEL, A. R., ANDREEV, A. A., KOTOV, B. A., MAMADALIEV, M., OKUNEVA, N. M., SMIRNOV, I. A., and SHADRICHEV, E. V. (1970). *J. non-cryst. Solids* **4**, 151.

RICE, T. M., BARKER, A. S., HALPERIN, B. I., and McWHAN, D. B. (1969). *J. appl. Phys.* **40**, 1337.

RICHTER, H. and BREITLING, G. (1958). *Z. Naturf.* **13a**, 988.

RIDLEY, B. K. (1963). *Proc. phys. Soc.* **82**, 954.

ROBERTS, G. G., TUTIHASI, S., and KEEZER, R. C. (1968). *Phys. Rev.* **166**, 637.

ROBINS, J. L. (1962). *Proc. phys. Soc.* **79**, 119.

ROBINSON, J. E. (1967). *Phys. Rev.* **161**, 533.

ROCKSTAD, H. K. (1970). *J. non-cryst. Solids* **2**, 192.

ROGACHEV, A. A. (1968). *Proceedings of the 9th international conference on the physics of semiconductors, Moscow*, p. 407. Nauka, Leningrad.

—— and SABLINA, N. I. (1969). *Soviet Phys. Semicond.* **2**, 768.

ROULET, B., GAVORET, J., and NOZIÈRES, P. (1969). *Phys. Rev.* **178**, 1072.

RUBIO, J. (1969). *J. Phys. C: Solid St. Phys.* **2**, 288.

SAITOH, M., FUKUYAMA, H., UEMURA, Y., and SHIBA, H. (1969). *J. phys. Soc. Japan* **27**, 26.

SANDROCK, R. (1968). *Phys. Rev.* **169**, 642.

SASAKI, W. (1965). *J. phys. Soc. Japan* **20**, 825.

—— (1970). *Proceedings of the 10th international conference on the physics of semiconductors, Cambridge, Massachusetts* (ed. S. P. Keller, J. C. Hensel, and F. Stern), p. 583. United States Atomic Energy Commission.

SAVAGE, J. A. and NIELSEN, S. (1965a). *Infrared Phys.* **5**, 195.

—— —— (1965b). *Physics and Chemistry of Glasses* **6**, 90.

SCHMID, A. P. (1968). *J. appl. Phys.* **39**, 3140.

SCHNAKENBERG, J. (1965). *Z. Phys.* **185**, 123.

—— (1968). *Phys. Stat. Solidi* **28**, 623.

SCHNYDERS, H., RICE, S. A., and MEYER, L. (1966). *Phys. Rev.* **150**, 127.

SCHOTTMILLER, J., TABAK, M., LUCOVSKY, G., and WARD, A. (1970). *J. non-cryst. Solids* **4**, 80.

SCHRIEMPF, J. T., SCHINDLER, A. I., and MILLS, D. L. (1969). *Phys. Rev.* **187**, 959.

SENTURIA, S. D., HEWES, C. R., and ADLER, D. (1970). *J. appl. Phys.* **41**, 430.

SHANKS, H. R., SIDLES, P. H., and DANIELSON, G. C. (1963). *Nonstoichiometric compounds* (Adv. Chem. Ser., 39; ed. R. Ward), p. 237.

SHAW, R. F., LIANG, W. Y., and YOFFE, A. D. (1970). *J. non-cryst. Solids* **4**, 29.

SHOCKLEY, W. (1950). *Electrons and holes in semiconductors.* Van Nostrand, Princeton, New Jersey.

SIENKO, M. J. (1964). *Solutions métal–ammoniac, Colloque Weyl 1963* (ed. G. Lepoutre and M. J. Sienko), p. 23. W. A. Benjamin, New York.

SIEMSEN, K. J. and FENTON, E. W. (1967). *Phys. Rev.* **161**, 632.

SIMMONS, J. G. (1967). *Phys. Rev.* **155**, 657.

SIMPSON, A. W. (1970). *Phys. Stat. Solidi* **40**, 207.

SIMPSON, J. H. (1949). *Proc. R. Soc.* **197**, 269.

SLATER, J. C. (1951). *Phys. Rev.* **82**, 538.

—— (1968a). *Phys. Rev.* **165**, 658.

—— (1968b). *J. appl. Phys.* **39**, 761.

SONDER, E. and STEVENS, D. K. (1958). *Phys. Rev.* **110**, 1027.

SPEAR, W. E. (1957). *Proc. phys. Soc.* B **70**, 669.

—— (1960). *Proc. phys. Soc.* **76**, 826.

—— (1969). *J. non-cryst. Solids* **1**, 197.

SPICER, W. E. and DONOVAN, T. M. (1970a). *J. non-cryst. Solids* **2**, 66.

—— and DONOVAN, T. M. (1970b). *Proceedings of the 10th international conference on the physics of semiconductors, Cambridge, Massachusetts* (ed. S. P. Keller, J. C. Hensel, and F. Stern), p. 677. United States Atomic Energy Commission.

SPRINGTHORPE, A. J., AUSTIN, I. G., and SMITH, B. A. (1965). *Solid St. Commun.* **3**, 143.

SRB, I. and VAŠKO, A. (1963). *Czech. J. Phys.* B **13**, 827.

SRINIVASAN, G. and COHEN, M. H. (1970). *J. non-cryst. Solids* **3**, 393.

STERN, F. (1971). *Phys. Rev.* B **3**, 2636.

STILES, P. J., CHANG, L. L., ESAKI, L., and TSU, R. (1970). *Appl. Phys. Lett.* **16**, 380.

STOCKER, H. J., BARLOW, C. A., and WEIRAUCH, D. F. (1970). *J. non-cryst. Solids* **4**, 523.

STOLEN, R. H. (1970). *Physics and Chemistry of Glasses* **11**, 83.

ŠTOURAČ, L., VAŠKO, A., SRB, I., MUSIL, C., and ŠTRBA, F. (1968). *Czech. J. Phys.* B **18**, 1067.

STRAUB, W. D., ROTH, H., BERNARD, W., GOLDSTEIN, S., and MULHERN, J. E. (1968). Phys. Rev. Lett. **21**, 752.

STREET, R. A., DAVIES, G. R., and YOFFE, A. D. (1971). *J. non-cryst. Solids* **5**, 276.

STUKE, J. (1969). *Festkörperprobleme* **9**, 46.

STUKE, J. (1970a). *J. non-cryst. Solids* **4**, 1.

—— (1970b). *Proceedings of the 10th international conference on the physics of semiconductors, Cambridge, Massachusetts* (ed. S. P. Keller, J. C. Hensel, and F. Stern), p. 14. United States Atomic Energy Commission.

—— and WEISER, G. (1966). *Phys. Stat. Solidi* **17**, 343.

SUNDFORS, R. K. and HOLCOMB, D. F. (1964). Phys. Rev. **136**, A810.

SZEKELY, G. (1951). *J. electrochem. Soc.* **98**, 318.

—— (1970). *Phys. Rev.* B **2**, 2104.

TABAK, M. D. (1970) *Phys. Rev.* B**2**, 2104.

—— (1971). *Proceedings of the third international conference on photoconductivity*, p. 87. Pergamon, Oxford.

—— and WARTER, P. J. JR. (1968). *Phys. Rev.* **173**, 899.

TANAKA, S. and FAN, H. Y. (1963). *Phys. Rev.* **132**, 1516.

TAUC, J. (1970a). *Optical properties of solids* (ed. F. Abelès), North-Holland, Amsterdam.

—— (1970b). *Mater. Res. Bull.* **5**, 721.

—— and ABRAHÁM, A. (1969). *Czech. J. Phys.* B **19**, 1246.

—— ——PAJASOVÁ, L., GRIGOROVICI, R., and VANCU, A. (1965). *Proceedings of the international conference on physics of non-crystalline solids, Delft*, p. 606. North-Holland, Amsterdam.

—— —— ZALLEN, R., and SLADE, M. (1970). *J. non-cryst. Solids* **4**, 279.

—— GRIGOROVICI, R., and VANCU, A. (1966). *Phys. Stat. Solidi* **15**, 627.

—— MENTHE, A., and WOOD, D. L. (1970). *Phys. Rev. Lett.* **25**, 749.

—— ŠTOURAČ, L., VORLÍČEK, V., and ZÁVĚTOVÁ, M. (1968). *Proceedings of the 9th international conference on the physics of semiconductors, Moscow*, p. 1251. Nauka, Leningrad.

TAYLOR, P. C., BISHOP, S. G., and MITCHELL, D. L. (1970). *Solid St. Commun.* **8**, 1783.

THOMPSON, J. C. (1965). *Solvated electrons* (Adv. Chem. Ser. No. 50), p. 96.

THORNBER, K. K. and FEYNMAN, R. P. (1970). *Phys. Rev.* B **1**, 4099.

THOULESS, D. J. (1970). *J. Phys. C: Solid St. Phys.* **3**, 1559.

TIÈCHE, Y. and ZAREBA, A. (1963). *Phys. kondens. Materie* **1**, 402.

TIMBIE, J. P. and WHITE, R. M. (1970). *Phys. Rev.* B **1**, 2409.

TOYOZAWA, Y. (1959). *Prog. theor. Phys. Suppl.* **12**, 111; *Prog. theor. Phys.* **22**, 455.

—— (1962). *J. phys. Soc. Japan* **17**, 986.

—— (1964). *Tech. Rep. Inst. Solid St. Phys. (Univ. Tokyo)* A, no. 119.

TREUSCH, J. and SANDROCK, R. (1966). *Phys. Stat. Solidi* **16**, 487.

TSU, R., HOWARD, W. E., and ESAKI, L. (1970). *J. non-cryst. Solids* **4**, 322.

TURNBULL, D. (1969). *Contemp. Phys.* **10**, 473.

TUTIHASI, S., ROBERTS, G. G., KEEZER, R. C., and DREWS, R. E. (1969). *Phys. Rev.* **177**, 1143.

TWOSE, W. D. (1959). Ph.D. Thesis, University of Cambridge.

UPHOFF, H. L. and HEALY, J. H. (1961). *J. appl. Phys.* **32**, 950.

URBACH, F. (1953). *Phys. Rev.* **92**, 1324.

URBAIN, G. and ÜBELACKER, E. (1966). *C.r. hebd. Séanc. Acad. Sci. Paris* C **262**, 699.

VAIPOLIN, A. A. and PORAI-KOSHITS, E. A. (1960). *Fizika tverd. Tela* **2**, 1656.

VAIPOLIN, A. A. and PORAI-KOSHITS, E. A. (1963). *Fizika tverd. Tela* **5**, 246.

VAN ZANDT, L. L., HONIG, J. M., and GOODENOUGH, J. B. (1968). *J. appl. Phys.* **39**, 594.

VASKO, A. (1970). *J. non-cryst. Solids* **3**, 225.

VELICKÝ, B., KIRKPATRICK, S., and EHRENREICH, H. (1968). *Phys. Rev.* **175**, 747.

VENGEL, T. N. and KOLOMIETS, B. T. (1957). *Soviet Phys. tech. Phys.* **27.2**, 2314.

VON MOLNAR, S. (1970). IBM Jl Res. Dev. **14**, 269.

—— and KASUYA, T. (1968). *Phys. Rev. Lett.* **21**, 1757.

VOLGER, J. (1960). *Prog. Semicond.* **4**, 205.

WACHTER, P. and WEBER, P. (1970). *Solid St. Commun.* **8**, 1133.

WAGNER, C. N. J. (1969). *J. Vac. Sci. Tech.* **6**, 650.

WALLEY, P. A. (1968a). Ph.D. Thesis, University of London.

—— (1968b). *Thin Solid Films* **2**, 327.

—— and JONSCHER, A. K. (1968). *Thin Solid Films* **1**, 367.

WALTERS, G. K. and ESTLE, T. L. (1961). *J. appl. Phys.* **32**, 1854.

WARREN, W. W. (1970a). *J. non-cryst. Solids* **4**, 168.

—— (1970b). *Solid St. Commun.* **8**, 1269.

WEAIRE, D. (1971). *Phys. Rev. Lett.* In press.

WEISER, G. and STUKE, J. (1969). *Phys. Stat. Solidi* **35**, 747.

WEISER, K. and BRODSKY, M. H. (1970). *Phys. Rev.* B **1**, 791.

—— FISCHER, R., and BRODSKY, M. H. (1970).

—— FISCHER, R., and BRODSKY, M. H. (1970). *Proceedings of the 10th international conference on the physics of semiconductors, Cambridge, Massachusetts* (ed. S. P. Keller, J. C. Hensel, and F. Stern), p. 667. United States Atomic Energy Commission.

WEMPLE, S. H. (1965). *Phys. Rev.* **137**, A1575.

WHITE, R. M. and WOOLSEY, R. B. (1968). *Phys. Rev.* **176**, 908.

WIGNER, E. (1938). *Trans. Faraday Soc.* **34**, 678.

WILSON, A. H. (1931). *Proc. R. Soc.* **133**, 458.

WILSON, T. M. (1969). *J. appl. Phys.* **40**, 1588.

—— (1970). *Int. J. quant. Chem.* 3S, 757.

WISER, N. and GREENFIELD, A. J. (1966). *Phys. Rev. Lett.* **17**, 586.

WOLF, E. L., LOSEE, D. L., CULLEN, D. E., and COMPTON, W. D. (1971), *Phys. Rev. Lett.* **26**, 438.

WONG, P. T. T. and WHALLEY, E. (1971). *Discuss. Faraday Soc.* No. 50. In press.

YAFET, Y., KEYES, R. W., and ADAMS, E. N. (1956). *J. Phys. Chem. Solids* **1**, 137.

YAMANOUCHI, C. (1963). *J. phys. Soc. Japan* **18**, 1775.

—— MIZUGUCHI, K., and SASAKI, W. (1967). *J. phys. Soc. Japan* **22**, 859.

YEARGAN, J. R. and TAYLOR, H. L. (1968). *J. appl. Phys.* **39**, 5600.

ZACHARIASEN, W. H. (1932). *J. Am. Chem. Soc.* **54**, 3841.

ZALLEN, R. (1968). *Phys. Rev.* **173**, 824.

ZENER, C. (1951). *Phys. Rev.* **82**, 403.

ZIMAN, J. M. (1960). *Electrons and phonons.* Oxford University Press.

ZIMAN, J. M. (1961). *Phil. Mag.* **6,** 1013.
—— (1967a). *Adv. Phys.* **16, ** 421.
—— (1967b). *Adv. Phys.* **16,** 551.
—— (1969). *J. Phys. C: Solid St. Phys.* **2,** 1230.
—— (1970). *J. non-cryst. Solids* **4,** 426.
ZIMMERER, G. (1970). Thesis, University of Marburg.
ZINAMON, Z. (1970). *Phil. Mag.* **21,** 347.
—— and MOTT, N. F. (1970). *Phil. Mag.* **21,** 881.
ZITTARTZ, J. and LANGER, J. S. (1966). *Phys. Rev.* **148,** 741.
ZLATKIN, L. B., MARKOV, YU. F., STEKHANOV, A. I., and SHUR, M. S. (1970).
  J. Phys. Chem. Solids **31,** 567.

AUTHOR INDEX

Abkowitz, M., 374
Abraham, A., 273, 301, 302, 304, 316
Abrahams, E., 17, 41, 104, 156
Acrivos, J. V., 151
Adams, E. N., 182
Adams, P. D., 70
Adkins, C. J., 42, 196
Adler, D., 38, 142, 366
Afromowitz, M. A., 245
Aldea, A., 54, 111
Alexander, J. H., 273, 274
Alexander, M. N., 161, 162, 164, 182
Allcock, G. R., 114, 115
Allgaier, R. S., 54, 63, 89, 90
Amitay, M., 54, 175
Amrhein, E. M., 218
Anderson, P. W., 3, 10, 16, 18, 19, 22
Andreev, A. A., 97, 99, 100
Andrews, P. V., 77
Andreychin, R. E., 337, 339, 340, 341
Andriesh, A. M., 258, 327, 334, 335, 337
  338, 342, 394
Animalu, A. O. E., 66, 67, 73
Antonov, V. N., 162
Appel, J., 115, 116
Ashcroft, N. W., 67
Ashley, E. J., 273, 288, 300, 301, 304
Austin, I. G., 109, 111, 113, 115, 118, 119,
  142, 170, 171, 174, 212, 218, 219, 261,
  358
Averbach, B. L., 371
Axmann, A., 373, 374

Baars, J. W., 307
Babaev, A. A., 336, 339, 350, 363
Baber, W. G., 63, 122
Bahl, S. K., 205, 224, 245, 272, 280, 283,
  289, 290, 298, 299, 366, 367, 368
Baidakov, L. A., 363
Bailey, M. W., 197, 374
Ballentine, L. E., 60, 73
Banus, M. D., 169
Banyai, L., 3, 31, 54
Bardasis, A., 256
Bardeen, J., 104
Barker, A. S., 127
Barlow, C. A., 269, 270
Beaglehole, D., 304, 307, 308, 310
Beckman, O., 182
Beeby, J. L., 60
Bell, R. J., 262

Belu, A., 281, 283
Bennett, J. M., 253, 287, 300, 301, 304
Berglund, C. N., 248
Bernard, W., 55
Betts, F., 38, 192, 365
Bhatia, A. B., 65
Bienenstock, A., 38, 192, 365
Bird, N. F., 262
Bishop, S. G., 219, 261, 358, 369, 370
Blakney, R. M., 382, 384
Blakemore, J. S., 230
Blinowski, J., 184
Böer, K. W., 54, 268
Bogomolov, V. N., 114, 117
Bonch-Bruevich, V. L., 245
Borland, R. E., 56
Borisova, Z. U., 363
Bosman, A. J., 119, 120, 170, 172
Bradley, C. C., 71
Brau, M., 191
Breitling, G., 195, 274
Briegleb, G., 374
Brinkman, W. F., 126, 132, 142, 176
Brinson, M. E., 166
Brodsky, M. H., 205, 230, 233, 234, 250,
  251, 262, 264, 265, 289, 291, 292, 293,
  294, 307, 309, 310, 327, 358, 359, 361,
  362, 363
Brust, D., 305
Bucher, E., 122
Bunker, D. L., 112
Busch, G., 269

Cabane, B., 92, 93, 94, 97
Callaerts, R., 317, 320
Cardona, M., 257, 258, 303
Caron, L. G., 132
Castellan, G. W., 160
Catterall, R., 120, 150, 151
Catterall, J. A., 75, 76
Červinka, L., 205, 245, 265, 315, 316, 318,
  319, 321, 323
Chang, L. L., 368
Chen, H. S., 270
Chen, I., 118, 235
Chittick, R. C., 273, 274, 280, 285, 286,
  287, 288, 292, 295, 298, 299, 301, 302,
  307
Chizhevskaya, S. N., 86
Cho, S. J., 128
Chopra, K. L., 192, 205, 224, 245, 272,

280, 283, 289, 290, 298, 299, 366, 367, 368
Chroboczek, J. A., 182
Cimpl, Z., 266, 345
Clark, A. H., 227, 272, 280, 281, 285, 288, 290, 298, 299
Clendenen, R. L., 122
Cohen, M. H., 22, 24, 38, 44, 52, 57, 136, 150, 199, 233, 366
Coleman, M. V., 274, 277
Collings, E. W., 74, 75, 99
Compton, W. D., 30, 31, 147, 155, 159, 160, 166, 167
Conwell, E. M., 152
Cook, B. E., 236
Coopersmith, M. H., 22
Crevecoeur, C., 119, 170, 172
Croitoru, N., 224, 267, 272, 274, 280, 281, 282, 288, 289, 290, 296, 298, 359, 360, 362
Crowder, B. L., 262
Cuevas, M., 152, 153, 159, 161, 163
Cullen, D. E., 30, 31
Cumming, J. B., 184
Cusack, N. E., 66, 74, 83
Cutler, M., 42, 47, 48, 54, 97, 98, 100, 101, 167, 168, 169, 170

D'Altroy, F. A., 156
Danielson, G. C., 148, 149
Darby, J. K., 68
Dash, W. C., 298, 299, 305, 308, 310
Davies, G. R., 217
Davis, E. A., 52, 53, 79, 134, 141, 146, 147, 155, 159, 160, 161, 166, 167, 200, 204, 212, 214, 216, 217, 237, 243, 249, 252, 253, 307, 336, 387, 393, 400
Dean, P., 262
de Boer, J. H., 122
de Gennes, P. G., 126, 176, 178
de Wit, H. J., 119
d'Heurle, F. M., 76
Denayer, M., 317, 320
Dernier, P. D., 145
des Cloizeaux, J., 137
Dévényi, A., 224, 274, 280, 281, 282, 283, 288, 289, 290, 296, 298
Dewald, J. F., 191
Dexter, D. L., 240, 241, 245
Dolezalek, F. K., 210, 384
Domb, C., 19
Doniach, S., 132
Donovan, T. M., 253, 254, 264, 272, 273, 287, 288, 298, 299, 300, 301, 304, 305
Dove, D. B., 366
Dow, J. D., 241, 242, 335, 394
Drake, C. F., 39, 173
Drews, R. E., 307, 337, 340, 347, 351, 392 394

Drickamer, H. G., 122
Dunstan, W., 166
Durkan, J., 182
Dussel, G. A., 268

Eckenbach, W., 132, 314
Economou, E. N., 57
Edmond, J. T., 205, 219, 221, 222, 245, 258, 259, 260, 327, 329, 330, 337, 339, 347, 348, 349, 351, 352, 353, 356, 361, 362, 363, 364, 365, 370
Edwards, S. F., 13, 22, 61, 73, 81
Efendiev, Sh. M., 258, 334, 335, 337, 338, 342, 349, 394
Egelstaff, P. A., 65, 70
Ehrenreich, H., 127
Elliott, R. J., 182
Emin, D., 54, 111, 116
Enderby, J. E., 65, 70, 97, 99
Esaki, L., 230, 233, 249, 251, 327, 366, 368
Estle, T. L., 265
Evans, B. L., 331
Evans, R., 70, 71

Faber, T. E., 63, 64, 68, 69, 71, 72, 73, 74, 81, 82
Fagen, E. A., 38, 205, 229, 230, 232, 245, 252, 366, 369
Fan, H. Y., 21, 156, 184, 245
Feldman, C., 267
Felty, E. J., 236, 250, 251, 342, 346, 347, 348, 354, 355, 357, 358, 363, 376
Fenton, E. W., 392
Ferrier, R. P., 84, 85, 86, 87
Feynman, R. P., 103, 115
Field, M. B., 97
Firsov, Yu A., 53, 114, 117
Fischer, J. E., 258, 303
Fischer, P., 191
Fischer, R., 230, 233, 234, 361, 363
Fistul, V. I., 166
Flaschen, S. S., 191
Franck, E. U., 83
Franz, W., 335, 350
Freake, S. M., 42, 196
Freiser, M. J., 181
Frenkel, J., 266
Friedel, J., 73, 94, 97, 178
Friedman, L., 53, 55, 72, 88, 225, 289
Frisch, H. L., 56
Fritzsche, H., 44, 52, 152, 153, 154, 155, 159, 161, 163, 166, 190, 197, 199, 205, 229, 230, 232, 245, 265, 268, 269, 290, 291, 369
Fröhlich, H., 31, 50, 114, 115
Froidevaux, C., 92, 93
Fry, J. L., 169

Fuhs, W., 281, 283, 312, 314
Fukuyama, H., 174
Fulenwider, J. E., 270

Garbett, E. S., 218, 219, 261, 358
Gatos, H. C., 205, 327, 364, 365
Gavoret, J., 75
Geballe, T. H., 51, 165, 184, 185
Getov, G. K., 337, 340, 341
Ghosh, P. K., 118
Gibbons, D. J., 208
Ginzbarg, A. S., 56
Gissler, W., 373, 374
Glagoleva, N. N., 86
Glazov, V. M., 86
Gleissman, J. R., 152
Goldstein, S., 55
Golin, S., 186, 187
Gomer, R., 78
Goodenough, J. B., 144
Goryunova, N. A., 320, 322, 323
Graczyk, J. F., 278, 279, 292
Grant, A. J., 354
Greene, M. P., 61, 68
Greenfield, A. J., 66
Greenwood, D. A., 9
Gregora, I., 316
Grigorovici, R., 192, 193, 196, 224, 272, 274, 275, 276, 277, 280, 281, 282, 283, 288, 289, 290, 296, 298, 301, 304, 307, 310, 371
Gross, E. F., 320, 322, 323
Grosse, P., 392
Grunwald, H. P., 382, 384
Gutzwiller, M. C., 132
Gubanov, A. I., 3, 31, 86
Gudat, W., 257
Güntherodt, H. J., 269
Gurney, R. W., 107

Haislip, R., 54
Haisty, R. W., 37, 191, 207, 377, 378, 379
Halbo, L., 182
Halperin, B. I., 31, 56, 57, 127, 137
Halpern, B., 78
Ham, F. S., 73
Hamilton, E. M., 42, 196
Hanamura, E., 182
Handrich, K., 151
Haneman, D., 265
Harrison, W. A., 68
Hartke, J. L., 210, 235, 236, 245, 267, 380, 382, 383, 384, 388, 389, 390, 391
Hartman, R., 63
Hartman, T. E., 267
Hasegawa, A., 68
Hashmi, F. H., 317, 320
Hattori, M., 363

Healy, J. H., 327, 338, 352, 361, 362
Heikes, R. R., 48
Heine, V., 36, 66, 67, 68, 73
Helland, J. C., 56
Hellwarth, R. W., 115
Henkels, H. W., 380
Hensel, F., 83
Heritage, M. B., 366
Herman, F., 255, 304, 306, 308
Herrell, D. J., 84, 85, 86, 87
Herring, C., 132
Herskowitz, G. J., 270
Hewes, C. R., 38, 366
Hill, R. M., 267
Hilton, A. R., 191
Hindley, N. K., 53, 103, 260
Hodgson, J. N., 82
Holcomb, D. F., 151, 161, 162, 164, 182
Holland, L., 192
Holmberg, S. H., 205, 245
Holstein, T., 53, 54, 55, 111, 116
Holtzberg, F., 181
Hone, D., 256
Honig, J. M., 144
Hopfield, J. J., 240
Höschl, P., 315, 316, 318, 319, 321, 323
Hosemann, R., 205, 245, 265, 315
Houston, B. B., 63
Howard, W. E., 205, 230, 233, 249, 251, 327, 366, 368
Howe, R. A., 70
Howe, S., 77, 78
Hrubý, A., 315, 316, 318, 319, 321, 323
Hubbard, J., 125, 131
Hull, G. W., 165
Hulls, K., 356
Hulthén, L., 133
Hung, C. S., 152

Iddings, C. K., 115
Ilschner, B. R., 84
Ing, S. W., 210, 235, 339, 342, 343, 344, 399, 400
Ioffe, A. F., 3, 7, 86, 192, 205, 206
Ipateva, V. V., 363
Ivanov, E. K., 320, 322, 323
Ivkin, E. B., 214, 215, 219, 355, 357

James, H. M., 56
Jayaraman, A., 122, 145
Jerome, D., 122, 138
Jones, H., 85
Jonscher, A. K., 267, 272, 280, 284, 289
Jortner, J., 79, 120
Jullien, R., 122, 138

Kagan, Yu., 103
Kaganov, M. I., 134

Kanamori, J., 132
Kaplow, R., 371
Kasen, M. B., 77
Kasuya, T., 177, 178, 179
Katcoff, S., 184
Katz, M. J., 62, 63
Keezer, R. C., 197, 247, 372, 374, 391, 392
Keil, T. H., 241
Keldysh, L. V., 137
Keller, H., 391
Kemeny, G., 132
Keyes, R. W., 182
Kirkpatrick, S., 127
Klima, J., 35, 197, 307
Knights, J. C., 392
Knox, R. S., 137, 240, 395
Kobe, A., 151
Koenig, S. H., 63
Kohn, W., 61, 68, 125, 129, 134, 137, 140
Kollmar, A., 373, 374
Kolomiets, B. T., 210, 214, 215, 219, 229,
  230, 258, 325, 327, 334, 335, 336, 337,
  338, 339, 342, 347, 349, 350, 354, 355,
  357, 361, 362, 363, 394
Kopaev, Yu. V., 137, 162
Korony, G., 281, 283
Kortum, R. L., 255
Kosek, F., 205, 245, 266, 332, 333, 334,
  345, 346, 347
Kotov, B. A., 97, 99, 100
Kramer, B., 396
Kravitz, S., 70
Krebs, H., 37, 191, 196, 207, 377, 378, 379
Krieger, J. B., 62
Krishnan, K. S., 65
Kudinov, E. K., 114, 117
Kubo, R., 106
Kuglin, C. C., 255
Kuhn, M., 290
Künzi, H. U., 269
Kataïtsev, V. I., 103

LaCourse, W. A., 381
Landau, L. D., 130
Landauer, R., 56, 57
Langer, J. S., 31
Langreth, D. C., 115
Lanyon, H. P. D., 243, 375, 389, 390
Lark-Horovitz, K., 166
Laurikainen, K. V., 133
Lax, M., 31, 56, 60
Lăzărescu, M., 267, 259, 360, 362
Leavy, J. F., 42, 54, 167
Lebedev, E. A., 210, 355
Le Comber, P. G., 210, 296, 297
Leiga, A. G., 307, 394
Lekner, J., 67, 78, 79
Liang, W. Y., 347, 348, 354

Lieb, E. H., 133
Lien, S. Y., 66
Lifshitz, I. M., 30, 31, 134
Lizell, B., 380
Lopez, A. A., 63
Losee, D. L., 30, 31
Lloyd, S. P., 56
Lucovsky, G., 235, 342, 355, 358, 363, 371,
  372, 374, 375, 376, 384, 385, 386, 389,
  400
Lueder, H., 269
Lukes, F., 305
Lukes, T., 245
Luttinger, J. M., 132
Lynch, R. W., 122
Lyubin, V. M., 230

McGill, T. C., 35, 197, 307
Mackenzie, J. D., 381
Mackenzie, R. C., 197
Mackinson, R. E. B., 56
Mackintosh, A. R., 148
McMillan, P. W., 356
McWhan, D. B., 122, 127, 138, 139, 142,
  143, 144, 145
Maczuk, J., 380
Mader, S., 76, 77
Mahan, G. D., 241
Mahr, H., 240
Maines, R. G., 122
Male, J. C., 55, 206, 207, 226, 329, 362
Mallon, C. E., 97, 100
Mamadaliev, M., 97, 99, 100
Mamontova, T. N., 336, 339, 350, 363
Mănăilă, R., 274, 275, 276, 277
Many, A., 208
March, N. H., 68, 182
Mark, P., 267
Markel, K., 258, 303
Markov, Yu. F., 323
Maschke, K., 305, 396
Massey, H. S. W., 16
Mattheiss, L. F., 128
Mattis, D. C., 178, 179
Matyáš, M., 266, 315, 316, 318, 319, 321,
  323, 345
Mazets, T. F., 229, 258, 334, 335, 337, 338.
  342, 349, 394
Meeks, T., 62
Mell, H., 227, 228, 281, 283, 298, 310
Menthe, A., 266, 335, 336, 345
Methfessel, S., 178, 179, 181
Meyer, L., 78
Miller, A., 17, 41, 104, 156
Miller, L. S., 77, 78
Mills, D. L., 122
Milward, R. C., 184
Minami, T., 363

Mitchell, D. L., 219, 261, 358, 369, 370
Mizuguchi, K., 161, 183
Moon, R. M., 144
Moorjani, K., 267
Mooradian, A., 372, 373
Moss, S. C., 278, 279, 292
Mott, N. F., 4, 12, 16, 20, 21, 22, 24, 26, 31, 32, 33, 34, 37, 41, 44, 46, 47, 48, 49, 52, 53, 56, 62, 63, 70, 73, 77, 79, 82, 84, 85, 89, 94, 101, 107, 109, 111, 113, 115, 118, 119, 120, 122, 123, 125, 126, 128, 129, 130, 132, 133, 134, 135, 137, 141, 144, 145, 146, 149, 150, 151, 154, 156, 158, 160, 161, 166, 167, 168, 169, 170, 171, 174, 176, 184, 200, 204, 212, 214, 216, 217, 237, 243, 249, 252, 253, 267, 268, 269, 271, 282, 284, 336, 354, 387, 393
Mueller, F. H., 218
Mulhern, J. E., 55
Müller, L., 267, 390
Müller, M., 267, 390
Musil, C., 379
Mycielski, J., 184
Myers, M. B., 236, 250, 251, 342, 346, 347, 348, 354, 355, 357, 358, 363, 376

Nagels, P., 317, 320
Nagaoka, Y., 126, 127
Nakamachi, F., 132, 363
Narayanamurti, V., 122
Nathan, M. I., 262
Negreskul, V. V., 363
Neuringer, L. J., 182, 184
Neustadter, H. E., 22
Newman, R., 298, 299, 305, 308, 310
Neyhart, J. H., 210, 235, 339, 342, 343, 344
Nielsen, S., 325, 347
Nikiforova, M., 339, 340, 341
Niklas, J., 314
Nishimura, H., 128
Nordheim, L., 61
North, D. M., 65, 70
Northover, W. R., 191
Norwood, T. E., 169
Nowick, A. S., 76
Nozières, P., 75
Nwachuku, A., 290

Okuneva, N. M., 97, 99, 100
Olechna, D. J., 395
Osmun, J. W., 290, 291
Overhauser, A. W., 136
Ovshinsky, S. R., 38, 44, 52, 190, 192, 197, 199, 233, 268, 269, 270, 365
Owen, A. E., 210, 214, 215, 217, 220, 245, 325, 326, 337, 339, 345, 352, 355, 356, 380, 387

Pai, D. M., 235, 399, 400
Pajasová, L., 304
Panova, G. Kh., 103
Pashintsev, Yu. I., 164
Papadakis, A. C., 208
Paul, W., 144
Pearson, A. D., 191, 270
Peck, W. F., 191
Peierls, R. E., 123
Penn, D. R., 136, 256
Penney, T., 180
Perez-Albuerne, E. A., 122
Perron, J. C., 94, 95, 96, 223
Pettit, G. D., 181, 250, 251, 292, 293, 294, 307, 309, 310
Phariseau, P., 60
Phillips, J. C., 56, 254, 256, 304, 314
Piller, H., 258, 303
Pippard, A. B., 181
Platakis, N. S., 205, 327, 364, 365
Platzman, P. M., 115
Polk, D. E., 277
Pollak, M., 51, 52, 54, 156, 175, 184, 185, 187, 212, 217, 361
Poole, H. H., 266
Popescu, C., 267, 359, 360, 362
Porai-Koshits, E. A., 331
Porile, N. T., 184
Postill, D. R., 83
Pratt, G. W., 132
Prohofsky, E. W., 182
Prosser, V., 391

Rakavy, G., 208
Rakov, A. V., 164
Raspopova, E. M., 354
Rawson, H., 190
Raz, B., 79
Redfield, D., 241, 242, 245, 335, 394
Reed, T. B., 169
Regel, A. R., 3, 7, 86, 97, 99, 100, 192, 205, 206
Regensburger, P. J., 235, 236, 245, 391
Remeika, J. P., 144, 145
Rice, S. A., 78
Rice, T. M., 122, 126, 127, 132, 137, 138, 139, 142, 143, 144, 176
Richter, H., 195, 274
Ridley, B. K., 269
Roberts, A. P., 56
Roberts, G. G., 247, 391, 392
Robertson, J. M., 210, 214, 215, 217, 220, 345, 352, 355, 356
Robeson, C. R., 77
Robins, J. L., 398
Robinson, J. E., 71
Rockstad, H. K., 215, 231, 245, 250, 251, 347, 358, 361, 362, 363

Rogachev, A. A., 138, 139, 164
Ross, R. G., 83
Roth, H., 55
Rowe, T. A., 371
Roulet, B., 75
Rubio, J., 60

Sablina, N. I., 164
Sadagopan, V., 205, 327, 364, 365
Saitoh, M., 174
Sandrock, R., 394, 395
Sasaki, W., 161, 175, 183, 184
Savage, J. A., 325, 347
Scanlan, I. F., 39, 173
Scanlon, W. W., 63
Schindler, A. I., 122
Schmid, A. P., 173
Schmidt, P. H., 122, 138, 139
Schnakenberg, J., 53, 111, 113
Schnyders, H., 78
Schottmiller, J., 374, 375, 376, 384, 385, 386, 389
Schriempf, J. T., 122
Schweiger, A., 269
Seguin, R. W., 205, 245
Seitz, F., 160
Senturia, S. D., 38, 365
Seraphin, B. O., 258, 303
Shadrichev, E. V., 97, 99, 100
Shafer, M. W., 181
Shanks, H. R., 148, 149
Shaw, R. F., 217, 347, 348, 354
Shay, J. L., 255
Shiba, H., 174
Shockley, W., 104, 208
Shur, M. S., 323
Sidles, P. H., 148, 149
Siemsen, K. J., 392
Sienko, M. J., 150
Šimeček, T., 315, 316, 318, 319, 321, 323
Simidchieva, P. A., 337, 339, 340, 341
Simmons, C. J., 97
Simmons, J. G., 267, 268
Simpson, J. H., 47
Simpson, A. W., 151
Sivertsen, J. M., 66
Škácha, J., 315, 316, 318, 319, 321, 323
Slack, L. H., 261, 369, 370
Slade, M., 273, 301, 302, 331
Sladek, R. J., 182
Slater, J. C., 127
Smirnov, I. A., 97, 99, 100
Smith, B. A., 170
Smith, J. E., 262
Somaratna, K. T. S., 245
Sonder, E., 174, 175
Sonntag, B., 257

Spear, W. E., 77, 78, 118, 208, 210, 236, 296, 297, 382, 384, 389
Spenke, E., 269
Spicer, W. E., 248, 253, 254, 264, 272, 273, 287, 288, 298, 299, 300, 301, 304, 305
Springer, T., 373, 374
Springthorpe, A. J., 170
Srb, I., 371, 379
Srinivasan, G., 52
Stekhanov, A. I., 323
Sterling, H. F., 273, 274
Stern, F., 34
Stevens, D. K., 174, 175
Stocker, H. J., 269, 270
Stolen, R. H., 262
Štourač, L., 315, 316, 318, 319, 320, 321, 323, 379
Stiles, P. J., 368
Straub, W. D., 55
Strauss, S., 62
Štrba, F., 379
Street, R. A., 217, 347
Stuke, J., 44, 89, 90, 91, 223, 224, 227, 228, 245, 247, 258, 280, 281, 282, 283, 288, 296, 298, 305, 308, 311, 312, 313, 314, 351, 391, 393, 394, 395
Sundfors, R. K., 151
Suits, J. C., 181
Szekely, G., 273

Tabak, M. D., 210, 235, 355, 374, 375, 376, 382, 384, 385, 386, 387, 388, 389, 398, 400
Takeda, T., 177
Tanaka, M., 363
Tanaka, S., 21, 184
Tauc, J., 53, 205, 243, 245, 248, 249, 266, 272, 273, 298, 299, 301, 302, 304, 315, 316, 318, 319, 320, 321, 323, 332, 334, 335, 336, 345, 346, 347
Taylor, H. L., 267
Taylor, P. C., 219, 261, 358, 369, 370
Taylor, W., 372
Teleman, E., 289
Thomas, D. J. D., 274, 277
Thomas, P., 305, 396
Thompson, J. C., 38, 150, 205, 245, 366
Thornber, K. K., 103, 115
Thouless, D. J., 18
Tièche, Y., 92
Timbie, J. P., 75
Title, R. S., 250, 251, 264, 265, 289, 291, 292, 293, 294, 307, 309, 310
Toyozawa, Y., 182, 240
Treusch, J., 394, 395, 396
Trotter, J., 75, 76
Trylski, J., 182

Tsu, R., 205, 230, 233, 249, 251, 327, 366, 368
Turnbull, D., 190
Tutihasi, S., 247, 391, 392
Twaddell, V. A., 381
Twose, W. D., 56, 62, 156, 158, 160, 161

Übelacker, E., 94
Uemura, Y., 174
Uphoff, H. L., 327, 338, 352, 361, 362
Urbach, F., 240
Urbain, G., 94
Ure, R. W., 48

Vaipolin, A. A., 331
van Daal, H. J., 119, 120
Van Dyke, J. P., 255, 304, 306, 308
Van Zandt, L. L., 144
Vancu, A., 272, 301, 304, 307, 310
Vasko, A., 371, 379, 398
Velický, B., 127
Vengel, T. N., 347, 361, 362, 363
Verwey, E. J. W., 122
Vescan, L., 267, 272, 280, 359, 360, 362
Vogel, W., 205, 245, 265, 315
Volger, J., 49, 55
von Molnar, S., 178, 180
Vorlíček, V., 315, 316, 318, 319, 320, 321, 323

Wachter, P., 180
Wagner, C., 84
Wagner, C. N. J., 76
Walley, P. A., 272, 274, 280, 284, 289, 291, 292
Walters, G. K., 265
Wang, T. T., 270
Ward, A., 374, 375, 376, 384, 385, 386, 389
Warren, W. W., 101, 269, 270
Warter, P. J., 210, 235, 388, 398, 399, 400
Weaire, D., 36
Weber, P., 180
Weiser, G., 258, 394
Weiser, K., 205, 230, 233, 234, 250, 251,

292, 293, 294, 307, 309, 310, 327, 358, 359, 361, 362, 363, 393
Weirauch, D. F. 269, 270
Wemple, S. H., 149
West, M. B., 77
Whalley, E., 262
White, R. M., 75, 176
Widmer, H., 76
Wigner, E., 135
Wilson, A. H., 121, 137
Wilson, E. G., 71
Wilson, T. M., 127, 128
Wiser, N., 66
Wolf, E. L., 30, 31
Wong, P. T. T., 262
Wood, D. L., 266, 335, 336, 345
Woolsey, R. B., 176
Wright, G. B., 372, 373
Wu, F. Y., 133
Wyttenbach, A., 184

Yafet, Y., 182
Yamanouchi, C., 161, 182, 183
Yanase, A., 177, 179
Yeargan, J. R., 267
Yoffe, A. D., 217, 347, 348, 354
Young, P. A., 331
Yu, P. Y., 257

Zachariasen, W. H., 277
Zallen, R., 218, 273, 301, 302, 331, 332, 347, 348
Zareba, A., 92
Závětova, M., 304, 307, 308, 310, 316, 318, 320
Zener, C., 175
Zhernov, A. P., 103
Ziman, J. M., 18, 35, 55, 60, 63, 64, 65, 68, 69, 71, 73, 74, 100, 122, 128
Zimmerer, G., 313
Zinamon, Z., 120, 126, 130, 132, 144, 145, 149, 169, 176, 184
Zittartz, J., 31
Zlatkin, L. B., 320, 322, 323

SUBJECT INDEX

a.c. conductivity,
  for hopping conduction, 49ff.
  in doped semiconductors, 184ff.
    amorphous semiconductors, 211ff.
      germanium, 289ff.
      As_2S_3, 215, 217, 345
      As_2Se_3, 215, 217ff., 355, 357
      $Tl_2Se.As_2Te_3$, 369ff.
      Te_2AsSi, $Te_{48}As_{30}Si_{12}Ge_{10}$, 215, 217
alternating currents, *see* a.c. conductivity
alloys,
  magnesium-bismuth 84ff.
  resistivity of liquid metal, 63ff.
ammonia,
  solutions of metals in, 120, 150ff.
amorphons, 274ff.
amorphous metal and semi-metal films,
  76ff., 84ff., 196
amorphous semiconductors, 31ff., 43ff.,
  52ff., 188ff.
  with tetrahedral coordination 272ff.
  chalcogenides, 324ff.
  selenium and tellurium, 371ff.
Anderson localization, 16ff.
  in liquid metals and semiconductors 80ff.
  of polarons, 119
  in doped semiconductors, 166ff.
  and the metal–non-metal transition,
    146ff.
  in cerium sulphide, 167ff.
    VO, 168ff.
    amorphous semiconductors, 43ff.
argon,
  charge transport in liquid, 78ff.
arsenic triselenide, amorphous, 347ff.
  a.c. conductivity of, 215, 217ff., 355,
    357
  drift mobilities in, 210, 355ff.
  electrical conductivity of, 90, 207, 221,
    327, 330, 351ff., 356
  electrotransmission experiments on, 349
  glass transition temperature of, 349,
    355, 357
  infrared absorption in, 218, 261, 358
  optical absorption in, 231, 244ff.,
    250ff., 258ff., 347ff.
  photoconductivity in, 231, 354ff.
  preparation of, 347
  pressure coefficient of gap in, 354
  recombination radiation in, 350
  reflectivity of, 350ff.
  structure of, 196, 347
  temperature coefficient of gap in,

    205, 222, 349, 351, 353ff.
  thermoelectric power of, 90, 221ff.,
    352ff.
arsenic trisulphide, amorphous, 331ff.
  a.c. conductivity of, 215, 217, 345
  effect of silver and other additives on,
    339ff., 345
  electrical conductivity of, 327, 330,
    337ff.
  electrotransmission experiments on, 335,
    337
  glass transition temperature of, 346
  magnetic susceptibitility of, 345
  optical absorption in, 244ff., 250ff., 332ff.
  photoconductivity in, 236, 335, 338,
    342ff.
  preparation of, 332
  recombination radiation in, 336, 339
  reflectivity of, 337, 340
  structure of, 331ff.
  temperature coefficient of gap in, 205,
    334ff.
arsenic tritelluride, amorphous, 358ff.
  a.c. conductivity of, 215, 217, 361
  electrical conductivity of, 207, 221, 327,
    358ff.
  optical absorption in, 231, 244ff., 250ff.,
    358ff.
  photoconductivity in, 231, 360
  preparation of, 358
  temperature coefficient of gap in, 205, 222
  thermoelectric power of, 221ff.
$As_2Se_3-As_2Te_3$, mixed binary system,
  amorphous, 221ff., 226, 231ff., 327ff.,
  330, 361ff.
$As_2Se_3-As_2S_3$, mixed binary system, amorphous, 328, 363
$As_2S_3-As_2Te_3$, mixed binary system, amorphous, 363
$As_2Se_3-Sb_2Se_3$, mixed binary system,
  amorphous, 327, 364ff.

Baber scattering, 63, 122
barriers, effect on a.c. conduction, 49
Bjerrum defects, 120
Bloch-Wilson theory, 34, 36

Cd,Ge,As_2 and similar ternaries, 315ff.
  electrical properties of, 316ff.
  magnetic susceptibility of, 315ff.
  optical properties of, 244ff., 320ff.
  preparation and structure of, 315
  temperature coefficient of gap in, 205

cerium sulphide, 167ff.
chemical rate theory, 112

Dangling bonds, 39, 52, 200, 264ff., 277, 280
deformation potential,
  in liquid rare gas elements, 78
  semiconductors, 104
density of states, 35ff.
  in amorphous As$_2$S$_3$, 341
    amorphous germanium, 264, 282, 288
    amorphous Mg–Bi, 84, 87
    amorphous semiconductors, 198ff.
    crystalline germanium, 306
  of liquid metals, 72ff., 79ff.
  from photo-emission studies, 262ff.
  in trigonal selenium, 396
dielectric relaxation time, 208
differential thermal analysis, 190, 197
drift mobility, 207ff.
  in amorphous As$_2$Se$_3$, 355ff.
    amorphous selenium and alloys, 382ff.
    amorphous silicon, 296ff.
    solid and liquid rare gases, 78
Drude equation, 13, 28, 49, 81ff., 211, 258

Electron–electron scattering, 63, 122
electron spin resonance, 264ff., 289, 291, 294, 374
electroreflectance, 257ff., 303ff., 393ff.
electrotransmission, 257ff., 335, 337, 349
europium compounds, 177ff.
excitonic insulator, 137ff.
excitons, 79, 240ff.
extended states, 10, 23, 44, 198

Franz–Keldysh effect, 241ff., 335, 394
free carrier absorption, 211, 258ff., 369ff.

Germanium, amorphous, 272ff.
  a.c. conductivity of, 289ff.
  density of states in, 288
  density of, 273, 304
  electrical conductivity of, 224ff., 279ff.
  electron spin resonance in, 264ff., 289.
  electroreflectance experiments on, 303ff.
  Hall effect in, 227, 288ff.
  infrared transmission spectra of, 301ff.
  magnetoresistance of, 227ff., 281, 283ff.
  optical properties of, 243, 253ff., 298ff.
  photoconductivity in, 290
  piezoresistance of, 281, 283
  preparation of, 272ff.
  radial distribution function in, 195, 274ff.
  refractive index of, 300ff.

structure of, 274ff.
thermoelectric power of, 223ff., 281ff.
tunnelling into, 289ff.
germanium, crystalline,
  band structure of, 255, 306
  conductivity and density change on melting, 205ff.
  impurity conduction in, 152ff.
  photoconductivity in, 138ff.
germanium telluride, amorphous, 205, 244ff., 365ff.
  electrical conductivity of, 327, 366ff.
  optical properties of, 244ff., 251, 366ff.
  photoconductivity in, 368
  preparation of, 365
  structure of, 38, 365ff.
glass formation, 189ff., 377ff.
  transition temperature, 189ff.
    in As–S system, 346
    As–Se system, 355, 357
    As$_2$Se$_3$, 349
glow discharge deposition, 273
grain boundaries, electrical resistance in the presence of, 77

Hall effect, Hall coefficient, Hall mobility, 53ff.
  in amorphous CdGe$_x$As$_2$, 318
    amorphous germanium, 227, 288ff.
    amorphous semiconductors, 225ff.
    chalcogenide glasses and liquids, 226, 329
    doped semiconductors, 163, 175
    liquid metals, 71ff., 88ff., 401ff.
      tellurium, 91ff.
      Te–Tl, 99
      Sb$_2$Se$_3$, 99ff
Hubbard Hamiltonian, 131

Impurity conduction, 152ff.
  in ionic materials, 170ff.
    magnetic semiconductors, 177ff.
interband absorption in amorphous materials, 52ff., 237ff., 248ff.
  As$_2$S$_3$, 244, 250, 332ff.
  As$_2$Se$_3$, 218, 244, 250, 347ff.
  As$_2$Te$_3$, 244, 250, 358ff.
  CdGeAs$_2$, 244, 320ff.
  chalcogenides, 231, 329ff.
  germanium, 298ff.
  GeTe, 244, 366ff.
  multicomponent glasses, 244, 252, 369ff.
  selenium and tellurium, 235ff., 244, 391ff.
  silicon, 250, 307ff.
  three-five compounds, 313ff.
intraband absorption, 258ff.
  see also free carrier absorption

Knight shift,
  of liquid metals, 74
    tellurium, 92ff.
  in doped semiconductors, 164
  relation to pseudogap, 101
Krypton, drift mobilities in, 78
Kubo–Greenwood formula, 9, 10ff., 61

Lifetime,
  recombination, 229
  of carriers injected into amorphous
    selenium alloys, 387ff.
liquid,
  alloys, 68ff.
  chalcogenides, 221, 226, 258ff.
  metals, 63ff.
  selenium, 89, 380, 392

Magnetic polarons, 175ff.
  semiconductors, 177ff.
  susceptibility of,
    amorphous As_2S_3, 345
      $CdGe_xAs_2$, 315ff.
    materials (theory), 28
    semiconductors, 265
    doped semiconductors, 28ff., 174ff.
    liquid metals, 74ff.
    solid and liquid tellurium, 94
magnetoresistance of
  amorphous semiconductors, 227
    germanium, 228, 281, 283ff.
    silicon, InSb, GeTe, 228
  doped semiconductors, 181ff.
mercury,
  amalgams, 70
  conductivity of, 83
metallic conduction,
  amorphous, 76ff.
  liquid, 63ff.
  Ziman's theory of, 63ff.
metal–non-metal transitions, 121ff.
  in doped semiconductors, 161ff.
minimum metallic conductivity, 26, 28, 42
  in liquid mercury at low densities, 83
  doped semiconductors, 166ff.
  cerium sulphide, 168
mobility,
  conductivity, in extended states, 43ff.,
    201, 209,
    strong fields, 268
  for hopping transport, 44ff.
  relationship to drift mobility, 207ff.
    Hall mobility, 53ff.
  mobility, drift, see drift mobility
  mobility, Hall, see Hall effect
  shoulder (or edge), 43ff., 198ff.
Mott g factor, 36ff., 71, 80ff.
  transition, 123ff., 133
    in doped semiconductors, 161ff.
Mott–Hubbard insulators, 123ff, 127ff.

Nickel oxide,
  impurity conduction in, 170ff.
  non-metallic property of, 126
  polarons in, 119
non-ohmic conduction, 266ff.

Ornstein–Zernike formula, 66, 78
optical properties of,
  crystalline semiconductors, 238ff., 253ff.
  amorphous, semiconductors, 52ff., 237ff.
    chalcogenides, 231, 329ff.
      (see also arsenic triselenide,
        trisulphide, tritelluride)
    $CdGeAs_2$, 320ff.
    germanium, 243, 253ff., 290, 298ff.
      telluride, 244ff., 251, 366ff, 368.
    selenium, 235ff., 244ff., 257, 391ff.
    silicon, 250, 298ff., 307ff.
    tellurium, 82, 391ff.
    three–five compounds, 313ff.
    liquid metals, 81
    semiconductors, 81ff.
oxygen, effect on properties of selenium,
  381

Phonons, 102ff.
  absorption by, 261ff., 322ff.
photoconductivity, 229ff.
  in arsenic triselenide, 231, 354ff.
    trisulphide, 335, 338, 342ff.
    tritelluride, 360ff.
  other chalcogenides, 230ff.
  germanium, 290
    telluride, 368
  selenium, 235ff., 398ff.
  silicon, 298
photo-emission, 262ff.
piezoresistance,
  in amorphous germanium, 281, 283
    three–five compounds, 314
polarons, 113ff.
  Anderson localization of, 119ff.
  degenerate gas of, 120ff.
  hopping by, 117ff.
  in liquids, 120
  thermopower due to, 118ff.
  effect on impurity conduction of, 170ff,
  in vanadate glasses, 172ff.
  magnetic, 175ff.
Poole–Frenkel effect, 266ff., 400
pseudogaps, 35, 56, 80ff., 88ff.
  due to overlapping Hubbard bands, 184
pseudopotentials, 60ff., 64ff.
  table of, 67

Quantum efficiency, 211, 229ff.
  in amorphous selenium, 235ff., 399ff.

Radial distributions functions, 194ff.
  of $CdGeAs_2$, 315

chalcogenide glasses, 331ff.
  germanium, 195, 274ff.
  selenium, 371
  silicon, 278ff.
Raman spectra, 262, 371ff.
rare gases, mobility of electrons in, 78ff.
recombination edge, 233
  radiation, 336, 339, 350, 363

Seebeck coefficient, *see* thermoelectric power
selenium, amorphous, 371ff.
  carrier lifetime in, 387ff.
  conductivity of, 380ff.
  drift mobility in, 210, 382ff.
  electron spin resonance in, 374
  electroflectance spectra of, 394
  optical properties of, 235ff., 244ff., 257, 391ff.
  photogeneration in, 235ff., 398ff.
  quantum efficiency in, 235ff., 399
  space-charge-limited currents in, 389ff.
  structure of, 372ff.
    alloys of, 374ff., 384ff., 388ff.
selenium, crystalline,
  band structure of, 395
  density of states in, 396
  structure of, 396
selenium, liquid,
  alloys with tellurium, 94ff.
  conductivity and thermoelectric power of, 89ff., 380
  structure of, 373ff.
semiconductors,
  amorphous, 188ff.
  degenerate, 61ff., 166ff.
  doped, 152ff.
  liquid, 86ff.
  magnetic, 177ff.
  theory of conduction in amorphous, 43ff.
semi-metals, 129
  amorphous, 84, 196
  crystalline, 196
  liquid, 86ff.
silicon, amorphous,
  conductivity of, 224ff., 291ff.
  drift mobility in, 296ff.
  electrical properties of, 291ff.
  electron spin resonance in, 264ff., 291, 294
  k-selection rule for, 307
  magnetoresistance of, 227
  optical properties of, 250ff., 298ff., 307ff.
  photoconduction in, 298
  preparation of, 274
  radial distribution function of, 279
  refractive index of, 294, 309, 311
  structure of, 274ff.
  thermoelectric power of, 224ff., 296, 298
silicon, crystalline,
  band structure of, 308

impurity conduction in 162, 165
  thermoelectric power of, 165, 296, 298
silver, effect on electrical properties of chalcogenides of, 339, 341, 345
space-charge-limited currents, 360, 389
spin polarons, *see* magnetic polarons
switching in amorphous films, 269ff.

$T^{\frac{1}{4}}$ law, *see* variable range hopping
tellurium, amorphous, 371ff.
  alloys, 374ff., 377
  optical properties of, 391ff.
tellurium crystalline, 395ff.
tellurium, liquid
  absorption in, 82
  alloys with selenium, 94ff.
    thallium, 97ff.
  conductivity of, 91ff.
  Hall effect in, 92
  Knight shift in, 92ff.
  magnetic susceptibility of, 94
  neutron spectroscopy of, 374ff.
  optical properties of, 82, 392
thermal conductivity, 362, 379
thermoelectric power,
  theory of, 47ff.
  of amorphous semiconductors, 219ff., chalcogenides, 90, 220ff., 329, 352ff., 362, CdGe$_x$As$_2$, 317ff., germanium, 281ff.
  doped semiconductors, 164ff.
    liquid metals, 70ff.
    selenium and its alloys, 96, 380ff.
    Te–Tl, 99
    Mg–Bi films, 87
    nickel oxide, 172
    silicon, 223ff., 296, 298
  three–five compounds, amorphous, 224ff., 227ff., 312ff.
titanium dioxide, conduction in, 117ff.
titanates, conduction in, 148ff.
tungsten bronzes, 148ff.
tunneling into amorphous germanium 289ff.

Urbach's rule, 238ff., 299, 329, 339, 293

Vacancies, random fields due to, 167ff.
vanadium glasses, 39, 172ff.
  oxides, 142ff., 168
variable-range hopping ($T^{\frac{1}{4}}$ law), 41ff., 171, 180, 202, 204, 284ff.
vibrational spectra, 218ff., 261ff., 322ff., 372ff.

Wilson transition, 122
Wigner crystallization, 135ff.

X-ray emission from liquid metals, 75ff.
Xerography, 397ff.

Ytterbium, conductivity of, 122, 138ff.